THEORETICAL PHYSICS IN THE TWENTIETH CENTURY

A Memorial Volume to Wolfgang Pauli

Wolfgang Pauli

THEORETICAL PHYSICS
IN THE
TWENTIETH CENTURY

A Memorial Volume to Wolfgang Pauli

Edited by

M. FIERZ
Zürich, Switzerland

and

V. F. WEISSKOPF
Cambridge, U.S.A.

INTERSCIENCE PUBLISHERS INC., NEW YORK

Interscience Publishers Ltd., London

First published 1960

LIBRARY OF CONGRESS CATALOG
CARD NUMBER 60-15886

Interscience Publishers Inc., 250 Fifth Avenue, New York 1, N.Y.

For Great Britain and Northern Ireland : Interscience Publishers Ltd.,
88–90 Chancery Lane, London, W.C.2

Made and printed in Great Britain by
William Clowes and Sons, Limited, London and Beccles

AUTHORS

V. BARGMANN
Department of Mathematical Physics, University of Princeton, New Jersey

NIELS BOHR, For.Mem.R.S.
Institute for Theoretical Physics, Copenhagen

H. B. G. CASIMIR
Philips Gloeilampenfabrieken, Research Laboratory, Eindhoven

C. P. ENZ
Institute for Advanced Study, Princeton, New Jersey

M. FIERZ
Eidgenössische Technische Hochschule, Zürich

W. HEISENBERG, For.Mem.R.S.
Max-Planck-Institut für Physik und Astrophysik, München 23

R. JOST
Eidgenössische Technische Hochschule, Zürich

R. KRONIG
Technological University of Delft

L. D. LANDAU, For.Mem.R.S.
Institute for Physical Problems, Academy of Sciences, Moscow

R. E. PEIERLS, F.R.S.
Department of Mathematical Physics, University of Birmingham

B. L. VAN DER WAERDEN
Mathematisches Institut der Universität, Zürich

F. VILLARS
Massachusetts Institute of Technology, Cambridge, U.S.A.

v

G. WENTZEL
   The Enrico Fermi Institute for Nuclear Studies, University of
   Chicago

C. S. WU
   Department of Physics, Columbia University, New York

PREFACE

Several years ago, when Pauli was still with us, a volume was planned to celebrate his 60th birthday on 25th April, 1960. Contrary to the usual practice of soliciting original papers from most of his pupils and friends, we had planned to collect a series of articles by some of his close collaborators describing and reviewing the present status of all the fields in physics to which Pauli has contributed. Soon we discovered that this was a formidable task, for there is practically no field in physics on which Pauli's ideas have not left a significant imprint. The literal realization of our plan would have been equivalent to writing a complete Handbook of modern physics. We were consequently obliged to reduce our aims and restrict ourselves to consideration of two particular kinds of articles. The first represents an attempt to summarize briefly the progress made in some of the topics in physics which were closest to Pauli's interests, and the others are reports on the heroic period of physics during the 1930's, when Pauli's own work and constant critical vigilance were decisive in the conception of the basic ideas of quantum mechanics.

Pauli's untimely death occurred during the preparation of this collection, and the birthday volume became a memorial volume. The inadequacy of our plan was painfully apparent against the background of this new obligation. No collection of articles could do justice to the memory of Pauli's work and his impact on modern physics. His memory lives among all physicists. Only further progress in physics carried out in his spirit can ever serve as a true memorial.

This volume was first initiated by Dr. Paul Rosbaud, a close friend of Pauli's, and we present it as a modest testimony to the debt which the world of Physics owes to Wolfgang Pauli.

M. F.
V. F. W.

CONTENTS

1* ix

FOREWORD

Progress of physical science in this century is marked not only by the exploration of vast fields of experience, but equally by the development of new frameworks for the analysis and synthesis of experimental evidence. In this development, Wolfgang Pauli, to whose memory this volume is dedicated, played a prominent part by his own outstanding achievements as well as by the inspiration and stimulation which we all received from him.

Pauli's penetrating insight and critical judgment came early to the fore in his famous encyclopaedia article on relativity theory, which he published when he was only 20 years old and which is still one of the most valuable expositions of the basis and scope of Einstein's original conceptions. His early familiarity with this radical revision of fundamental physical concepts, and his mastery of the mathematical tools indispensable for the proper formulation of the new ideas, became the background for Pauli's important contributions to quantum physics.

While the theory of relativity, both as regards the principles and their application, had already in Einstein's hands reached a high degree of completion, the situation in quantum theory was very different indeed. Far from offering a general account of phenomena on the atomic scale, Planck's epoch-making discovery of the quantum of action rather represented a challenge to incorporate an entirely new elementary feature into a consistent description of physical phenomena. As is well known, the way to this goal was beset with many obstacles and was only gradually paved by the collaboration of a whole generation of physicists.

After his school days in Vienna, Pauli pursued his studies in Munich under the inspiration of Sommerfeld who with his unique mastery of the methods of mathematical physics exerted a deep influence on all his pupils. In later years, Pauli kept close contact with his old teacher of whom he often spoke with admiration and affection. When Pauli, after working with Born in Göttingen, came to Copenhagen in 1922, he at once became, with his acutely critical and untiringly searching mind, a great source of stimulation to our group. Especially he endeared himself to us all by his

1

intellectual honesty, expressed with candour and humour in scientific discussions as well as in all other human relations.

In those years, no comprehensive methods of quantum physics were yet developed and the interpretation of experimental evidence was guided mainly by the so-called correspondence argument which expressed the endeavour to uphold a description in classical terms to the utmost extent compatible with the individuality of atomic processes. By such a tentative procedure it proved possible in a more or less consistent manner to utilize spectral data to obtain a survey of the bindings of electrons in atoms, and in particular a first approach to an interpretation of the relationships between the physical and chemical properties of the elements.

I vividly remember discussions with Pauli, in which he expressed his dissatisfaction with the weak argumentation underlying the attempt to explain the peculiar stability of closed electron shells, so decisive for the periodicities exhibited by the properties of the elements when arranged according to their nuclear charge. The pertinence of his remarks would indeed be most strikingly vindicated by Pauli's continued work in the following years, resulting in the enunciation of the exclusion principle which expresses a fundamental property of systems of identical particles for which, as for the quantum of action itself, classical physics presents no analogy.

The ingenuity with which Pauli in those years mastered the application of correspondence arguments within their proper scope is illustrated by his beautiful analysis of the Compton scattering of radiation by free electrons. Inspired by Einstein's general statistical considerations of energy and momentum exchange in radiative processes, he showed that the scattering probability depends on the intensity of both radiation components involved in the process. The line followed in this work is indeed very closely related to the general dispersion theory, formulated by Kramers, which was to prove so important for the subsequent great developments.

To Pauli, with his abhorrence for any kind of ambiguity in physical theories, the advent of a rational quantum mechanics, excluding all irrelevant use of classical pictures, was a tremendous relief. In particular, it need hardly be recalled how this development permitted an harmonious incorporation of Pauli's exclusion principle in proper quantum statistics. The vigour with which Pauli threw himself into the exploration of the new methods, and the mastery of these which he soon acquired, are evidenced by his article on the foundations of quantum mechanics in *Handbuch der Physik* (1932), which retains a similar position in scientific literature as his old exposition of relativity theory.

Pauli's whole background made it inevitable that he would be deeply pre-occupied with the problem of adapting the fundaments of quantum physics to relativistic requirements. Not only did he from the beginning take a prominent part in the formulation of the quantum theory of electromagnetic fields, but also his contribution to the relativistic theory of the electron was most helpful in promoting the full understanding of its implications. In the elucidation of the apparent paradoxes to which the subsequent discussion of the measurability of field components and electric charges gave rise, Pauli's active interest was also a great stimulation.

In subsequent years, Pauli became ever more deeply occupied with the problems of the elementary particles and their associated quantized fields. At an early stage, he made a fundamental contribution to this development by the introduction of the concept of the neutrino, which ensured the upholding of the conservation laws in the β-decay of atomic nuclei. In this connection, it is also interesting to recall that Pauli, in 1926, was the first to draw attention to the source of information about nuclear spins and electromagnetic moments offered by the hyperfine structure of spectral lines.

In this memorial volume, experts in the various fields have surveyed Pauli's many-sided pioneering work and its background at the successive stages of development of physical science. When contemplating Pauli's great life-work, it is important to remember the inspiration he gave not least to the many pupils whom he gathered around him, first in Hamburg and later in Zürich where, apart from an interruption in the war years which he spent in Princeton, he worked for the last 30 years of his life. Still, through his participation in scientific symposia and his extensive correspondence with colleagues and friends, Pauli's influence reached much wider circles.

Indeed, everyone was eager to learn about Pauli's always forcefully and humorously expressed reactions to new discoveries and ideas, and his likes and dislikes of the prospects opened. We always benefited by Pauli's comments even if disagreement could temporarily prevail; if he felt he had to change his views, he admitted it most gracefully, and accordingly it was a great comfort when new developments met with his approval. At the same time as the anecdotes around his personality grew into a veritable legend, he more and more became the very conscience of the community of theoretical physicists.

Pauli's searching mind embraced all aspects of human endeavours. In Zürich he found colleagues sharing his many-sided interests, and his studies of historical, epistemological and psychological questions found expression in a number of highly suggestive essays. Also there he had the good fortune of meeting a life-companion who by her fine understanding of the power of his intellect and the integrity of his character gave him that peace of mind which he needed so much in his great research and teaching activity. With Wolfgang Pauli's death we have lost not only a brilliant and inspiring fellow worker, but a true friend who to many of us appeared as a solid rock in a turbulent sea.

NIELS BOHR

THE TURNING POINT

R. KRONIG

Il y a tant de manières de dire la vérité sans la dire tout entière! L'absolu détachement des choses n'admettrait-il aucun regard jeté de loin sur celles que l'on désavoue? Et quel est le cœur assez sûr de lui pour répondre qu'il ne se glissera jamais un regret entre la résignation, qui dépend de nous, et l'oubli qui ne peut venir que du temps?

Eugène Fromentin

On 7 January 1925, at the age of 20 and inexperienced in many ways, I arrived in the small and picturesque German university town of Tübingen, taking lodgings at the Hotel zum Goldenen Ochsen. I had gone there as travelling fellow of Columbia University with the intention of visiting Landé and Gerlach, who held chairs in theoretical and experimental physics, respectively, at the university, and of meeting Back. At the Institute of Physics I was kindly received by Landé with the remark that I was coming at a very opportune moment since he was expecting Pauli the following day. In fact Pauli had written him a long and very interesting letter, which he gave me to read. In this connection it will be useful to draw a sketch of the state of physics at that time, making clear the reasons for the quest that had led me to Tübingen.

During the second half of the last century the noble edifice of classical phenomenological physics had been consolidated, finding its ultimate completion at the beginning of the present century in the theory of relativity. Of course many special problems still awaited analysis: the behaviour of systems involving non-linear terms in the theory of elasticity, the phenomenon of turbulence in hydrodynamics, and diffraction effects in acoustics and optics. However, they all had this in common: the basic framework in which a solution had to be constructed was known, and the difficulties to be overcome were primarily of a mathematical nature.

In the field of atomic theory, which had received strong impulses in the nineteenth century from the study of chemical reactions and of electrolysis, from the thermodynamic investigation of matter and, finally, from the discovery of cathode rays and

5

radioactivity, the situation was quite different.   Here it had been gradually recognized that classical physics was inadequate for giving a satisfactory description of the observations.

Already the first, decisive, step clearly demonstrated that in atomic physics new features enter which are quite foreign to classical physics.   This was the introduction by Planck (1900) of the quantum hypothesis into the mechanics of the linear harmonic oscillator and the success with which it met in leading to a formula for black body radiation in harmony with the empirical data: the notion that such an oscillator, of frequency v, is capable only of discrete energy values, differing successively by the amount hv as claimed by Planck, contrasts with the possibility of a continuous variation of the energy in Newtonian mechanics.   In the theory of light quanta Einstein (1905) had extended the hypothesis of Planck from a mechanical system to electromagnetic vibrations and was thereby enabled to give a simple interpretation of the photo-electric effect.   In electromagnetic waves of frequency v, as well, the energy was to be available only in integral multiples of the amount hv, the energy of a light quantum or photon.   In both Planck's and Einstein's contributions the quantity h, of the dimension of an action, entered as a new universal constant.

The biggest field for the application of quantum ideas, however, was made accessible by the idea of the nuclear atom, proposed by Rutherford (1913) and deduced directly from his brilliant ex-periments on the scattering of α-particles by matter.   The synthesis of this picture and the quantum theory was the great achievement of Bohr (1913, 1914, 1915).   In his familiar first postulate he introduced the general concept of stationary states with well defined values of the energy as applicable to any atomic system, the linear harmonic oscillator being only a special case; more particularly, it was recognized by him that *discrete* stationary states are to be expected for *closed* systems, the implication being that for *open* systems the energy will in general still be capable of continuous variation.   In this postulate the observed stability of atoms and molecules had found expression.   In the second postulate the radiation emitted or absorbed by them was associated with transitions between pairs of stationary states, the frequency v of the radiation being related to the energies W_j and W_k by the equation

$$hv = W_j - W_k \qquad \qquad \dots . (1)$$

in conformity with Einstein's hypothesis of light quanta.   On this basis an interpretation of the combination principle of Rydberg and Ritz, stating that the wave numbers in the spectrum of any atomic system can always be represented as differences between pairs of a series of quantities characteristic of the system, the spectroscopic terms, could immediately be given if the terms were identified with the energies of the stationary states, divided by h and by the velocity of light c.

On the one hand the contrast between classical and quantum physics was thus sharply brought out. On the other hand, Bohr (1918) at a very early date clearly realized the need for seeing quantum physics as a generalization of classical physics. At a time when a precise formulation of quantum physics was not yet possible, his correspondence principle, claiming a qualitative analogy between the two theories, proved an invaluable guide for further research and permeated as leaven his whole *œuvre* as well as that of his collaborators, leading ultimately to the development of quantum mechanics in the hands of Heisenberg.

Stimulated by the postulates of Bohr, physicists in the middle years of the second decade of the present century were searching for general principles that would furnish the energies of stationary states in harmony with experiment. For closed systems of one degree of freedom, described by a coordinate q, the answer seemed to be provided by the method of the phase integral which maintained that for a stationary state the relation

$$\oint p \, dq = nh, \quad n = 0, 1, 2 \cdots \qquad \qquad \ldots\ldots(2)$$

has to be fulfilled, in which p is the momentum conjugate to q, given as a function of q by the laws of classical mechanics, while the integration is to be extended over one complete cycle of the (periodic) motion. In the case of the linear harmonic oscillator this requirement leads back to Planck's original hypothesis. By considering circular orbits in atoms with one electron, the hydrogen-like atoms, Bohr (1913) came to the conclusion that the angular momentum of the motion was quantized, being an integral multiple of $h/2\pi$. Moreover, the classical interdependence of energy and angular momentum, assuming Coulomb interaction between nucleus and electron, led Bohr (1914) to the energy values

$$W = -\frac{2\pi^2 Z^2 e^4 \mu}{h^2(1+\mu/M)} \cdot \frac{1}{n^2}, \quad n = 1, 2, 3 \cdots \qquad \ldots\ldots(3)$$

Z being the atomic number of the nucleus, e the electronic charge, μ the electronic mass and M the nuclear mass.

The great initial success of Bohr's theory was due to the fact that (1) together with (3) gave directly an expression for the frequencies in hydrogen-like spectra such as had been empirically found by Balmer and Paschen and by Fowler and Pickering respectively for hydrogen and ionized helium in the visible and near infra-red region of the spectrum, while in the ultra-violet and far infra-red new series of lines were predicted that were later confirmed experimentally.

It has been one of the fortunate coincidences in the history of physics that the method of the phase integral leads to energy values in *quantitative* conformity with spectroscopic evidence, both in the case of the linear harmonic oscillator and in the case of the hydrogen-like atoms, although we now know that in general it has only approximative significance. The same remark may be made as regards the application of classical mechanics by Rutherford to the interpretation of his scattering experiments with α-particles. Unquestionably in both cases the agreement found, although essentially fortuitous, was an enormous stimulant for further research along the chosen path.

A by-product of Bohr's investigations was the recognition of a quantum of magnetic moment, now known as the Bohr magneton. Indeed, in an atom in which the heavy nucleus might be regarded as practically at rest, and thus the orbital angular momentum as predominantly due to the electrons, the classical relation between magnetic moment and angular momentum, claiming that the ratio between them is equal to $e/2\mu c$, gave rise to the expectation that atomic magnetic moments would always be integral multiples of the quantity $eh/4\pi\mu c$.

The quantization of the circular orbits of hydrogen-like atoms must be seen as one of the first attempts to extend the application of quantum theory to systems of one degree of freedom beyond the linear harmonic oscillator. In reality, however, the two particles in these atoms move in three-dimensional space, and a generalization of the method of quantization to systems with more than one degree of freedom was thus called for. Such an extension was given in particular by Sommerfeld (1915, 1916a and b) for so-called multiply-periodic systems in which a separation of the partial differential equation of Hamilton–Jacobi is possible in suitably chosen generalized coordinates q_r. Denoting the conjugate momenta by p_r, each p_r being a function of the corresponding q_r following from the separation, the natural generalization of (2) consisted in requiring that

$$\oint p_r \, dq_r = n_r h, \quad n_r = 0, 1, 2 \cdots \qquad \cdots\cdots(4)$$

where again the integration was to be extended over one complete cycle of each q_r. In this way the allowed motions were to be selected from all motions possible according to classical mechanics, the energy of the stationary states appearing as a function of the quantum numbers n_r.

Among the apparently successful applications of (4) several deserve particular attention. In the hands of Bohr (1913, 1914, 1915) the hydrogen-like atoms yielded to treatment without any restriction to circular orbits. In this connection Bohr emphasized the special character of the motion of an electron in a Coulomb field, where the orbits of negative energy are ellipses and hence closed, so that the motion involves only one period. Such a system is called degenerate, being separable with different choices of the coordinates q_r, and (4) must then be replaced by the lesser requirement

$$\oint \sum_r p_r \, \mathrm{d}q_r = \oint 2T \, \mathrm{d}t = nh, \quad n = 0, 1, 2 \cdots \qquad \ldots (5)$$

T being the kinetic energy, t the time, n the total quantum number. For the hydrogen-like atoms the value $n = 0$ had to be excluded because it would correspond to the electron falling into the nucleus. On the basis of (5) the energy of the stationary states was again found to be given by (3).

It was Sommerfeld (1916b) who first took fully into account the relativistic variability of mass in the case of the hydrogen-like atoms, bringing about a slow precession of the elliptic orbit in its plane. While in the case of the non-relativistic motion (5) fixes only the major axis of the orbit, leaving the eccentricity and the orientation in space undetermined, the occurrence of a second period in the motion now gives rise to a quantization of the angular momentum which again becomes an integer, the azimuthal quantum number l in present-day notation, times $h/2\pi$. Also the energy depends now explicitly both on n and l, and a fine structure of the energy levels and of the spectral lines results. This was apparently confirmed by experiment, although here again a fortunate coincidence came into play.

By applying the conditions (4) to a hydrogen-like atom in a constant magnetic field, where the Larmor precession introduces a third frequency into the motion, Debye (1916) and Sommerfeld (1916c) could show that the component of angular momentum in the field direction is also quantized, having values $mh/2\pi$, where the magnetic quantum number m takes integral values from $-l$ to $+l$ (with the normalization of l adopted today). In this way the important concept of space quantization, soon confirmed by the experiments of Stern and Gerlach, made its entry into physics. Also it could be shown that the magnetic field caused an energy change equal to

$$\Delta W = m \frac{eh}{4\pi\mu c} H, \quad m = -l, -l+1, \cdots, l \qquad \cdots . (6)$$

so that an interpretation of the normal Zeeman effect of the spectral lines now became possible on the basis of the frequency relation (1).

The discussion of the (non-relativistic) hydrogen-like atom in the presence of a constant electric field led to further successes. The energy values found by Epstein (1916) on the basis of a separation of the problem in parabolic coordinates were in agreement with measurements on the Stark effect of the hydrogen line spectrum.

Finally the treatment of diatomic molecules as vibrating rotators with the help of (4) led, in the hands of different authors, to an understanding of the salient features of the band spectra of such molecules.

In all these cases the theoreticians were confronted with a new task. The frequency rule of Bohr in conjunction with the energy values resulting from the method of quantization led to possible values of the frequencies in the spectrum of the system considered. Experience showed that not all spectral lines thus predicted actually did occur, but that many have the intensity zero, being forbidden by selection rules that could be formulated in terms of the quantum numbers. More generally the question arose in which way the intensities of spectral lines could be computed next to their frequencies.

The way was in part prepared by a fundamental paper of Einstein (1917) in which this author introduced the concept of transition probabilities A_{jk}, B_{jk} and B_{kj} for spontaneous and stimulated emission and for absorption of radiation, the number of transitions per unit time in an assembly of systems being given respectively by $N_j A_{jk}$, $N_j B_{jk}\rho(\nu)$, $N_k B_{kj}\rho(\nu)$, with N_j and N_k the number of systems in the upper and lower states j and k and $\rho(\nu)$ the specific radiation density at the frequency ν of transition. The problem was thus reduced to a computation of these transition probabilities from the properties of the system.

Here the correspondence principle came into action. It claimed, in analogy with classical physics, that the electric moment of the system is decisive in this respect. If this quantity is analysed in a Fourier series involving the various fundamental frequencies ω_r of the multiply-periodic motion and their harmonics $\sum_r \tau_r \omega_r$, then the square of the amplitude of such a harmonic was to be considered as a qualitative measure of the transition probability for a transition in which the changes Δn_r of the quantum numbers n_r are equal to the τ_r. If in particular the amplitude vanishes, then the corresponding transition was assumed not to take place. A successful application of this view-point to the intensity and polarization of the Stark components in hydrogen-like spectra was given by Kramers (1919, 1920).

It was natural that an extension of the theory from hydrogen-like atoms to atoms with more than one electron was eagerly sought for in the years around 1920. In the interior of the atom, where the nuclear field predominates over the interactions of the electrons, the chances for such an extension appeared most favourable. Indeed, the experimental work on X-ray spectra of Barkla, Moseley and their successors, notably Siegbahn and Coster, showed that the energies required to remove various firmly bound electrons beyond the region of nuclear attraction lay more or less close to the values given by (3). The deviations could easily be understood as due to the perturbing influence of the other electrons; by introducing a shielded nuclear charge $Z'e$ instead of the real nuclear charge Ze they could also be formally accounted for. X-ray levels could thus be classified by means of the quantum numbers n and l, belonging to the electron which had undergone removal and previously encountered in the relativistic treatment of hydrogen-like atoms.

The simple structure, already long known to the spectroscopists, of the optical spectra of the alkalis and the alkaline earths also invited an application to these atoms of the principles so far established. Sommerfeld (1915, 1916a) in particular suggested that the spectra in question should be ascribed to transitions of the valence electron which moves in the field of the nucleus, shielded by the inner electrons. Assuming that this shielded field still has essentially a central symmetric character, a classification of the stationary states by the two quantum numbers n and l is appropriate here too. Sommerfeld was thus led to the conclusion that the different series of terms, established with the aid of the combination principle, correspond to different values of the azimuthal quantum number l, the terms within any one series being distinguished by the value of the total quantum number n. The possibility of ascribing l in such a way that the selection rule $\Delta l = \pm 1$ is obeyed can be understood as a direct consequence of the correspondence principle.

A very important distinction in this connection was made by
Bohr (1922) by introducing the concept of orbits penetrating into
the atomic core, as against those which do not. For the latter
the shielding of the nuclear field by the electrons of the core is
practically complete, and hence the corresponding energy values
differ only slightly from those of hydrogen-like atoms. For the
penetrating orbits, on the other hand, the total quantum number
n must be larger than the total quantum number of the electrons
with the same l-value forming the core. On the basis of a more
quantitative consideration the so-called Rydberg formula can be
derived for the energy values, approximately given by the
expression

$$W = -\frac{2\pi^2 Z_{\text{eff}}^2 e^4 \mu}{h^2} \cdot \frac{1}{[n+a(l)]^2} \qquad \ldots(7)$$

where Z_{eff} is now the resultant number of elementary charges of
the core while $a(l)$ is a function of l, independent of n.

Along these lines Bohr (1923) ultimately arrived at his comprehensive vision of the way in which the periodic system of the
elements arises by successive capture of electrons in the nuclear
field. Combining the evidence of the X-ray absorption and
emission spectra with that of the optical spectra and also with the
facts of chemistry and magnetism (Bohr and Coster, 1923), he
was led to the notion of a shell structure of the atom based on the
classification of the electronic orbits by the quantum numbers n
and l. That in the various types of orbits only a limited number of
electrons can be accommodated, was an additional hypothesis
required to cover the empirical data, once the key for deciphering
them had been found. This hypothesis may be considered
as a precursor of the exclusion principle to be discussed
later.

It is at this point that a review of the contributions made by
Pauli during the period in question can most appropriately be
given. Pauli had already made a name for himself by writing, at
the age of 20, the chapter on the theory of relativity in the
Enzyklopädie der Mathematischen Wissenschaften, a review article
which still, today, can be recommended to those who wish to
inform themselves on this fundamental subject of classical physics.
As a pupil of Sommerfeld at Munich, Pauli soon became interested
in atomic physics.

In this connection should be mentioned in the first place an
investigation (Pauli, 1920) on the diamagnetism of monatomic
gases. By taking into account the Larmor precession impressed

upon the atom by the magnetic field, the diamagnetic susceptibility per unit volume is computed by him to be

$$\chi = -\frac{Ne^2}{6\mu c^2}\overline{\sum R^2} \quad\quad ....(8)$$

where N is the number of atoms per unit volume, R the distance of an electron from the nucleus, while the summation is to be extended over all electrons and the bar means an average over all orientations. This formula has retained its validity in quantum mechanics if the averaging is replaced by taking the diagonal matrix element of the quantity concerned. A significant remark is made at the beginning of the derivation, namely that absence of paramagnetism will not only occur when the atoms in question have a vanishing magnetic moment, but also when, in the presence of a non-vanishing moment, they do not redistribute themselves over different orientations according to the Maxwell–Boltzmann formula. This situation is just what occurs, not indeed for atoms, but for the free electrons in a conductor which are subject to the exclusion principle, and it was on this basis that Pauli (1927a) seven years later could develop his theory of the paramagnetism of metals which does not depend on temperature.

A little later Pauli (1921) investigated the theory of the dielectric polarization of a gas consisting of rigid diatomic molecules with a permanent dipole moment p along their internuclear axis. This problem had already been treated by Debye on the basis of classical physics and had led him in the case of sufficiently weak electric fields to the relation

$$\frac{3}{4\pi}\frac{\epsilon-1}{\epsilon+2} = \frac{Np^2}{3kT} \quad\quad ....(9)$$

for the dielectric constant ϵ, N being the number of dipoles per unit volume, k Boltzmann's constant and T the absolute temperature. By considering the molecules as rotators with an angular momentum having the quantized values $Jh/2\pi$ ($J = 0, 1, 2\cdots$), by applying the concept of space quantization to the orientation of this angular momentum in the external field and by introducing the Maxwell–Boltzmann formula for the distribution of the molecules over the various orientations, Pauli could derive an equation of the type (9), but with a different numerical factor on the right-hand side. That a difference between the classical and the quantum-theoretical result thus remained at high temperatures too was a hint even at that time that all was not well with the older quantum theory.

A further publication (Pauli, 1922) on the hydrogen molecule ion covers in the main the results of Pauli's doctoral dissertation. In this paper the system consisting of two hydrogen nuclei fixed in space and one electron is quantized according to the rules previously described, the internuclear distance serving as a parameter on which the energy values of the stationary states depend. A separation of variables is possible here in elliptic and hyperbolic coordinates. The calculations are interesting from a historical point of view, the author not only considering the quantization, but also the stability of the orbits selected by the quantum conditions against small perturbations. Indeed, at that time the belief was held by many that unstable orbits had to be excluded even if they satisfied the quantum conditions.

In this period fell the fundamental discovery by A. H. Compton of the effect named after him. A quantum of radiation scattered by a free electron undergoes a change in wavelength $\Delta\lambda$, which can be demonstrated in the X-ray region. Compton (1923), and at the same time Debye (1923), gave a theoretical interpretation of this phenomenon. Already Einstein (1917) had suggested that a light quantum not only has an energy $h\nu$, but also a momentum $h\nu/c$ in the direction of propagation so that the emission and absorption of radiation by an atom will be accompanied by momentum transfer. As Einstein could show, this momentum transfer ensures that in a gas of atoms in equilibrium with radiation obeying Planck's law the Maxwellian velocity distribution is maintained. To account for the wavelength shift in X-ray scattering, Compton and Debye ascribed momenta $h\nu/c$ and $h\nu'/c$ to the incident and scattered photon respectively, the vector difference being taken up by the scattering electron while the corresponding energy has to be furnished by the radiation. For an electron originally at rest ν' will hence be smaller than ν, and by using relativistic mechanics the authors mentioned above could derive the well known relation for the change in wavelength

$$\Delta\lambda = \frac{2h}{\mu c}\sin^2 \tfrac{1}{2}\vartheta \qquad \ldots\ldots(10)$$

ϑ being the angle of scattering.

These results led Pauli (1923b) to study the thermal equilibrium between a gas of free electrons and black body radiation with an energy distribution given by Planck's law. If the momentum transfer between the electrons and the radiation field is assumed to take place through the classical mechanism of radiation pressure, then, as had already been shown by Lorentz and Fokker, neither the spectral energy distribution of the radiation nor the Maxwellian velocity distribution of the electrons will be maintained. Pauli could demonstrate that this difficulty disappears when the elementary scattering mechanism proposed by Compton and Debye is used as a basis for the discussion with suitable assumptions for the probability of the scattering process.

Only mentioning in passing publications by Born and Pauli (1922) on perturbation methods in the older quantum theory and by Kramers and Pauli (1923) on the quantization of molecular rotations, we come now to two important papers (Pauli, 1923a, 1923c) devoted to a phenomenon which was to prove of great importance for the further development of atomic physics: the anomalous Zeeman effect. We have already mentioned the efforts which had been made to arrive at an understanding of the optical spectra of atoms with more than one electron and the success which had been gained for elements in the first column of the periodic table. One feature we intentionally did not mention before is the so-called fine structure. Indeed, the energy levels giving rise to the optical spectra of the alkalis are not exhaustively characterized by their total and azimuthal quantum numbers n and l, but show for $l \neq 0$ a doublet structure that necessitates the introduction of a further quantum number.

At the time under consideration it was assumed that somehow the core of the alkali atoms had an angular momentum $s = \frac{1}{2}$ and that this angular momentum was to be vectorially composed with the angular momentum l of the valence electron in its orbit to give a resultant angular momentum $j = l \pm \frac{1}{2}$, excepting for $l = 0$, in which case j would be equal to $\frac{1}{2}$. The angular momenta l and s were supposed to precess uniformly about their resultant j, and the correspondence principle led then immediately to the selection rule $\Delta j = 0, \pm 1$ as actually confirmed by the spectroscopic data. Similarly in the alkaline earths an angular momentum was ascribed to the core which could have either the value 0 or 1. By combining it vectorially with the angular momentum l of the valence electron, singlet and triplet terms were thus to be expected. The correspondence principle furthermore led, in the hands of Sommerfeld and Heisenberg (1922), to approximate predictions as regards the relative intensities of the various fine structure components.

A considerable extension of the material to which these ideas could be applied was provided by the analysis of multiplets in more complicated spectra, such as those of the transition elements in the first long period of the periodic system. Especially through the work of Bechert, Catalan, Laporte and Russell it became established, in analogy with what was known for the alkalis and alkaline earths, that the sub-levels of multiplet terms could be considered as arising from a coupling of two angular momenta L and S, to form a resultant angular momentum J according to the rule

$$J = |L-S|, |L-S|+1, \cdots, L+S \qquad \cdots (11)$$

The spacing of the sub-levels suggested that the vectors L and S are subject to an interaction energy proportional to the cosine of the angle between them. Next to the number of sub-levels found, the observance of the selection rules $\Delta L = 0, \pm 1, \Delta J = 0,$ ± 1 was essential in attributing proper values of L, S and J to the various energy levels. A new feature discovered by Laporte in this connection was the occurrence of two types of levels, distinguished as even and odd, such that only levels of different types could combine under emission or absorption of radiation.

A study of the influence of magnetic fields on the spectra in question had revealed that in all cases where a multiplicity of terms occurs the Zeeman effect is not normal as described by (6), but of a more complicated type. The vector model for the interpretation of the multiplet structure suggested a treatment of this anomalous Zeeman effect by means of the methods evolved for quantizing multiply-periodic systems. This programme was dealt with in the two papers of Pauli (1923a, 1923c) already quoted. Magnetic moments were to be associated with the angular momenta S and L, that corresponding to S being $2S$ Bohr magnetons, that corresponding to L being L Bohr magnetons. The double magnetism associated with S was introduced *ad hoc* at the time without going into the theoretical reasons for it. By discussing the behaviour of the system under the simultaneous influence of the coupling energy between the angular momenta L and S and of the interaction of the associated magnetic moments with the external magnetic field, Pauli could follow the complete transition from the case of weak fields to that of strong fields. In weak fields the resultant angular momentum J undergoes space quantization, the multiplet level splitting into $2J+1$ equidistant components, to be distinguished by the magnetic quantum number M which represents the component of J in the direction of the field. Equation (6) must be replaced by

$$\Delta W = gM \frac{eh}{4\pi\mu c} H, \quad M = -J, -J+1, \cdots, J \quad \cdots (12)$$

with a splitting factor g for which an expression in terms of L, S and J had already been given by Landé (1923):

$$g = \frac{3}{2} + \frac{S(S+1) - L(L+1)}{2J(J+1)} \quad\quad \ldots\ldots(13)$$

In strong fields the angular momenta L and S undergo space quantization separately with components M_L and M_S in the field direction. This behaviour of the energy levels manifests itself in the spectra as the Paschen–Back effect. A more explicit discussion is given in Van der Waerden's article in this book.

Here another investigation of Pauli's (1924) can suitably be recalled. Many energy levels J of multiplets under very high resolution show a further splitting of a smaller order of magnitude, known as hyperfine structure. Pauli was the first to suggest that this phenomenon should be ascribed to an angular momentum I of the atomic nucleus, accompanied by a small magnetic moment, I being coupled to J to form a resultant F in a way similar to the coupling of S and L to form the resultant J. The various sublevels F then manifest themselves in the radiative transitions as a further splitting of the spectral lines.

This then describes in general terms the situation prevailing in atomic physics at the end of 1924 when I left New York for Europe. It is interesting to recall at this point the state of physics in the United States at that period. While in experimental physics a number of investigators like Michelson, Millikan, Langmuir, Compton and R. W. Wood, ranking among the foremost in the world, continued a tradition of pioneer research that went back to Franklin, Henry and Rowland, theoretical physics, after the meteoric appearance of Gibbs, could not boast of a similar record. In my university training I had received a thorough grounding in classical theoretical physics, but I had been obliged to acquire a knowledge of atomic physics to a large extent by autodidactic methods. There was, it is true, a somewhat disperse group of younger men in America, endeavouring to come up to scratch in this subject, of which I should mention Kemble, Van Vleck, Breit, Slater and Mulliken, but their mutual contacts were limited. Like most young physicists of that period I was greatly inspired by Sommerfeld's book *Atombau und Spektrallinien*. Also a meeting with Ehrenfest, lecturing in America in 1924, had made a strong impression on me, and I took to heart his suggestion to go abroad and in particular to visit his institute.

It had led me first to Cambridge, then to Leiden where I spent several weeks. At that time Ornstein and his pupils at Utrecht had been able to show by careful measurements on the Zeeman components of spectral lines and on the components of multiplets that the intensities stand in a simple rational relationship, obeying the so-called sum rules. Together with Goudsmit, then at Leiden, I arrived at a general formula for the relative intensities of the Zeeman components, expressing them in terms of the quantum numbers J and M (Goudsmit and Kronig, 1925). The correspondence principle suggested that these intensities are polynomials of the second degree in J and M. The requirement that Ornstein's empirical rules were to be satisfied led to a determination of the coefficients. Next to the selection rules and the g-formula of Landé this was one of the first attempts to replace the qualitative statements of the correspondence principle by a quantitative result, which was later confirmed by quantum mechanics.

It was natural under these circumstances that I desired to see the persons who had contributed so largely to a better comprehension of the Zeeman effect, and it was for this reason that, as mentioned before, I found myself in Tübingen early in 1925. Also, Pauli was for me much more than just a name and, looking forward to meeting him, I eagerly read the letter which Landé had lent me on my arrival. This letter actually contained an exposition of the exclusion principle in the clear and critical style so characteristic of its author. It set forth that in an atom in a strong magnetic field *each* electron should be classified by four quantum numbers *such as were used to label the terms of an alkali atom due to the excitation of the valence electron,* namely the total quantum number n, the azimuthal quantum number l and two magnetic quantum numbers m_1 and m_2. Of these m_1 represented the component of angular momentum in the direction of the magnetic field, being the sum of the component m_l of the orbital angular momentum l and of the component $m_s = \pm \frac{1}{2}$ of the angular momentum $s = \frac{1}{2}$, which was previously mentioned and in the case of the alkalis had hitherto been assigned to the atomic core. On the other hand, $m_2 = m_l + 2m_s$ represented the magnetic interaction energy with the external field, in suitable units. In addition, the hypothesis was made that in a state labelled by a given set of values of the four quantum numbers there is room for one and only one electron.

On the basis of these assumptions a great many facts immediately fell into line. The maximum occupational numbers of the shells introduced by Bohr in his theory of the periodic system follow directly from them. By regarding the quantities $\sum m_1$ and $\sum m_2$

for all the electrons of the atom as furnishing respectively the component of total angular momentum in the direction of the field and the total magnetic interaction energy with the external field, it furthermore became possible to predict which multiplets can arise if the number of electrons with given n and l is known. Thus it is an immediate consequence that a closed shell has $L = S = 0$ and that a closed shell from which k electrons have been removed gives the same manifold of multiplets as a shell containing k electrons. In particular, the observed doublet structure of the X-ray levels thus became intelligible, since for them the possible presence of loosely bound electrons outside closed shells may be neglected, the coupling between these and the inner electrons in general being too weak to manifest itself.

For the interpretation of the optical spectra the new view-point was exceedingly fruitful. In the case of the elements in the first and third columns of the periodic table, where normally all but one electron are contained in closed shells, the quantum numbers l and s of this electron are identical with the quantum numbers L and S of the atomic configuration as a whole. For the elements in the second column of the periodic table, generally l vanishes for one of the electrons outside closed shells, so that the l of the other one may still be identified with L; while for S the values 0 and 1, leading to singlet and triplet terms, become possible. Familiar results could thus be seen in the light of the general scheme. More interesting was the case of argon, the complicated spectrum of which had previously been analysed by Paschen. Except for the ground state we have here a closed shell with one electron removed, together with one electron outside the shell. As regards the manifold term the system therefore behaves formally as a system with two electrons outside closed shells, showing singlet and triplet levels. The richest harvest was gained, however, in the prediction of the multiplets possible for elements in the other columns of the periodic table and for the transition elements. The purpose of Pauli's visit to Tübingen was specifically the verification of such predictions by means of concrete examples. The spectra of elements in the fourth column of the periodic table, more in particular of lead, had been studied by Back, and the low-lying levels formed a test case for Pauli's considerations.

It is a unique experience to meet a creative mind at its sources, an experience which one does not easily forget. Pauli's letter made a great impression on me and naturally my curiosity was aroused as to the meaning of the fact that *each individual* electron of the atom was to be described in terms of quantum numbers familiar from the spectra of the alkali atoms, in particular the two angular momenta l and $s = \frac{1}{2}$ encountered there. Evidently s could now no longer be attributed to a core, and it occurred to me immediately that it might be considered as an intrinsic angular momentum of the electron. In the language of the models which before the advent of quantum mechanics were the only basis for discussion one had, this could only be pictured as due to a rotation of the electron about its axis. Such a picture, it is true, was subject to a number of serious difficulties, which will be referred to elsewhere. Yet it was a fascinating idea and the same afternoon, still quite under the influence of the letter I had read, I succeeded in deriving with it the so-called relativistic doublet formula.

The size of the fine structure splitting of the levels in the optical spectra of the alkalis was a great puzzle at that time, to which in particular Landé (1924) had explicitly drawn attention. On the picture of a magnetic interaction between the orbit of the valence electron and a magnetic moment corresponding to an angular momentum of the electrons in the core a proportionality of fine structure intervals with the third power of an effective nuclear charge was to be expected while actually proportionality with the fourth power was found. This fourth-power dependence was a source of consternation also in the so-called relativistic X-ray doublets. Now if, in conjunction with its intrinsic angular momentum $s = \frac{1}{2}$, an intrinsic magnetic moment of one Bohr magneton was acribed to the electron, then it would not only suffer an electrostatic attraction in its motion around the (screened) nucleus, but also a magnetic coupling. Indeed, in passing from a reference system in which the nucleus is at rest to one moving with the velocity $\mathbf{v}$ of the electron, a Lorentz transformation applied to the radial electric field $\mathbf{E}$ of the (screened) nucleus gives rise to a magnetic field

$$\mathbf{H} = \frac{\mathbf{E} \times \mathbf{v}}{(c^2 - v^2)^{1/2}}$$

perpendicular to the orbital plane in the latter system. By introducing the interaction of the intrinsic magnetic moment b (of one Bohr magneton) of the electron with this magnetic field, given by $\mp bH$ for an orientation parallel or antiparallel to $\mathbf{H}$, as a small perturbation, a doublet splitting resulted which depended on the nuclear charge in just the way derived from the empirical data by Landé.

Of course it was necessary that this interpretation should not come into conflict with the experimental facts on the fine structure of the hydrogen-like spectra, of which Sommerfeld seemed to have given a full account. The hope was that the relativistic precession of the orbit in its plane and the interaction of the intrinsic magnetic moment of the electron with the orbital motion would compensate each other in such a way as to make levels with different l but the same j coincide, giving the same number and pattern of energy levels as predicted by Sommerfeld's original treatment. The circumstance that both effects were proportional to the fourth power of the atomic number encouraged such a hope, but closer examination showed that the new coupling was too large by a factor of 2, which will be referred to again later. On reporting my findings to Landé he said that I should surely tell them to Pauli when he came.

On the next day we went to fetch Pauli from the station. For some reason I had imagined him as being much older and as having a beard. He looked quite different from what I had expected, but I felt immediately the field of force emanating from his personality, an effect fascinating and disquieting at the same time. At Landé's institute a discussion was soon started, and I also had occasion to put forward my ideas. Pauli remarked: 'Das ist ja ein ganz witziger Einfall', but did not believe that the suggestion had any connection with reality. The spectrum of lead was then duly gone into and was found to be in harmony with the expectations raised by Pauli's work. This appeared in print a few months later (Pauli, 1925), elaborated in some respects, but in its essentials identical with the contents of the letter I had seen.

From Tübingen I went for a short time to Göttingen, another centre of atomic research. Here Born and Franck held chairs in theoretical and experimental physics and were surrounded by a group of young investigators. One of the subjects to which attention had been given was the calculation of the energy levels of the neutral helium atom. On the basis of perturbation methods results had been obtained by Born and Heisenberg (1923) which were quite at variance with experiment, and the conviction had daily been growing stronger that the current methods of quantization would have to be revised. From Göttingen I passed through Berlin, visiting Grotrian whose book on the spectra of elements with one, two or three valence electrons was then the bible of all spectroscopists, and from there to Copenhagen.

At the institute of Bohr new and exciting developments were taking place. In the preceding year a paper had been published by Bohr, Kramers and Slater (1924) in which it had been suggested as a radical possibility that in elementary processes of emission and absorption of radiation energy and momentum might perhaps be only statistically conserved. This extremist notion gave, of course, rise to much discussion, which was silenced only when Geiger and Bothe showed experimentally that nature has not made use of this possibility.

More important in the long run was the development by Kramers and Heisenberg (1925) of a formula for the scattering moment of atomic systems under the influence of radiation, an extension of earlier work of Ladenburg (1921) and of Ladenburg and Reiche (1923). This went beyond the qualitative statements of the correspondence principle and actually represented a result that is derivable by quantum mechanics in its present form. In it there occur, besides the energy values of the stationary states, the values of the amplitudes of the electric moment corresponding to the transitions between stationary states, or, in the language of today the non-diagonal matrix elements of the electric moment. Continuing the earlier work on the intensities of the Zeeman components of spectral lines I set about finding formulae for the relative intensities of the multiplet components in harmony with the experimental findings of Ornstein and his school (Kronig, 1925). This problem was also solved simultaneously and independently by Sommerfeld and Hönl (1925) and by Russell (1925). In modern quantum mechanics the results are a direct outcome of the properties of Legendre functions. Finally, Kuhn (1925) and Thomas (1925) arrived at a formula for the sum of the squares of the amplitudes of the electric moments belonging to all the transitions which start from the same energy level, which also retained its quantitative validity in the later developments.

In this way a number of results had become available which pretended exactness and which made the call for an integrating synthesis all the more urgent. How unsatisfactory the situation was generally considered appears clearly from a letter I had from Pauli, dated 21 May 1925, in which he writes:

'Die Physik ist momentan wieder sehr verfahren, für mich ist sie jedenfalls viel zu schwierig und ich wollte ich wäre Filmkomiker oder so etwas und hätte nie etwas von Physik gehört!'

I should not wonder if in the period preceding Newtonian mechanics a similar feeling had been prevalent. Then, too, a number of particular results on the statics and dynamics of material bodies was known, such as the law of moments, the kinematic behaviour of freely falling objects, the theorems governing the elastic and inelastic impact of spheres and the laws of Kepler on planetary motion. They stood loosely side by side until the principles of Newton brought unity to their interpretation.

It was in this atmosphere that Heisenberg's quantum mechanics was born in the summer of 1925. I cannot refrain from giving in full a passage from a letter of Heisenberg, written from Göttingen during the period of gestation and dated 5 June 1925*:

Nun will ich Ihnen noch ein bischen von meinen eigenen Intensitäts-betrachtungen erzählen und ich hoffe auf Ihre (möglichst scharfe) Kritik.

Der Grundgedanke ist: In der klassischen Theorie genügt die Kenntnis der Fourierreihe der Bewegung um *alles* auszurechnen, nicht etwa nur

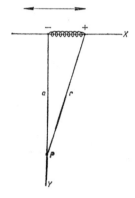

das Dipolmoment (und die Ausstrahlung), sondern auch das Quadrupol-moment, höhere Pole u.s.w. Um ein Beispiel zu geben: Ein anhar-monischer Oszillator schwinge in der x-Richtung,

$$x = a_0 + a_1 \cos \omega t + a_2 \cos 2\omega t + \cdots;$$

dann kann man z.B. die periodische Kraft auf einen Punkt P (im Abstande a vom Nullpunkt) ausrechnen und findet

$$K = -\frac{e^2}{a^2} + \frac{e^2}{a^2 + x^2} = \frac{e^2}{a^2}\left(-1 + \frac{1}{1 + x^2/a^2}\right).$$

Die Fourierentwicklung von $1/(1 + x^2/a^2)$ sei

$$b_0 + b_1 \cos \omega t + b_2 \cos 2\omega t + \cdots,$$

dann findet man

(1) $\quad b_0 = 1 - \dfrac{a_0^2 + \frac{1}{2}a_1^2 + \cdots}{a_2} + \dfrac{\cdots}{a^4}; \quad b_1 = -\dfrac{2(a_0 a_1 + \frac{1}{2}a_1 a_2 + \cdots)}{a^2};$

$$b_2 = \ldots$$

Also die Fourierkoeffizienten sind durch die ursprünglichen a_n ausdrück-bar. Es liegt nun nahe, anzunehmen, dass auch in der Quantentheorie

* As the reader will note, there is an error in the second equation of this letter which presumably was written in a hurry. The error is of no impor-tance for the general argument.

durch die Kenntnis der Übergangswahrscheinlichkeiten, oder der korrespondierenden Amplituden alles gegeben ist. Man wird daher versuchen, die Gleichungen (1) quantentheoretisch umzudeuten, und zwar ergibt sich eine Umdeutung zwangläufig, z.B. etwa so

$$b_1(n, n-1) = -\frac{1}{a^2}[a_0(n)a_1(n, n-1) + a_1(n, n-1)a_0(n-1)$$
$$+ a_1(n-1, n-2)a_2(n, n-2) + a_2(n+1, n-1)a_1(n+1, n) + \cdots].$$

Das Wesentliche an dieser Umdeutung scheint mir, dass die Argumente der quantentheoretischen Amplituden so gewählt werden müssen, wie es dem Zusammenhang der Frequenzen entspricht. Wenn also z.B. in der klassischen Theorie gilt

$$(2) \qquad b_2 e^{2i\omega t} = (a_1 e^{i\omega t})^2,$$

so muss die quantentheoretische Verwandlung davon heissen:

$$b_2(n, n-2)e^{i\omega(n, n-2)t} = a_1(n, n-1)a_1(n-1, n-2)e^{i\overbrace{[\omega(n, n-1)+\omega(n-1, n-2)]}^{=\;\omega(n,\,n-2)}t},$$

also

$$b_2(n, n-2) = a_1(n, n-1)a_1(n-1, n-2).$$

Wenn man nun zugibt, dass wirklich eine solche Berechnung und quantentheoretische Verwandlung sinnvoll ist, so hat man auch schon die quantentheoretischen Intensitätsgesetze. Denn in der klassischen Theorie bestehen immer Beziehungen zwischen den Intensitäten von der Art (2). Als Beispiel nehme man wieder den anharmonischen Oszillator und setze

$$x = \lambda a_0 + a_1 \cos \omega t + \lambda a_2 \cos 2\omega t + \lambda^2 a_3 \cos 3\omega t + \cdots \lambda^{\tau-1}a_\tau \cos \tau\omega t \cdots$$

Die Bewegungsgleichung lautet

$$\ddot{x} + \omega_0^2 x + \lambda x^2 = 0.$$

Daraus folgt in 1. Näherung, $\omega^2 \approx \omega_0^2$,

$$a_2(-4\omega^2 + \omega_0^2) = -\tfrac{1}{2}a_1^2,$$
$$a_3(-9\omega^2 + \omega_0^2) = a_1 a_2 \text{ u.s.w.}$$

Die quantentheoretische Verwandlung davon lautet offenbar:

$$a_2(n, n-2) \cdot 3\omega_0^2 = \tfrac{1}{2}a_1(n, n-1)a_1(n-1, n-2),$$
$$a_3(n, n-3) \cdot 8\omega_0^2 = \tfrac{1}{2}[a_1(n, n-1)a_2(n-1, n-3)$$
$$+ a_2(n, n-2)a_1(n-2, n-3)].$$

Entnimmt man aus der Theorie des harmonischen Oszillators, dass, was die Abhängigkeit von n betrifft, a gegeben ist durch $\sqrt{n}$ (auch in der Quantentheorie), so folgt, dass man hat:

In der klassischen Theorie

$$a_\tau(n) = \lambda^{\tau-1}k(\tau)\sqrt{n^\tau}.$$

In der Quantentheorie

$$a_\tau(n, n-\tau) = \lambda^{\tau-1}k(\tau)\sqrt{n(n-1)(n-2)\cdots(n-\tau+1)}.$$

Diese Formel ist nun in der Tat die seinerzeit schon besprochene (vgl. die Diskussionen mit Pauli), und ich könnte mir denken, dass man damit wirklich ein allgemeines Gezetz der Berechnung der Intensitäten hat: Aus den Bewegungsgleichungen ergeben sich einfache Beziehungen zwischen den a_τ, die (bei f Freiheitsgraden bis auf f unabhängige Konstante) die a_τ bestimmen. Diese Beziehungen übernehme man, nach quantentheoretischer Verwandlung, direkt in die Quantentheorie und hat (wieder bis auf f unabhängige Konstante) die Intensitäten. Die Bestimmung der Konstanten ist noch ein Kapitel für sich und ich will darüber heute nichts schreiben. Aber man kann z.b. zeigen, dass Ihre Intensitätsformeln der Multipletts und Zeemaneffekte auch aus dem eben ausgeführten Schema zu folgen scheinen.

Was mir an diesem Schema gefällt, ist, dass man wirklich alle Wechselwirkungen zwischen Atom und Aussenwelt dann auf die Übergangswahrscheinlichkeiten reduzieren kann (von Entartungsfragen abgesehen). Nicht zufrieden bin ich zunächst mit der mathematischen Seite (ich sehe bis jetzt keine Möglichkeit einer einfachen Berechnung der Intensitäten) und der Bestimmung der f Konstanten. Die physikalische Bedeutung des obengenannten Schemas zur Berechnung der Intensitäten gibt auch wieder sehr sonderbare Gesichtspunkte.

From this letter it appears how the law for the multiplication of quantum-mechanical quantities, later expressed in matrix terminology, was beginning to take shape. The determination of the f constants referred to by Heisenberg was ultimately achieved by the quantum-mechanical commutation rule for canonically conjugate variables, which in fact expressed in a new language the content of the above-mentioned sum rule of Kuhn and Thomas for the intensities.

The actual development of quantum mechanics by Heisenberg himself and by others will be dealt with elsewhere in this book, so that only the connection with spectroscopy has been touched upon here. In July 1925, when I again spent a short time in Göttingen, the work of Born and Jordan, who had formulated Heisenberg's theory in terms of matrices, stood in the foreground. Also Goudsmit (1925) and Hund (1925) were systematizing the consequences of the exclusion principle regarding the multiplets which can arise from a given electronic configuration of the atom. From Göttingen I went to San Vito di Cadore in the Dolomites, where I spent my vacation with Fermi and a group of Italian mathematicians, and I returned to Copenhagen early in September.

The great feeling of relief, generally felt with regard to the new situation, appears clearly from another letter of Pauli to me, dated 9 October 1925:

'Die Heisenbergsche Mechanik hat mir wieder Lebensfreude und Hoffnung gegeben. Die Lösung des Rätsels bringt sie zwar nicht, aber ich glaube, dass es jetzt wieder möglich ist vorwärts zu kommen. Man muss zunächst versuchen die Heisenbergsche Mechanik noch etwas mehr vom Göttinger formalen Gelehrsamkeitsschwall zu befreien und ihren physikalischen Kern noch besser blosszulegen. Dann müsste man einerseits versuchen, durch Vertiefung der Grundlagen auch den "Zwang" mit einzubegreifen und anderseits sie mit den Stosserscheinungen in einen natürlichen Konnex zu bringen.'

The last-mentioned problem was clarified only after the advent of wave mechanics a year later when Born, interpeting the wave function as a probability amplitude, showed the way for dealing with collision phenomena. The other one, designated by the word 'Zwang', referred to the notion, then current in Copenhagen and put forward strongly by Bohr (1923, 1925), that the doubling of terms which appeared in the fourth quantum number, as required by Pauli in the formulation of his exclusion principle, is a phenomenon induced in atoms with more than one electron and makes only a partial appearance for helium. For this element, the apparent doublet structure of the orthohelium terms had, by reason of insufficient spectroscopic resolution, not yet been unmasked as a triplet structure at the time. (For more details see the article by Van der Waerden.) The view-point I had arrived at in Tübingen of an intrinsic angular momentum residing in the electron did not fit in with these ideas.

In the late fall of 1925 a note appeared by Uhlenbeck and Goudsmit (1925) in which these authors independently set forth the idea of an intrinsic angular momentum of the electron, accompanied by a magnetic moment of one Bohr magneton without, however, realizing the nature of the coupling of this moment to the orbital motion and the possibility of deriving the dependence of the resulting fine structure on the atomic number according to a fourth power law. In an interesting review of his work Uhlenbeck (1955) stresses the moral support he and Goudsmit had had in this matter from Ehrenfest. At the end of November 1925, in a lecture on the interpretation of spectra which I gave before Fysisk Forening, the Danish physical society, and which was attended by most physicists then at Copenhagen, I drew attention anew to the notion of an intrinsic angular momentum of the electron, referring to the note of Uhlenbeck and Goudsmit, without receiving any response at all.

About 10 December 1925 I returned to America to commence a teaching position in New York. Through the experiments of B. Davis on the refraction of X-rays by solids I became interested in the theory of dispersion of a substance having continuous absorption bands instead of discrete absorption lines. By a generalization of the dispersion theory of Kramers and Heisenberg (1925) there resulted an integral formula, known today as one of the dispersion relations (Kronig, 1926a). The converse one expressing the absorption index in terms of the index of refraction was published by Kramers (1927), approaching the problem from the mathematical side. It is interesting to note that the dispersion relations later proved to be of much wider applicability (Kronig, 1946). Actually they were re-discovered independently by electrical engineers, as applying to the real and imaginary parts of electric impedances.

In March 1926 there appeared a second note by Uhlenbeck and Goudsmit (1926), dealing with the hydrogen spectrum. Already previously these authors (Goudsmit and Uhlenbeck, 1925) had proposed a formal re-numbering of the hydrogen levels in analogy with the classification of the stationary states for the alkali atoms. Introducing three quantum numbers, n, l, j, they had *assumed* the levels of equal j, but different l, to coincide in pairs, without, however, suggesting the nature of the interaction which would bring this about. The type of coupling which was sketched above in connection with my experiences in Tübingen came to their notice through Heisenberg. Uhlenbeck (1955) refers to this as follows:

'Eind October verscheen onze mededeling* en zij trok direct dee aandacht. Enige dagen na het verschijnen kregen wij reeds een brief van Heisenberg, waarin hij schreef dat met ons model de doubletsplitsing in de alkalispectra er goed uitkwam afgezien van een factor twee en hij vroeg onze opinie over deze moeilijkheid.'

In a letter dated 26 March 1926 Bohr wrote to me on this same subject:

'Now I even suspect that it is from yourself that the understanding of the mutual coupling between spin and orbital motion has come to the notice of the physicists. In fact, when on my return from Leiden I discussed in Göttingen the problems with Heisenberg, from whom the Leiden people had learnt the cause of the coupling, he told me that he had heard it himself a year before from somebody, but he could unfortunately in no way remember who it had been.'

As set forth in detail in Van der Waerden's article, the understanding of the coupling turned the scales, the quantum-mechanical strain was broken, and Bohr wrote a commendatory addendum to

* Uhlenbeck and Goudsmit, 1925.

the last note of Uhlenbeck and Goudsmit (Bohr, 1926). In these notes the term spin occurs for the first time.

In view of this complete *volte face* of the leading physicists in the matter of the quantum-mechanical strain, the only thing remaining for me to do was to call attention to all the difficulties still in the way of the proposed explanation (Kronig, 1926b). These difficulties are also fully referred to in the article by Van der Waerden.

The development in the following years threw an entirely new light on this complex of problems, to the clearing up of which Pauli made decisive contributions. It is therefore appropriate at the present stage to look more carefully into the history of quantum theory between 1926 and 1928.

As already mentioned, the considerations of Heisenberg (1925) were the starting-point for the matrix formulation of quantum mechanics which Born, in cooperation with Jordan, set up (Born and Jordan, 1925; Born, Heisenberg and Jordan, 1926). Indeed the relation between the amplitudes, already sketched out in the previously quoted letter of Heisenberg, is nothing else than the application of the rule for matrix multiplication. In close agreement with the ideas of Bohr's correspondence principle the formal aspects of classical mechanics were retained, non-commutative matrices taking the place of ordinary quantities in the Hamiltonian canonical equations

$$\dot{q}_r = \frac{\partial H}{\partial p_r}, \qquad \dot{p}_r = -\frac{\partial H}{\partial q_r} \qquad \ldots\ldots(14)$$

supplemented by the commutation relations

$$\left.\begin{array}{l} q_r q_s - q_s q_r = 0, \\ p_r p_s - p_s p_r = 0, \\ p_r q_s - q_s p_r = (h/2\pi i)\delta_{rs} \end{array}\right\} \qquad \ldots\ldots(15)$$

Truly one might speak here of new wine being put into old bottles. Independently, Dirac (1925, 1926b) arrived at results essentially equivalent to those of the above-mentioned authors.

After the treatment by Heisenberg (1925) of the linear harmonic oscillator, leading to conclusions in agreement with those of the older quantum theory except for the appearance of a zero-point energy, it became imperative to show that also for hydrogen-like atoms the correct energy values (3) result on the new basis. At a stage when the mathematical technique of the matrix calculus had been introduced, but before that of wave mechanics had become available, this was a task of considerable difficulty. In an ingenious treatment Pauli (1926) could show by the matrix method that quantum mechanics does, indeed, give the same results as the older theory.

If

$$\mathbf{P} = \mu \mathbf{r} \times \mathbf{v}$$

represents the constant angular momentum of the electron around the nucleus,

$$\mathbf{p} = \mu \mathbf{v}$$

the linear momentum, then it can be deduced from the equations of motion of classical mechanics that the vector

$$\mathbf{A} = \frac{1}{Ze^2\mu} \mathbf{P} \times \mathbf{p} + \frac{\mathbf{r}}{r}$$

is a constant in time. By scalar multiplication with $\mathbf{r}$ it follows that

$$\mathbf{A} \cdot \mathbf{r} = -\frac{1}{Ze^2\mu} \mathbf{P}^2 + r$$

Taking the square of the last equation but one it follows further that

$$1 - \mathbf{A}^2 = -\frac{2W}{Z^2e^4\mu} \mathbf{P}^2$$

where W denotes the energy. Pauli showed that in quantum mechanics vector matrices $\mathbf{A}$ and $\mathbf{P}$ can be introduced which formally obey the same equations. By making use of the exchange relations (15) he obtained a system of matrix formulae in which only the matrices $\mathbf{A}$, $\mathbf{P}$ and W are involved while the coordinates are eliminated. The solution of these equations, which can be carried out in an elementary way, leads to the energy values (3) (for infinite nuclear mass).

About this time the investigations described became confluent with another approach that also had its origin in 1925. In that year de Broglie (1925) published a remarkable paper which, however, did not immediately receive all the attention that it deserved. In it the suggestion was made that the duality in the nature of light, long recognized as a wave motion, but also manifesting corpuscular properties when interacting with material particles, has its counterpart in the behaviour of matter with which a wave phenomenon is to be associated, in addition to its having corpuscular character. On the basis of the theory of relativity, de Broglie was led to postulate a relation between the momentum **p** and the energy W of a free particle on the one hand and the wave vector **k** and the frequency ν of the associated plane wave on the other hand in the form

$$\mathbf{p} = h\mathbf{k}, \qquad W = h\nu \qquad \ldots \ldots (16)$$

A test for the first relation was soon provided by the experiments of Davisson and Germer and of G. P. Thomson and others on electron diffraction by crystals.

While de Broglie had confined his attention essentially to a free particle, making only some qualitative suggestions for other cases, Schrödinger (1926) extended his work, in the first place, to the problem of a particle of mass μ, subject to a force derivable from a potential energy V and with the restriction to non-relativistic motions. Partly by intuitive reasoning he arrived at the time-dependent wave equation

$$-\frac{h^2}{8\pi^2\mu}\Delta\Psi + V\Psi = -\frac{h}{2\pi i}\frac{\partial\Psi}{\partial t} \qquad \ldots \ldots (17)$$

to be obeyed by the wave function Ψ. For systems in a stationary state with energy W, characterized by a wave function with time-dependence of the form

$$\Psi = \psi e^{-2\pi i Wt/h}$$

there arises from it the time-independent wave equation

$$-\frac{h^2}{8\pi^2\mu}\Delta\psi + V\psi = W\psi \qquad \ldots \ldots (18)$$

which leads to an eigenvalue problem for the parameter W if a reasonable mathematical behaviour of ψ is required everywhere. A determination of the energy values of the stationary states was thus made possible along lines which at first sight seemed to be remote from the approach provided by the matrix method.

Schrödinger himself was able, however, to demonstrate the essential equivalence of the two theories. In fact the view-point developed by him provided the means for computing in a systematic way the matrix elements in the theory of Heisenberg, Born and Jordan. In the first place he could extend his results to systems of more than one particle and to forces derivable from a vector potential, making use, if so desired, of generalized coordinates $q_1, q_2 \cdots, q_n$ instead of rectangular coordinates. The wave function is then a function in the abstract multi-dimensional configurational space of the q. The salient point in the construction of the quantum-mechanical matrices is that the peculiar rules of computation, which according to Born, Heisenberg and Jordan are obeyed by functions of the $2n$ quantities $q_1, q_2, \cdots, q_n$; $p_1, p_2, \cdots, p_n$, are completely conformal to the rules of computation which are valid in the field of ordinary analysis for the linear differential operators in the domain of the n variables $q_1, q_2, \cdots, q_n$. The coordination has to be carried out in such a way that in the function every p_r is replaced by the operator $\partial/\partial q_r$. Indeed, the operator $\partial/\partial q_r$ commutes with $\partial/\partial q_s$ for arbitrary m; with q_s, however, only if $s \neq r$. The operator obtained for $s = r$ by commutation and subtraction,

$$\frac{\partial}{\partial q_r} q_r - q_r \frac{\partial}{\partial q_r}$$

applied to an arbitrary function of the q's, on the other hand reproduces the function and is hence the identity operator. Making use of a complete normalized set of eigenfunctions $u_1(q), u_2(q) \cdots$ in the space of the variables q with a density function $\rho(q)$, the matrix elements in the quantum mechanics of Born, Heisenberg and Jordan are then given by

$$F_{jk} = \int u_j^\star(q)[F u_k(q)]\rho(q)\,\mathrm{d}q$$

Schrödinger's investigations also elucidated the relation between quantum mechanics and classical mechanics, the former appearing as a generalization of the latter in a similar sense as physical optics is a generalization of geometrical optics. An entire branch of mathematics, that of partial differential equations and their solution in terms of eigenfunctions, so fruitful in other sections of theoretical physics, had thus at one stroke been made available for the handling of the problems of atomic physics.

The deeper significance of the wave function Ψ naturally became a subject of much discussion, particularly after Schrödinger had shown that the quantity $\Psi^\star\Psi$ obeys a conservation law in configurational space. While de Broglie and Schrödinger originally cherished the hope of re-introducing by its means the determinism into physics which had been abandoned in such concepts as the transition probabilities, it soon became apparent that the full benefits of the new view-point could only be reaped by an even further relinquishment of a deterministic description. Born (1926) in particular stressed at an early date, in connection with collision problems, the necessity of interpreting the wave function as a probability amplitude and its square $\Psi^\star\Psi$ as a probability density of encountering the system in a particular configuration of its coordinates. Bohr brought forward his whole

2*

authority to make clear the complementary character of the particle and wave pictures, so strikingly formulated by Heisenberg (1927b) in his uncertainty relations

$$\Delta q \Delta p \approx h \qquad \qquad \dots (19)$$

for canonically conjugate variables.

At the period in question long and instructive discussions took place in Copenhagen on this subject between Bohr and Einstein, the latter advocating a more deterministic formulation of physics, although it was he himself to whom we owe in such a large measure the concept of transition probability with its non-deterministic implications. Since then this issue has been raised anew from time to time, but it was always felt by the great majority of physicists, and is still felt so today, that the probability interpretation of quantum theory has come to stay and is an adequate framework for answering all the questions to which observations on atomic systems may give rise.

In the formulation of quantum mechanics reported so far, the material particles were considered as characterized by positional coordinates only. It now became an urgent task to incorporate the phenomenon indicated by the term 'spin' into the new scheme of things. The initial steps were taken by Pauli (1927b) himself, who proposed that the wave function of an electron, besides being determined by the continuously variable positional coordinates, should be considered as also depending on a spin variable, capable of two values only. We refer the reader to the article by Van der Waerden as regards the details of this development. A basis for discussing spectroscopic problems and in particular the anomalous Zeeman effect was thus provided which no longer took recourse to classical models of a charge rotating about an axis through its centre. Thereby Pauli paved the way for the relativistic theory of the electron and of hydrogen-like atoms which we owe to Dirac (1928).

In fact, one of the shortcomings of the theories hitherto discussed, with the exception of the original investigation of de Broglie for free particles and some suggestions of Schrödinger, was that they represented a quantum-theoretical translation of non-relativistic classical mechanics. The fundamental nature of this restriction as well as the fact that in the case of hydrogen-like atoms relativistic effects lead to the observable phenomenon of the fine structure in the spectrum made it highly desirable to take the requirements of the theory of relativity properly into account. Dirac showed that for a single electron in external electric and magnetic fields a relativistically invariant wave equation could be formulated, not indeed as one might first have expected after Pauli's work, with a wave function depending on a spin variable capable of two values only, but with a four-component wave function.

In Dirac's theory of the electron, the last fundamental step necessary for the interpretation of spectra was taken (if we disregard the small radiative corrections to energy levels envisaged in quantum field theory). Dirac's wave equation removed at one stroke all the remaining difficulties. Applied to hydrogen-like atoms it gives the observed fine structure proportional to the fourth power of the nuclear charge. In the presence of an external magnetic field, energy shifts arise which can be represented as due to two angular momenta: one, the orbital angular momentum, carrying normal magnetism, the other, the spin angular momentum vector, carrying double magnetism. Also, these magnetic moments can both be understood as due to a current distribution extending over the entire atomic dimensions.

There was one further feature implicit in the wave equation of Dirac which was fully understood only much later. The introduction of a four-component wave function instead of the two-component wave function suggested by Pauli entailed a further doubling of the manifold of stationary states: to every state of positive energy there corresponds one with negative energy. This opened a way for the theory of the positron which will be dealt with elsewhere in connection with the quantization of fields.

Interesting and fundamental aspects of wave mechanics were recognized by Heisenberg (1926, 1927a) when the invariance of the wave equation with respect to various transformations was investigated. It is clear that such an invariance exists with respect to an interchange of the coordinates of identical particles, e.g. of two electrons in an atom or of two nuclei of the same kind in a molecule. As a consequence, the wave function of a non-degenerate stationary state must either remain unchanged or may only change sign when this transformation is applied to it. It was soon realized from spectroscopic evidence that, for a given kind of particle, nature makes use of one type of wave function only, e.g. for electrons and protons of the antisymmetric type, for ^{4}He-nuclei of the symmetric type. Indeed, in this way Pauli's exclusion principle for electrons found a formulation in terms of wave mechanics. In the article by Van der Waerden this subject is discussed in greater detail.

A more systematic study of the significance which the invariance of the wave equation of an atom against rotations of the coordinate system and against interchange of the coordinates of electrons has for spectroscopy we owe in particular to Wigner (1926, 1927). He was the first to apply the methods of group theory to the problems in question. In this connection he also pointed out that, besides the transformations already referred to above, reflection at the origin is an operation which leaves the wave equation unaltered. In this way a further division of the stationary states into two classes, even and odd states, can be accomplished. While for atomic spectroscopy this concept of parity gave a theoretical basis to results known for some time, it has become of great importance recently in the case of the non-electrodynamic forces that govern the behaviour of the atomic nucleus and which fall outside the discussion of this article.

It was natural that after the clarification of atomic spectroscopy the application of quantum mechanics to molecular spectra, in particular to those of diatomic molecules, became urgent. The resulting investigations, while contributing much to a better understanding of molecular structure, added nothing to the fundamental principles of physics. In connection with the earlier references it may be mentioned that the problem of the dielectric constant for a gas of rotating molecules was taken up anew in papers by Mensing and Pauli (1926) and by Kronig (1926c) in which it was shown that the classical Debye formula (9) for the dielectric constant in weak fields keeps its validity also in quantum mechanics. Another investigation which deserves separate mention is the interpretation by Heitler and London (1927) of the chemical binding in homopolar molecules on the basis of quantum mechanics, which opened large vistas in the field of theoretical chemistry.

A great extension of the possibilities for a theoretical treatment of problems in atomic physics was brought about as regards collision problems. In this field the older quantum theory had allowed few quantitative predictions. In wave mechanics collision problems were translated into an investigation of the scattering of a plane wave, representing the incoming particles, by the atomic system. Born (1926) first showed the way to deal with this subject. The calculation of the scattering of electrons in a central field of force by Faxén and Holtsmark (1927), using mathematical methods which go back to Lord Rayleigh, was an early prototype of this kind of work. Approximation methods also became available soon for handling cases in which, besides elastic scattering, there occurs inelastic scattering of the incident particles with energy transfer to the atomic system.

The development of quantum theory had important repercussions on statistical mechanics. Already in 1924 Einstein (1924) was led to the conclusion that for a system of identical particles in a common field of force, e.g. the molecules of a gas in a box, the enumeration of different states giving rise to the same macroscopic configuration had to be revised in a way first proposed by Bose (1924) in a derivation of Planck's law of black body radiation. Transferring this method from the case of photons to that of material particles with finite mass, Einstein arrived at an equation of state which later played an important role in the discussion of the properties of liquid helium. In a second paper Einstein (1925) pointed to the connection of these results with the work of de Broglie (1925).

While in the Bose–Einstein statistics no exclusion principle was assumed, so that this formalism was applicable to systems of particles described by wave functions symmetrical in the coordinates, Fermi (1926) and Dirac (1926b) discussed the analogous problem for systems of particles governed by antisymmetrical wave functions, in particular electrons.

The two statistics were characterized by the expression for the probability f in thermodynamic equilibrium of a non-degenerate stationary state being occupied, the relevant formulae being

$$f = \frac{1}{e^{(W-\zeta)/kT} \mp 1} \qquad \ldots (20)$$

where ζ is the thermodynamic potential, k Boltzmann's constant and T the absolute temperature, while the upper sign refers to the Bose–Einstein statistics, the lower sign to the Fermi–Dirac statistics. Applications for the latter were soon found in the previously mentioned work of Pauli (1927b) on the paramagnetism of metals and in the investigation by Sommerfeld (1928) of their electrical properties.

In the present survey, intended chiefly as a recapitulation of the older quantum theory in its relation to spectroscopy and of the development from it of modern quantum mechanics for systems with a finite number of degrees of freedom, the more prominent further developments can only be briefly indicated.

In publications by Jordan and Klein (1927) and by Jordan and Wigner (1928) it was shown that the results of non-relativistic quantum mechanics, obtained with a description of the system by a wave function in configuration space, could equally well be derived in three-dimensional space by applying the method of second quantization. The importance of this result lies in the fact that the way is thereby prepared for field theories which form the subject of another chapter.

In the realm of spectroscopy an exhaustive study of the energy levels of atoms built into crystal lattices was made by Bethe (1929) with the help of group theory. A revival of spectroscopy occurred after World War II when the application of microwave techniques permitted the study of spectra in a region hitherto inaccessible to the experimenter. Thus the investigation of the transitions between the different Zeeman levels of an atomic or molecular term, known as magnetic resonance, became possible both in the case where electronic magnetic moments and where nuclear magnetic moments come into play. Interesting applications to the study of problems of chemical constitution and of solid state physics were made, without, however, anything novel being added to fundamental principles.

In the region of extremely short wavelengths a new branch of experimentation, γ-ray spectroscopy, came into being. Here it is the nucleus, whose stationary states and radiative transitions are studied. All the concepts known from the case of the atom make their reappearance here: energy levels, parity, angular momenta of individual nucleons and their composition to give a resultant angular momentum, the exclusion principle, selection rules and transition probabilities. A greater richness of phenomena is provided by the fact that two kinds of particles, protons and neutrons, are involved in the emission of the spectra and by the additional circumstance that, next to electric dipole transitions, magnetic dipole transitions as well as transitions due to higher poles are often observed. Also in the reaction of nuclei to bombardment by fast particles the counterpart of atomic collisions is to be seen. All the available evidence appears to prove that the fundamental concepts of quantum mechanics are just as applicable to the description of the nucleus as to that of the atom.

I should like to end this survey by some personal reminiscences. In 1928 Pauli was nominated to the chair of Theoretical Physics at the Eidgenössische Technische Hochschule at Zürich. Late in 1927 he asked me if I would care to come there as his assistant. In a letter dated 22 November 1927 he writes about the position:

'Lästige Verpflichtungen wären für Sie kaum damit verbunden; Ihre Aufgabe wäre, jedesmal, wenn ich etwas sage, mir mit ausführlichen Begründungen zu widersprechen'.

I accepted and I always look back on the time I spent in Zürich, not only as one of the most instructive, but also as one of the most exhilarating periods of my life. Pauli began his new task at the end of April 1928, arriving a day before his birthday, and Scherrer cheered up his room on the occasion by having put some flowers on his writing desk. It was the best part of the year to be in Zürich, and as the days got warmer Scherrer, Pauli and myself often went swimming at the Strandbad, eating our lunch in bathing suits. One of my tasks, not agreed upon beforehand, was to watch out that Pauli should limit his consumption of ice cream at Sprüngli's Konditorei at the Paradeplatz where we often went in the afternoon. I recall in particular ordering an 'Eisschokolade' and, on being asked by the waitress whether it should be solid or fluid, replying that I preferred it fluid, my companion on the other hand in gaseous form. Such expeditions were often interspersed with discussions on subjects from physics, in which Pauli was unwilling to tolerate sloppy thinking, but was always ready to give honours where honours were due and to admit a mistake on his part if one could counter him with good arguments. Also he was quite willing to let you compensate the advantages he had when swimming in the Zürichsee by coming along on a Sunday walking tour where he had a handicap against persons of a lighter build.

I am sure that the many physicists who have succeeded me in the post I then held will look back on their stay in Zürich with as much gratitude as I do. After our first meeting, Pauli's orbit and my own have crossed repeatedly and in various ways, leaving me with the feeling of having received more than I ever could give in the vital atmosphere which surrounds him.

Note added 31 December 1958

The last paragraphs of the preceding text were written on the evening of 14 December, the night preceding Pauli's death, which came as a great shock to all his friends. In their memory, as well as in the history of physics, he will always hold a singular place.

REFERENCES

Bethe, H. (1929) *Ann. Phys. Lpz.* **3**, 133
Bohr, N. (1913) *Phil. Mag.* **26**, 1, 476, 857
— (1914) *Phil. Mag.* **27**, 506
— (1915) *Phil. Mag.* **29**, 332; **30**, 394
— (1918) *K. danske vidensk. Selsk. Nat. Mat. Afd.* Series IV, **8**, 1
— (1922) *Z. Phys.* **9**, 1

Bohr, N. (1923) *Ann. Phys. Lpz.* **1**, 228
— (1925) *Nature, Lond.* **116**, 845
— (1926) *Nature, Lond.* **117**, 265
— and Coster, D. (1923) *Z. Phys.* **12**, 342
— Kramers, H. A. and Slater, J. C. (1924) *Z. Phys.* **24**, 69
Born, M. (1926) *Z. Phys.* **37**, 863; **38**, 803
— and Heisenberg, W. (1923) *Z. Phys.* **16**, 259
— — and Jordan, P. (1926) *Z. Phys.* **35**, 557
— and Jordan, P. (1925) *Z. Phys.* **34**, 858
— and Pauli, W. (1922) *Z. Phys.* **10**, 137
Bose, S. N. (1924) *Z. Phys.* **26**, 178
Broglie, L. de (1925) *Ann. Phys. Lpz.* **3**, 22
Compton, A. H. (1923) *Phys. Rev.* **21**, 483
Debye, P. (1916) *Phys. Z.* **17**, 507
— (1923) *Phys. Z.* **24**, 161
Dirac, P. A. M. (1925) *Proc. Roy. Soc. A* **109**, 642
— (1926a) *Proc. Roy. Soc. A* **110**, 561; **111**, 279
— (1926b) *Proc. Roy. Soc. A* **112**, 661
— (1928) *Proc. Roy. Soc. A* **117**, 610; **118**, 351
Einstein, A. (1905) *Ann. Phys. Lpz.* **17**, 132
— (1917) *Phys. Z.* **18**, 121
— (1924) *S. B. preuss. Akad. Wiss.* 261
— (1925) *S. B. preuss. Akad. Wiss.* 3
Epstein, P. S. (1916) *Ann. Phys. Lpz.* **50**, 489
Faxén, H. and Holtsmark, J. (1927) *Z. Phys.* **45**, 307
Fermi, E. (1926) *Z. Phys.* **36**, 902
Goudsmit, S. (1925) *Z. Phys.* **32**, 794
— and Kronig, R. (1925) *Naturwissenschaften* **13**, 90
— and Uhlenbeck, G. E. (1925) *Physica* **5**, 266
Heisenberg, W. (1925) *Z. Phys.* **33**, 879
— (1926) *Z. Phys.* **38**, 411; **39**, 499
— (1927a) *Z. Phys.* **41**, 239
— (1927b) *Z. Phys.* **43**, 172
Heitler, W. and London, F. (1927) *Z. Phys.* **44**, 455
Hund, F. (1925) *Z. Phys.* **33**, 345; **34**, 296
Jordan, P. and Klein, O. (1927) *Z. Phys.* **45**, 751
— and Wigner, E. (1928) *Z. Phys.* **47**, 631
Kramers, H. A. (1919) *K. danske vidensk. Selsk. Nat. Mat. Afd.* Series III,
    8, 3
— (1920) *Z. Phys.* **3**, 199
— (1927) *Atti Congr. dei Fisici Como*, p. 545
— and Heisenberg, W. (1925) *Z. Phys.* **31**, 681
— and Pauli, W. (1923) *Z. Phys.* **13**, 351
Kronig, R. (1925) *Z. Phys.* **31**, 885; **33**, 261
— (1926a) *J. opt. Soc. Amer.* **12**, 547
— (1926b) *Nature, Lond.* **117**, 550
— (1926c) *Proc. nat. Acad. Sci., Wash.* **12**, 488, 608
— (1946) *Physica* **12**, 543
Kuhn, W. (1925) *Z. Phys.* **33**, 408
Ladenburg, R. (1921) *Z. Phys.* **4**, 451
— and Reiche, F. (1923) *Naturwissenschaften* **11**, 584
Landé, A. (1923) *Z. Phys.* **15**, 189
— (1924) *Z. Phys.* **24**, 88; **25**, 46
Mensing, L. and Pauli, W. (1926) *Phys. Z.* **27**, 509
Pauli, W. (1920) *Z. Phys.* **2**, 201
— (1921) *Z. Phys.* **6**, 319
— (1922) *Ann. Phys. Lpz.* **68**, 177

Pauli, W. (1923a) *Z. Phys.* **16**, 155
— (1923b) *Z. Phys.* **18**, 272
— (1923c) *Z. Phys.* **20**, 371
— (1924) *Naturwissenschaften* **12**, 741
— (1925) *Z. Phys.* **31**, 765
— (1926) *Z. Phys.* **36**, 336
— (1927a) *Z. Phys.* **41**, 81
—' (1927b) *Z. Phys.* **43**, 601
Planck, M. (1900) *Verh. dtsch. phys. Ges.* **2**, 237
Russell, H. N. (1925) *Nature, Lond.* **115**, 835
Rutherford, E. (1913) *Phil. Mag.* **21**, 669
Schrödinger, E. (1926) *Ann. Phys. Lpz.* **79**, 361, 489, 734; **80**, 437; **81**, 109
Sommerfeld, A. (1915) *S.-B. bayer. Akad. Wiss.* 425, 459
— (1916a) *S.-B. bayer. Akad. Wiss.* 131
— (1916b) *Ann. Phys. Lpz.* **51**, 1
— (1916c) *Phys. Z.* **17**, 491
— (1928) *Z. Phys.* **47**, 1, 43
— and Heisenberg, W. (1922) *Z. Phys.* **11**, 131
— and Hönl, H. 1925 *S.-B. preuss. Akad. Wiss.* 141
Thomas, W. (1925) *Naturwissenschaften* **13**, 627
Uhlenbeck, G. E. (1955) *Oude en Nieuwe Vragen der Natuurkunde*, Amsterdam; Noord-Hollandse Uitgeversmaatschappij
— and Goudsmit, S. (1925) *Naturwissenschaften* **13**, 953
— — (1926) *Nature, Lond.* **117**, 264
Wigner, E. (1926) *Z. Phys.* **40**, 492, 883
— (1927) *Z. Phys.* **43**, 624

ERINNERUNGEN AN DIE ZEIT DER ENTWICKLUNG DER QUANTENMECHANIK

W. HEISENBERG

Pauli hat an der Entwicklung der Quantentheorie in den kritischen Jahren von 1922 bis 1927 mit dem intensivsten wissenschaftlichen Interesse und mit seiner ganzen Arbeitskraft teilgenommen. Von seinen Beiträgen sind die von ihm damals veröffentlichten Arbeiten und sein Handbuchartikel über die Quantentheorie allgemein bekannt geworden. Diese Veröffentlichungen enthalten aber, wie dies bei der ungewöhnlich kritischen Einstellung Paulis begreiflich ist, nur einen kleinen Teil der wirklich von ihm geleisteten Arbeit. Pauli berichtete in seinen Abhandlungen über die fertigen Ergebnisse, aber nicht über den langen und oft mühevollen Weg, der zu ihnen geführt hatte, und auch nicht über unfertige Versuche. Ein Teil seiner im Stillen geleisteten Arbeit hat sich in dem umfangreichen Briefwechsel niedergeschlagen, der in jener Zeit swischen Pauli und mir geführt wurde, und wenn mir auch heute leider nur noch die Briefe zugänglich sind, die ich damals an Pauli schrieb, und die Pauli gelegentlich mit Notizen am Rand versah, nicht aber Paulis Antworten, so geben diese Briefe doch ein lebendiges Bild von dem Ringen um die Grundprobleme der Quantentheorie, an dem damals nur ein kleiner, überschaubarer Kreis von Physikern beteiligt war. Der erhalten gebliebene Teil des Briefwechsels soll also hier dazu benützt werden, um den Inhalt jener leidenschaftlichen Diskussionen über physikalische Grundfragen wenigstens teilweise zu rekonstruieren.

Zu Beginn jener Zeit waren drei Problemkreise in der unübersichtlichsten Weise miteinander verwoben, und ihre Trennung und Aufklärung bereitete die größten Schwierigkeiten. Es waren dies: Der durch den Elektronenspin bedingte anomale Zeemaneffekt vieler Spektrallinien, das Ausschließungsprinzip, und schließlich als wichtigstes die mit dem Dualismus Korpuskel–Welle verknüpften Grundfragen der Quantentheorie. Erst am Ende jener Periode wußte man, daß es sich dabei um drei grundsätzlich verschiedene Probleme handelte. In der Anfangszeit aber war es bei ben Mißerfolgen fast jedes theoretischen Versuchs, der über eine rein phänomenologische Beschreibung der experimentellen Tatsachen hinausging, zunächst immer unklar, ob es sich um das Versagen einer bestimmten Modellvorstellung (z.B. des kugelsymmetrischen Elektrons) oder aller Arten von Modellvorstellungen überhaupt, oder um ein falsches Auswahlprinzip bei der Festlegung der stationären Zustände handelte.

Ein erstes Ergebnis von entscheidender Bedeutung war der von Pauli (im Sommer 1922) geführte Nachweis, daß man durch Anwendung der Bohr-Sommerfeldschen Quantenbedingungen auf das Wasserstoffmolekül-Ion nicht zu den richtigen stationären Zuständen kommen konnte. Zwar genügte dieses Resultat noch nicht, um die Atommodelle bei den Physikern ein für allemal zu diskreditieren; dafür waren die Erfolge der Modelle beim Wasserstoffatom, dem Starkeffekt und Zeemaneffekt seiner Spektrallinien, und beim Periodischen System der Elemente viel zu groß und überraschend gewesen. Aber der Glaube an die anschaulich beschreibbaren Modelle wurde durch Paulis Arbeit doch zum ersten Male ernstlich erschüttert. In dieser Situation waren die empirischen Ergebnisse beim anomalen Zeemaneffekt von großer Wichtigkeit. Dort stellte sich nämlich durch die Arbeiten von Sommerfeld, Landé und anderen heraus, daß man durch ein verhältnismäßig einfaches, anschauliches Modell die empirischen Formeln zwar qualitativ, aber nicht quantitativ ableiten konnte. Man mußte am Schluß der Rechnungen immer noch Änderungen von der Art vornehmen, daß man etwa die Quantenzahl k durch $k - \frac{1}{2}$, oder l^2 durch $l(l+1)$ ersetzte. In den Diskussionen, die sich darüber zwischen Pauli und mir entspannen, wurde schon im Oktober 1923 einmal der Satz aufgeschrieben: 'Die Modellvorstellungen haben prinzipiell nur einen symbolischen Sinn, sie sind das klassische Analogon zur "diskreten" Quantentheorie'. Damit war also in aller Schärfe die Frage aufgeworfen, wie die 'diskrete' Quantentheorie, oder wir wir heute sagen, die Quantenmechanik, mathematisch aussehen könnte.

Aber die Theorie der Feinstruktur und des anomalen Zeemaneffektes enthielt noch andere Rätsel. Pauli hatte schon früh bemerkt, daß die Abzählung der stationären Zustände im Periodischen System der Elemente nicht in Ordnung war, und daß insbesondere die Feinstruktur der Röntgenlinien, so wie sie empirisch beobachtet wurde, niemals aus der Sommerfeldschen Theorie der relativistischen Feinstruktur folgen konnte; denn die Anzahl der diskreten Zustände war größer, als sie nach der Sommerfeldschen Theorie sein durfte.

Im Dezember 1924 schickte mir Pauli seine neue Arbeit über dieses Problem: Man mußte dem Elektron noch einen weiteren, vierten Freiheitsgrad geben, der nur zweier Werte fähig war; Pauli sprach von einer mechanisch nicht beschreibbaren Verdopplung der Zustände. Damit konnte man die Abzählung in Ordnung bringen und zu einer ungezwungenen Beschreibung des Periodischen Systems mit Hilfe des hier formulierten Paulischen Ausschließungsprinzips kommen. Jeder Quantenzustand durfte nur einfach besetzt werden. Die anschauliche Bedeutung des neuen Freiheitsgrades war damals allerdings noch unbekannt, ebenso natürlich der Zusammenhang zwischen dem Ausschließungsprinzip und den Symmetrieeigenschaften der Wellenfunktion.

Weitere wichtige Punkte unserer Diskussion waren dann die Ornsteinschen Intensitätsregeln bei den Multipletts, sowie die Kramers'sche Dispersionstheorie. In beiden Fällen waren Pauli und ich uns einig darüber, daß hier der Übergang von der nur symbolisch brauchbaren und daher nur qualitativ richtigen Modell-Mechanik im Sinne der Bohr-Sommerfeldschen Bedingungen zur wirklichen Quantenmechanik durch Erraten gelungen war; daß man das Bohrsche Korrespondenzprinzip hatte mathematisch soweit verschärfen können, bis man zu den richtigen Formeln vorgedrungen war. Also war es vielleicht auch möglich, einfach durch geschicktes Erraten eines Tages den Übergang zum vollständigen mathematischen Schema der Quantenmechanik zu vollziehen.

Ich versuchte zunächst im Frühjahr 1925, durch Studium der Fourierentwicklung der Keplerbahn im Wasserstoffatom zu Intensitätsformeln für das Wasserstoffspektrum zu gelangen in der Hoffnung, die richtigen quantentheoretischen Intensitätsformeln schließlich einfach erraten zu können. Das Keplerproblem erwies sich hierfür allerdings als zu schwierig, aber es ergab sich dabei von selbst die Vorstellung, daß die Gesamtheit der 'Übergangselemente' die Koordinaten eines Elektrons genau so gut repräsentieren könne, wie in der klassischen Physik die Fourierreihe dies tut. Die Zusammenfassung der empirisch greifbaren Informationen in der Koordinatenmatrix des Elektrons oder allgemein in den für jede vernünftige physikalische Größe zu bildenden Matrizen, blieb ein noch nicht ganz klar formuliertes Ergebnis jener Rechnung. Im Mai 1925 wandte ich diese Vorstellungen dann auf ein einfacheres Problem an, nämlich auf den anharmonischen Oszillator. Ein durch eine leichte Heufiebererkrankung verursachter Zwangsaufenthalt auf der Insel Helgoland Ende Mai 1925 gab mir die erwünschte Gelegenheit, den anharmonischen Oszillator nach den neuen Vorstellungen in allen Einzelheiten durchzurechnen. Obwohl es mir zunächst nicht gelang, ganz allgemein zu beweisen, daß die Energie dabei notwendig zu einer Diagonalmatrix wurde, daß also die Energie erhalten blieb, so sah das ganze Verfahren doch so vernünftig aus, daß ich es nach meiner Rückkehr nach Göttingen schon am 24. Juni Pauli in einem Brief mitteilte. Die Darstellung begann mit dem Satz: 'Grundsatz ist, bei der Berechnung von irgendwelchen Größen, wie Energie, Frequenz usw., dürfen nur Beziehungen zwischen prinzipiell beobachtbaren Größen vorkommen'. Paulis Antwort war ausgesprochen positiv, und ermunterte mich in der weiteren Ausarbeitung. Die mathematische Ausgestaltung zu einer in sich geschlossenen Theorie wurde bekanntlich in den nächsten Monaten unabhängig von Born und Jordan in Göttingen einerseits, von Dirac in Cambridge andererseits, durchgeführt. Ich selbst war damals etwas unglücklich darüber, daß es mir nicht gelingen wollte, auch nur das einfache Wasserstoffspektrum aus der neuen Theorie abzuleiten. Schon im Oktober des gleichen Jahres aber überraschte mich Pauli mit der vollständigen Quantenmechanik des Wasserstoffatoms. Mein Antwortbrief vom 3. November beginnt mit dem Satz: 'Ich brauche Ihnen wohl nicht zu schreiben, wie sehr ich mich über die neue Theorie des Wasserstoffs freue, und wie sehr ich es bewundere, daß Sie diese Theorie so schnell herausgebracht haben'.

Etwa um die gleiche Zeit erschien auch die Arbeit von Goudsmit über den Drehimpuls des Elektrons. Auch diese Arbeit bildete einen wichtigen Diskussionsgegenstand in Paulis Briefen. Doch soll über die Theorie des Elektronenspins im vorliegenden Buch an anderer Stelle berichtet werden. Dem von Pauli formulierten vierten Freiheitsgrad des Elektrons war damit eine einfache, anschauliche Deutung gegeben, deren Durchführbarkeit in unseren Briefen im einzelnen erörtert wurde.

Im Sommer 1925 bildeten auch schon die Anfänge der Wellenmechanik einen wichtigen Diskussionspunkt. Der Gedanke, daß die Versuche von Ramsauer einerseits, von Davisson und Kunsman andererseits durch Elektronenbeugung zu erklären seien, gewann, unterstützt durch eine Arbeit von Einstein, langsam an Boden. Im Frühjahr 1926 folgten dann die berühmten Arbeiten Schrödingers über das Wasserstoffatom, und damit die vollständige mathematische Formulierung der Wellenmechanik. Die Diskussionen über Schrödingers Theorie beschäftigten Pauli und mich sehr. Während wir den großen mathematischen Fortschritt sofort erkannten, blieben wir hinsichtlich der physikalischen Interpretation skeptisch. Der Versuch, die Wellenvorstellung zum physikalischen Mittelpunkt der Theorie zu machen, beunruhigte mich tief. In Briefen aus dem Sommer 1926 stehen die Sätze: 'Je mehr ich über den physikalischen Teil der Schrödingerschen Theorie nachdenke, desto abscheulicher finde ich ihn. Schrödinger wirft ja alles quantentheoretische, nämlich den lichtelektrischen Effekt, die Franckschen Stöße, den Stern-Gerlacheffekt usw. einfach über Bord. Dann ist es nicht schwer, eine Theorie zu machen; aber sie stimmt eben nicht mit der Erfahrung. Die große Leistung der Schrödingerschen Theorie ist die Berechnung der Matrixelemente.'

So wendete sich unser Interesse von selbst der immer noch unverstandenen Interpretation des mathematischen Formalismus der Quanten- und Wellenmechanik zu. Born entwickelte im Sommer 1926 seine Theorie der Stoßprozesse, und interpretierte die Welle im mehrdimensionalen Konfigurationsraum—in Fortbildung eines früheren Gedankens von Bohr, Kramers und Slater —richtig als Wahrscheinlichkeitswelle. Pauli setzte mir daraufhin in einem Brief auseinander, daß die Bornsche Interpretation nur ein Spezialfall einer viel allgemeineren Interpretationsvorschrift sei. So könne man zum Beispiel $|\psi(p)|^2\,dp$ als Wahrscheinlichkeit dafür deuten, daß das Teilchen einen Impuls zwischen p und $p+dp$ habe. Das paßte auch gut zu Überlegungen, die ich selbst über Schwankungserscheinungen angestellt hatte. Im Herbst 1926 entwickelte Dirac seine Transformationstheorie, in der dann allgemein das Absolut-Quadrat der Matrixelemente der unitären Transformationsmatrix als Wahrscheinlichkeit gedeutet wurde.

In den Sommermonaten des gleichen Jahres wurde auch der Zusammenhang des Paulischen Ausschließungsprinzips mit der Wellen- und Quantenmechanik klargestellt. Man konnte einerseits an der Quantenmechanik des Heliumatoms, mit dem ich mich beschäftigt hatte, nachweisen, daß man die richtigen, dem Pauliprinzip genügenden Terme nur dann erhielt, wenn man die Antisymmetrie der Wellenfunktion in den Teilchenkoordinaten forderte; und andererseits konnten Fermi und Dirac zeigen, daß ganz allgemein die Forderung der Antisymmetrie der Wellenfunktion bei Vertauschung der Koordinaten zweier beliebiger Elektronen dem Paulischen Prinzip äquivalent war, und bei Anwendung auf ein ideales Gas zu einer neuen Statistik führte. Damit war der physikalische Sinn des Paulischen Ausschließungsprinzips endgültig klargestellt.

Um diese Zeit, im Herbst 1926, gewann auch schon die

Unbestimmtheitsrelation im Briefwechsel zwischen Pauli und mir allmählich Gestalt. In einem Brief vom 28. Oktober 1926 steht der Satz: 'Die Gleichung $pq - qp = -i\hbar$ entspricht also immer in der Wellenvorstellung der Tatsache, daß es keinen Sinn hat, von einer monochromatischen Welle in einem bestimmten Zeitpunkt (oder sehr kurzem Zeitintervall) zu sprechen'. Pauli bemerkte dazu am Rande: 'In einem gegenüber der Periode kurzen Zeitintervall hat es auch keinen Sinn, vom Zustand (Energiewert) zu sprechen'. Weiter heißt es in dem Brief: 'Analog hat es keinen Sinn, von der Lage einer Korpuskel bestimmter Geschwindigkeit zu reden. Nimmt man es aber mit Geschwindigkeit und Lage nicht so genau, so hat das sehr wohl einen Sinn.' Pauli versuchte in seinem Antwortbrief die Hypothese, man müsse grundsätzlich den Phasenraum in endliche Zellen der Größe h einteilen, und man könne von einem Teilchen nur angeben, in welcher Zelle es sich befinde. Ich wandte dagegen ein: 'Wenn Sie die Wände der Zellen scharf vorgeben und doch bestimmen können, wieviele Partikel in jeder Zelle sind, kann man dann durch Wahl der Zellenwände benachbart zur ursprünglichen nicht die Anzahl der Atome in beliebig kleinen Zellen finden? Ich meine, ist die Wahl bestimmter Zellwände physikalisch sinnvoll? Vielleicht ist es so, daß man nur zum Beispiel das Verhältnis der beiden Zellwände vorgeben kann, nicht aber die Lage einer bestimmten Zellwand.'

So dicht diese Überlegungen schon an der richtigen Interpretation der Quantentheorie lagen, vergingen doch noch etwa drei Monate, bis die Formulierung so klar wurde, daß Pauli und ich wagten, von einem endgültigen Verständnis der Quantentheorie zu sprechen. In diesen Monaten sprach ich auch mit Bohr in Kopenhagen fast täglich über die Grundprobleme der Quantentheorie. Bohr versuchte, den Dualismus zwischen Wellenbild und Korpuskularbild zum Ausgangspunkt der physikalischen Interpretation zu machen, während ich mich bemühte, ohne Anleihe bei der Wellenmechanik den Weg zu Ende zu gehen, der durch die Quantenmechanik und die Diracsche Transformationstheorie vorgezeichnet schien. Diese intensiven, und an immer neuen physikalischen Beispielen wiederholten Diskussionen hatten nicht nur den Erfolg, allmählich eine Brücke zwischen den beiden, zunächst so verschiedenen Ausgangspunkten zu schlagen, sondern sie lieferten auch immer neuen Stoff, der in jeder der beiden Auffassungen mit Gewinn verarbeitet werden konnte. Trotz aller dieser Bemühungen wollte es uns aber nicht gelingen, wirklich Klarheit in die Quantentheorie zu bringen. Die neuen

Zusammenhänge waren so ungewohnt, so verschieden von dem, was in der Physik als gesichertes, überliefertes Gedankengut galt, daß wir uns in ihnen noch nicht vollständig zurechtfinden konnten. Am 23. November 1926 schrieb ich an Pauli nach einer längeren Erörterung der Diracschen Transformationstheorie: 'Über den eigentlichen Sinn dieser ganzen formalen Zusammenhänge denke ich oft nach, aber es ist schauderhaft schwer, daraus klug zu werden'.

Die Diskussionen über die Deutung der Quantentheorie wurden durch die Weihnachtsferien nur kurz unterbrochen. Vielleicht war es ein Zeichen der für uns alle durch die dauernden Diskussionen entstandenen Erschöpfung, daß Bohr Mitte Februar 1927 zur Erholung nach Norwegen reiste. Sicher hatte er den Wunsch, die Zeit neben dem Skilauf auch zum ruhigen und ungestörten Nachdenken über die Grundlagen der Quantentheorie auszunützen. Auch mir wurde es in dieser Zeit leichter, meine eigenen Gedanken zu sammeln, und so schrieb ich am 23. Februar an Pauli einen 14 Seiten langen Brief, dessen Inhalt im wesentlichen mit dem Inhalt der späteren Arbeit über die Unbestimmtheitsrelation identisch war. Paulis Antwortbrief klang viel positiver, als ich zu hoffen gewagt hatte. 'Es wird Tag in der Quantentheorie', so etwa lautete seine Antwort, die mich ermutigte, den ganzen Inhalt der Überlegung in einer ausführlichen Arbeit zu Papier zu bringen. Diese Arbeit schickte ich noch wenige Tage später zur Kritik ebenfalls an Pauli, so daß ich Bohr bei seiner Rückkehr schon die von Pauli begutachtete Arbeit zeigen konnte. Bohr war dann allerdings mit einigen Punkten der Arbeit noch mit Recht unzufrieden, so daß sie erst einige Zeit später mit wichtigen Verbesserungen zum Druck geschickt werden konnte. Inzwischen hatte Bohr auch den von ihm geprägten Begriff der Komplementarität soweit entwickelt, daß der physikalische Inhalt der Quantentheorie von den verschiedenen Ausgangspunkten aus in gleicher Weise klar zu überschauen war. Wenn noch Unterschiede der Auffassung bestanden, dann bezogen sie sich eben auf den verschiedenen Ausgangspunkt, oder auf eine verschiedene Sprechweise, aber nicht mehr auf die physikalische Deutung der Theorie. Über diese Deutung war jetzt vollständig Klarheit gewonnen, und Pauli war der erste außerhalb des eigentlichen Kopenhagener Kreises, der der neuen Deutung, zu der er selbst so viel beigetragen hatte, auch ohne Vorbehalt zustimmte.

Den äußeren Abschluß dieser ganzen Entwicklung bildete dann die Solvay-Konferenz, die im Herbst 1927 in Brüssel abgehalten wurde, und an der Einstein und H. A. Lorentz die für uns Kopenhagener wichtigsten Gesprächspartner über die Deutung der Quantentheorie waren. Die Diskussionen zwischen Bohr und Einstein beherrschten die Konferenz, und wenn es auch nicht gelang, Einstein davon zu überzeugen, daß die neue Deutung der Quantentheorie in jeder Weise befriedigend sei, so mußte Einstein doch schließlich zugeben, daß sie in sich geschlossen und widerspruchsfrei war. Auch Pauli hatte an diesem Ausgang der Konferenz, in der er oft das Wort ergriff, entscheidenden Anteil.

QUANTUM THEORY OF FIELDS
(UNTIL 1947)

GREGOR WENTZEL

1. EARLY QUANTUM ELECTRODYNAMICS

The basic idea of field quantization is some 50 years old. A particularly clear anticipation of later trends is found in a paper by Ehrenfest (1906). Commenting on Planck's theory of the Hohlraum radiation, Ehrenfest discusses the thermal equilibrium spectrum by means of the Rayleigh–Jeans normal modes analysis, exploiting the analogy of the amplitude of a proper vibration of the cavity with the coordinate of a material oscillator. Whereas the classical equi-partition of energies leads to the Rayleigh–Jeans spectrum, how can one modify the theory to obtain the Planck spectrum? As a possibility, suggested by Planck's quantization of material oscillators, Ehrenfest mentions the following hypothesis: the amounts of field energy residing in a normal mode of frequency ν can only be integral multiples of $h\nu$. The same assumption enabled Debye (1910) actually to derive the Planck spectrum. As we know today, such a quantization of the field energy results in exhibiting the corpuscular aspects of the system; but this connection with Einstein's light quantum hypothesis (1905) remained obscure until much later. Once the wave–particle dualism was understood, after the advent of wave mechanics, Debye's theory was seen to be equivalent to Bose's photon gas statistics (1924). The characteristic features of Bose's counting of states (namely, a permutation of n identical photons does not give a new state) corresponds to the non-degeneracy of the quantum state n of a linear oscillator (Born, Heisenberg and Jordan, 1926).

If it is true that an elementary light wave is equivalent to a harmonic oscillator, with energy eigenvalues $n h\nu(+\tfrac{1}{2}h\nu)$, it would then seem natural to apply quantum mechanics also to the *amplitude* of the wave and interpret it as an operator or, more specifically, as a matrix with respect to the oscillator quantum number n, similar to the coordinate matrix of the linear oscillator

48

$$(n'|q|n) = \begin{cases} n^{1/2} & \text{for} \quad n' = n-1 \\ (n+1)^{1/2} & \text{for} \quad n' = n+1 \\ 0 & \text{otherwise} \end{cases}$$

This idea was already used by Born, Heisenberg and Jordan (1926) to derive the mean square energy fluctuation of the Hohlraum radiation, but its major implications were discovered by Dirac (1927a) in his theory of the interaction of radiation with atomic matter. The interaction Hamiltonian (of first order) contains the matrices q as factors and will give rise, according to first-order perturbation theory, to atomic transitions in conjunction with transitions $n \to n \mp 1$ of the radiation oscillators or, in other words, with absorption or emission of photons. The energy of the combined system, atoms plus photons, is conserved within the limits of the uncertainty principle. The transition probabilities per unit time, involving the squares of the matrix elements, are proportional to the initial photon occupation numbers n in the case of absorption, and proportional to $(n+1)$ in the case of emission, where the parts $\sim n$ and ~ 1 correspond, respectively, to induced and spontaneous emission.

Today, the novelty and boldness of Dirac's approach to the radiation problem may be hard to appreciate. During the preceding decade it had become a tradition to think of Bohr's correspondence principle as the supreme guide in such questions, and, indeed, the efforts to formulate this principle in a quantitative fashion had led to the essential ideas preparing the eventual discovery of matrix mechanics by Heisenberg. A new aspect of the problem appeared when it became possible, by quantum-mechanical perturbation theory, to treat atomic transitions induced by given external wave fields, e.g. the photoelectric effect. The transitions so calculated could be interpreted as being caused by absorptive processes, but the 'reaction on the field', namely the disappearance of a photon, was not described by this theory, nor was there any possibility, in this framework, of understanding the process of spontaneous emission. Here, the correspondence principle still seemed indispensable, a rather foreign element (a 'magic wand' as Sommerfeld called it) in this otherwise very coherent theory. At this point, Dirac's explanation in terms of the q matrix came as a revelation. Known results were re-derived, but in a completely unified way. The new theory stimulated further thinking about the application of quantum mechanics to electromagnetic and other fields.

In a consecutive paper, Dirac (1927b) applied second-order

perturbation theory to the atom-field interaction and re-derived the Kramers–Heisenberg (1925) formula for the scattering of light by atomic systems. Finer aspects of radiative processes, like line widths due to damping, required a more elaborate mathematical treatment (Weisskopf and Wigner, 1930; for further literature see Heitler, 1954). Questions regarding the propagation velocity of light, or the coherence of scattered light, can best be answered by remembering that, for any quantum-mechanical system, the expectation values of observable quantities obey the equations of motion of the corresponding classical system. In application to the electromagnetic field operators, this leads to the classical field equations (Heisenberg, 1931), and much of classical wave optics is seen to remain valid.

In Dirac's radiation theory it is not the entire electromagnetic field that is subjected to quantization, but only its 'radiative part' consisting of plane transverse light waves. Electrostatic fields, on the other hand, are taken care of by including the Coulomb interaction energies into the Hamiltonian of the material system. This unsymmetric treatment of the two field parts not only appears contrary to the spirit of Maxwell's theory, but also raises questions from the view-point of relativity theory. A Lorentz transformation mixes the two field parts; the splitting is not invariant. The problem was now clearly this: how to formulate a general quantum theory of the Maxwell field interacting with charged particles, in a Lorentz invariant fashion. It certainly seemed a formidable programme in 1927, even though not all obstacles to be encountered could have been foreseen at that time.

One preliminary step was the Lorentz invariant formulation of the commutation rules for the charge-free field (i.e. Dirac's radiation field) by Jordan and Pauli (1928). Time-dependent field operators were introduced, and the commutators of two field components, taken at different space-time points, were expressed in terms of the, now famous, 'invariant Delta function'. The physical meaning of these results in relation to basic uncertainties in field measurements was later analysed by Bohr and Rosenfeld (1933).

A relativistic description of electrons, either force-free or subject to given external fields, was provided by Dirac's (1928) wave-mechanical theory of particles with spin 1/2. This theory, however, was beset with the difficulties coming from the 'states of negative energy', and these difficulties stayed with quantum electrodynamics until the mathematical development of the positron theory (see section 2) brought some relief.

Heisenberg and Pauli (1929) were the first to attempt a general formulation of quantum electrodynamics by setting up a general scheme for the quantization of fields which they hoped would be applicable to the Maxwell field. Since quantum mechanics, in its usual form, starts with a Hamiltonian characterizing the system, Heisenberg and Pauli assumed that the field equations, like the equations of motion of mechanics, are derivable from an action principle which allows us to define fields P_α 'canonically conjugate' to the original field components Q_α so that 'canonical commutation relations', together with a Hamiltonian, can be constructed. The commutation relations could be proved to be invariant under infinitesimal Lorentz transformations, if the Lagrangian density is invariant (see also Rosenfeld, 1930).* This canonical formalism, which later was to become so successful when applied to scalar and other fields, turned out to be insufficient in the case it was intended for: electrodynamics. Taking the Lagrangian density for the charge-free field in the customary form

$$L = -\tfrac{1}{4} \sum_{\alpha\beta} \left(\frac{\partial Q_\alpha}{\partial x_\beta} - \frac{\partial Q_\beta}{\partial x_\alpha} \right)^2 = \tfrac{1}{2}(\mathbf{E}^2 - \mathbf{H}^2)$$

where $Q_\alpha =$ four-potential ($\alpha = 1 \cdots 4$, $x_4 = ict$), then P_4 is found to vanish identically, and also the divergence of $\mathbf{P} = -\mathbf{E}$ vanishes. Under these circumstances, the canonical commutation relations cannot be applied. Only later was it recognized that this failure is connected with the zero rest mass of the photon and the existence of the gauge group

$$Q_\alpha \to Q_\alpha + \partial\chi/\partial x_\alpha$$

Heisenberg and Pauli (1929, 1930) found two ways to overcome the difficulty in a formal manner. The first was to add a term $\tfrac{1}{2}\epsilon(\sum_\alpha \partial Q_\alpha/\partial x_\alpha)^2$ to the Lagrangian density, prescribing the limit $\epsilon \to 0$ to be taken in the final result. In their second paper (1930), they chose the special gauge $Q_4 = 0$ (so that a Lorentz transformation entails a gauge transformation); one has then to require that the (time-independent) space function $C = \mathrm{div}\, \mathbf{E} + \rho$ vanish identically. Both these approaches can be carried through consistently, but appear somewhat artificial and not quite appropriate to a fundamental entity like the electromagnetic field. It was a particular disappointment that the basic difficulty of the classical Lorentz theory, the infinite value for the self-energy of the point electron, seemed to survive in the quantized version (see also Waller, 1930; Oppenheimer, 1930).

* With regard to this proof, Pauli used to say: 'Ich warne Neugierige'.

Closer to the line of the later development was a new (and independent) start by Fermi (1929–30). Here, the Lagrangian is chosen such as to give the field equations in the form

$$\sum_{\beta} \frac{\partial^2}{\partial x_{\beta}^2} Q_{\alpha} = -s_{\alpha}$$

(s_{α} = current and charge density) which, in order to yield Maxwell's equations, have to be supplemented by the 'Lorentz condition'; i.e. the four-divergence

$$\Omega \equiv \sum_{\alpha} \partial Q_{\alpha}/\partial x_{\alpha}$$

should vanish. Fermi (treating all quantities in Fourier transform) observed that, in quantum theory, the Lorentz condition need not be postulated as an identity for the field operators Q_{α}, but it is sufficient to impose corresponding subsidiary conditions or 'constraints' on the state vector Ψ:

$$\Omega\Psi = 0, \quad \text{and} \quad \dot{\Omega}\Psi = 0 \quad \left(\dot{\Omega} = \frac{i}{\hbar}[H, \Omega] \right),$$

stating that the operators Ω and $\dot{\Omega}$ annihilate Ψ at all times. These conditions are admissible because they are equivalent to two initial conditions for Ψ (at $t = 0$, say) which are compatible (the corresponding operators commute). By solving explicitly the subsidiary conditions, one can then immediately write down how Ψ depends on the 'scalar' potential (Q_4) and the longitudinal part of the 'vector' potential (div **Q**). Then, for the remaining factor in Ψ, one obtains a reduced Schrödinger equation

$$i\hbar \frac{\partial \Psi'}{\partial t} = H'\Psi'$$

where H' turns out to be the Hamiltonian of Dirac's radiation theory, including the Coulomb interactions between the charged particles (and also their infinite self-energies). (In the Heisenberg–Pauli versions, the Coulomb terms were derived in second-order perturbation theory only.) Since the primary formulation of Fermi's theory, which involves the static and wave fields in a unified fashion, can be set up in an arbitrary Lorentz frame of coordinates, it thus turns out that Dirac's quantum theory of radiation is in effect a relativistically invariant scheme provided the charged particles are also properly relativistically described, for instance by Dirac's wave mechanics for spin 1/2 electrons.

Fermi did not bother to verify explicitly that his quantization procedure (e.g. field commutation relations) remains invariant under Lorentz transformations although this might have been done by examining infinitesimal transformations and then invoking their group properties as Heisenberg and Pauli did in their versions of the theory. However, a much more transparent and elegant proof of Lorentz invariance emerged from a generalization of the theory which was discovered by Dirac, Fock and Podolsky (1932).

In all previous formulations, Lorentz invariance was far from obvious because of the non-symmetric treatment of time and space coordinates: each electron has its own position vector $\mathbf{r}_n$ (in a configuration space treatment), the fields are defined as functions of another space vector $\mathbf{r}$, but only *one* time coordinate t appears (in the state vector Ψ if the 'Schrödinger representation' is used). This lack of symmetry is removed in the 'multiple time' formulism of Dirac, Fock and Podolsky where an individual time coordinate t_n is assigned to each charged particle and the state vector Ψ, considered as a function of all four-vectors $(\mathbf{r}_n, t_n)$, is subjected to several Dirac wave equations, one for each electron. These wave equations involve the four-potential of the Maxwell field in a time-dependent representation (today, this is called 'interaction representation'):

$$Q_a(\mathbf{r}, t) = \exp\left(\frac{i}{\hbar} H_F t\right) Q_a(\mathbf{r}) \exp\left(-\frac{i}{\hbar} H_F t\right)$$

(H_F = field Hamiltonian without interaction); Q_a is to be taken at $(\mathbf{r}_n, t_n)$ in the wave equation for the nth electron. As a function of the field amplitudes, Ψ must again be subjected to a subsidiary condition $\Omega \Psi = 0$ which is a generalized form of Fermi's constraint. All these equations, as well as the commutation relations for the field operators, are manifestly Lorentz invariant, and also gauge invariant. If one, then, considers Ψ only in a single-time subspace (all $t_n = t$), one comes back to Fermi's theory, and finally to Dirac's radiation theory, and no further invariance proofs are necessary for these derived forms of the theory. Bloch (1934) further analysed the multiple-time theory as to internal consistency (the particles must be kept in space-like positions relative to each other:

$$c|t_n - t_{n'}| < |\mathbf{r}_n - \mathbf{r}_{n'}|)$$

and pointed out the physical meaning of the generalized state function Ψ: it bears on measurements made on the particles at their individual times t_n.

The Dirac–Fock–Podolsky theory is the direct forerunner of

later theories (Tomonaga, 1946; Schwinger, 1948) in which the charged particles are no longer described in configuration space but, instead, by a quantized field (e.g. electron field), and the set of discrete world-points (r_n, t_n) is replaced by a space-like 'surface' in Minkowski space. How this formalism served as a tool in the re-normalization programme of quantum electrodynamics will be reported elsewhere in this volume.

In the classical field theory corresponding to the multiple-time theory, the field functions depend explicitly on the particle times t_n (Wentzel, 1933). One can make use of this generalized Lorentz theory to re-formulate the classical equations of motion of charged point particles in such a way that the self-force of the particles becomes finite; in particular, the electromagnetic mass (inertia) vanishes. This is achieved by introducing a limiting process into the definition of the Lorentz force which lets the 'field point' approach the 'particle point' in time-like directions. In this way one can avoid all self-energy troubles in the *classical* theory of point electrons interacting through a Maxwell field, and it was hoped that similar limiting processes might eliminate the corresponding difficulties in the quantized theory. This hope turned out to be futile. Only the infinities of the classical, electromagnetic mass, type (diverging linearly with the cut-off momentum k_c) are affected by such a limiting process. But the quantum theory gives rise to other kinds of infinities, like Waller's (1930) term $(\sim k_c^2)$ calculated for an isolated Dirac spin electron (negative energy levels empty). At a later time when the hole theory of the positron became more acceptable, one had to deal with only logarithmic singularities, but even these survived all attacks by mathematical tricks until the idea of mass re-normalization came up, with the promise of a new consistent interpretation. Meanwhile, however, the discussion about mathematical re-formulation went on for many years. Dirac (1939), after discovery of another formulation of the classical theory (Dirac, 1938), tried to modify the field commutation relations by means of a small time-like vector ('λ-limiting process') but then found that he had to introduce other artifices, like light quanta of negative energy and negative probabilities (Dirac, 1942). A review and criticism of these efforts can be found in a paper by Pauli (1943).

All this work on the self-energy problem is today superseded and of historic interest only. In spite of all failures, the general confidence in quantum electrodynamics as a supreme, though as yet imperfect, tool of atomistic theory remained alive. It is true that most special applications were based on Dirac's radiation theory, and infinities, where they appeared, were dealt with in a heuristic manner (straight subtraction or cut-off). No contradictions with experimental facts were apparent (the 'Lamb shift' was suspected but still doubtful at that time). Nevertheless, the awareness of the basic difficulties weighed heavily on our minds.

To complete the picture, it should be recalled that in the early 30s the self-energy was not the only worry. The negative energy states of the Dirac electron have been mentioned already, and the toilsome development of the 'hole theory' will be reviewed later. There was also the infinite zero-point energy ($\sum \frac{1}{2}h\nu$) of the radiation field, and although today it may seem trivial to throw away an infinite additive constant in the energy by plain subtraction, people like Pauli (1933) went out of their way to cast the Hamiltonian density in a form which, in effect, eliminates the zero-point energy.

An infinity of a different kind is that referred to as the 'infra-red catastrophe' because the divergence occurs at small frequencies, as contrasted to the 'ultra-violet catastrophe' in the self-energies. One meets with this in problems like Bremsstrahlung if one asks for the total probability of any radiative process (photon emission); treating the field-electron interaction as small, the perturbation theory gives a result diverging as $\int d\nu/\nu$ at $\nu = 0$. Bloch and Nordsieck (1937) observed that this is really the fault of the perturbation method; the interaction is too large at low frequencies. Instead, they started by constructing the stationary states of free electrons in motion, with their proper fields attached, plus additional free photons. A weak external force (*this* is now the weak perturbation) induces transitions between such stationary states, and if initially no free photons were present there is a probability of their presence in the final state, as a consequence of the change of the proper field in the transition. It turns out that the mean number of photons emitted is infinite (concentrated at the lowest frequencies), but the total energy emitted is finite, and so is the total cross-section for the electron to be scattered into a certain solid angle. This cross-section is the same as one would calculate it from the Born approximation ignoring the field altogether. The formulae show why the expansion into powers of e (the field-electron coupling strength), though formally leading back to the original perturbation theory, is inadmissible at low frequencies. Pauli and Fierz (1938) re-examined this theory, replacing the 'electron' by an extended charged body; now the cut-off (which was also needed in Bloch's and Nordsieck's work and tended to obscure a possible connection with the

3+P.M.V.

self-energy divergence) has a physical cause and is specified by a form factor. The size of the body is taken large enough to make the electromagnetic mass terms negligible. Non-relativistic energies are used, but otherwise the energy conservation is treated rigorously. The result of this more detailed analysis agrees with that of Bloch and Nordsieck except for the observation that the probability of very small energy losses depends on the size (formfactor) of the charged body, in such a manner as to 'render immediate application to real electrons impossible'. Although the authors thus concluded on a pessimistic note, the general expectation was that the low-frequency end of the spectrum would eventually be amenable to a consistent treatment if only one could visualize a theory of point electrons free of the more serious high-frequency divergences.

2. ELECTRON FIELD QUANTIZATION

When Jordan (1927) first sought to quantize the electron wave field, this must have seemed a rather strange idea to many of us. Contrary to photons, electrons have charge and mass (and spin $\frac{1}{2}$). Wave mechanics of many-electron systems in configuration space representation was well developed and seemed entirely satisfactory, at least as a non-relativistic theory. Pauli's exclusion principle was known to be equivalent to the postulate of antisymmetry of the state functions.

On the other hand, Dirac (1927), in the preparation of his theory of light emission and absorption, had already discussed the quantization of a (complex) Schrödinger wave function, replacing the probability amplitudes of the 'unperturbed states' by operators raising or lowering by one the occupation numbers of these unperturbed states, with commutation rules

$$b_r b_s^\star - b_s^\star b_r = \delta_{rs}, \qquad b_r b_s - b_s b_r = 0$$

If the Hamiltonian is now written as

$$\sum_r W_r b_r^\star b_r + \sum_{rs} V_{rs} b_r^\star b_s$$

this quantized theory gives nothing new for a single particle

$$\sum_r b_r^\star b_r = 1$$

the equivalent Hamiltonian matrix being

$$H_{rs} = W_r \delta_{rs} + V_{rs}$$

but N identical particles behave as they should do according to

Bose–Einstein statistics, namely in accordance with configuration space wave mechanics using symmetric wave functions. In other words: for a system of identical bosons, the configuration space is not needed if the wave function in ordinary space is quantized. This procedure was called 'second quantization' or 'hyperquantization', because the use of a Schrödinger wave function amounts to a 'first' quantization. Jordan and Klein (1927) generalized this theory by admitting interaction terms $\sim b_r{}^\star b_s{}^\star b_k b_l$, e.g. Coulomb interactions between charged bosons. They pointed out that the Coulomb self-energy of the particles is formally eliminated by writing the non-commuting operators b, $b^\star$ in that particular order (two annihilation operators to the right).

The future prospects of this theory, in particular with regard to relativistic generalizations, were rated highly by Jordan who set out immediately to invent a similar formalism for fermions. Since the Pauli exclusion principle prohibits occupation numbers > 1, the b_r operators must be cut down to 2×2 matrices

$$\begin{pmatrix} 0 & 1 \\ 0 & 0 \end{pmatrix}_r$$

times unit matrices $(s \neq r)$. The final formulation of the theory, equivalent to configuration space wave mechanics with anti-symmetric state functions, was achieved by Jordan and Wigner (1928). Here, new operators a_r are introduced which differ from the b_r only by a judiciously chosen $\pm$ sign and obey 'anticommutation relations'

$$a_r a_s{}^\star + a_s{}^\star a_r = \delta_{rs}, \qquad a_r a_s + a_s a_r = 0$$

which are obviously invariant under unitary transformations $(a_r \rightarrow S^{-1} a_r S;\ S^\star = S^{-1})$. In actual applications, the explicit matrix representation with the $\pm$ sign need never be written out because the anticommutation relations suffice to express all results in terms of physical quantities like expectation values of the occupation numbers $N_r = a_r{}^\star a_r$. This fact, however, did not become common knowledge until much later (as also in the case of the Dirac matrices γ_μ: $\gamma_\mu \gamma_v + \gamma_v \gamma_\mu = 2\delta_{\mu v}$).

As a non-relativistic many-electron theory, the Jordan–Wigner formalism was to become a very helpful tool, for instance, for the study of the 'electron gas' in metallic conductors (a topic which cannot be followed in this report), but, was it more than a tool for special purposes? Would it be an essential element in the construction of a relativistic theory, in conjunction with quantum electrodynamics?

Dirac's relativistic wave mechanics of the spin electron, and its 'negative energy' troubles, have already been mentioned. As a possible remedy, Dirac (1930) proposed to consider as the 'vacuum' that state in which all (and only) negative energy levels are 'occupied' without, however, producing any observable charge density. A 'hole' in the negative energy 'sea' behaves like a particle of positive energy and 'positive' charge, and Dirac tried first to identify it with a proton. This interpretation soon proved untenable. Oppenheimer (1930) pointed out that, then, the hydrogen atom would lack stability, because of its rapid annihilation into two photons. A particularly lucid comment is found in H. Weyl's book *The Theory of Groups and Quantum Mechanics* (translated from the second German edition, 1931, by H. R. Robertson. New York; Dutton and Co.) on p. 263: according to Dirac's theory 'the mass of a proton should be the same as the mass of the electron; furthermore, no matter how the action is chosen (so long as it is invariant under interchange of right and left), this hypothesis leads to the essential equivalence of positive and negative electricity under all circumstances—even on taking the interaction between matter and radiation rigorously into account'.

Then, in 1932, came the experimental discovery of the positron, and the hole theory was given much credit for the prediction; but there was, as yet, no consistent mathematical formulation of this theory. Only certain perturbation calculations, pertaining, e.g. to the scattering of light by electrons, radiative pair creation and annihilation, or positron–electron scattering (with exchange effects: Bhabha, 1936), could be carried through at this stage because the difficulties appear only in higher order terms which one neglects.

The central problem was that of the 'vacuum polarization': an external electromagnetic field distorts the single electron wave functions of the negative energy sea and thereby produces a charge–current distribution which again affects the field. How is the subtraction of 'vacuum quantities', which is trivial in the field-free case, to be made now? Even if the external field is weak, it creates virtual electron–positron pairs, and their total contribution to the charge density, or polarization, appears as a divergent integral. What finite part of it, if any, will correspond to an observable vacuum polarization?

This problem, which was tackled from various points of view, proved to be very frustrating. This may be seen from the following quotations. Peierls (1934): 'One does not know whether the necessary changes in the theory will be only of a formal nature, just mathematical changes to avoid the use of infinite quantities, or whether the fundamental concepts underlying the equations will have to be modified essentially.' Furry and Oppenheimer (1934): 'The difficulties are of such a character that they are apparently not to be overcome merely by modifying the electromagnetic field of an electron within ... small distances but require here a more profound change in our notions of space and time. ...' It is noteworthy that Furry and Oppenheimer employed the Jordan–Wigner formalism of electron field quantization, but without much benefit.

However the pessimists were wrong this time: a workable though very complicated formulation of the hole theory was accomplished through the efforts of Dirac (1934) and Heisenberg (1934). Dirac, adopting a Hartree self-consistent field approximation, introduced time-dependent density matrices like

$$\sum \psi_{\sigma'}(\mathbf{x}'t')\psi_{\sigma''}{}^{\star}(\mathbf{x}''t'')$$

(summed, e.g. over the occupied states), and examined their singularities on the light cone

$$[|\mathbf{x}' - \mathbf{x}''|^2 = c^2(t' - t'')^2],$$

with the aim of subtracting singular functions depending explicitly on the field such that the finite remainder, for $\mathbf{x}' = \mathbf{x}''$, $t' = t''$, might serve to define observable quantities. Heisenberg used the conservation laws for charge, energy and momentum, to eliminate remaining ambiguities in the subtraction prescription. He also emphasized the shortcomings of the Hartree approximation ('anschauliche Theorie' as he called it) and proceeded to generalize the subtraction rules, now making use of the Jordan–Wigner electron field quantization which at this point starts to play its essential role. The theory is formally Lorentz invariant, and symmetric under interchange of electrons and positrons. It can be combined with quantum electrodynamics in a straightforward way and, in this form, constitutes a general theory of electrons, positrons and photons, in interaction. The smallness of the coupling constant $e^2/\hbar c = 1/137$ is essential in that expansions into powers of the electronic charge are freely made use of. (For a condensed description of this theory, see G. Wentzel, *Einführung in die Quantentheorie der Wellenfelder*, Franz Deuticke, Wien, 1943, pp. 186–191; English translation: Interscience Publishers, New York, 1949, pp. 196–202.)

However, as mentioned earlier, the self-energy difficulty

survived. Compared with the single electron theory, the situation in the hole theory looked slightly less detrimental in that only logarithmic divergences remained (Weisskopf, 1934): the more strongly divergent terms, attributed to the spin energy and to the 'forced vibrations under the influence of the zero-point fluctuations of the radiation field', cancel each other (Weisskopf, 1939). Also in the terms of higher order in $e^2/\hbar c$, the divergences remain logarithmic ($\sim$ powers of log k_c: Weisskopf, 1939). A suitable cut-off would then reduce the electronic self-energy to a small fraction ($\sim 1/137$) of mc^2. It was commonly taken for granted that the cut-off implied a violation of relativistic invariance unless one wanted to ignore the self-energy altogether.

More serious was the fact that, according to the positron theory, the photon also acquires an infinite self-energy, owing to its capability to create virtual electron–positron pairs. Heisenberg's (1934) version of the theory reduces the divergence (in the term $\sim e^2$) to a logarithmic one. No remedy seemed available to save the relativistic and gauge invariance of the theory. Heisenberg expected that a solution to these problems could only come about in a theory 'which gives the Sommerfeld constant $e^2/\hbar c$ a determined value'. Many years later, 'regularization' combined with re-normalization was to provide at least a mathematically consistent framework. (See F. Villars' report in this volume.)

While these obscure aspects of the theory had to be set aside, an extensive exploration of the vacuum polarization phenomenon came under way. Already at the Solvay Congress 1933, Dirac had reported on the case of a weak static potential, studied by first-order perturbation theory. For the charge density $\delta\rho$, induced by the potential ϕ, he derived an expression of the form

$$\delta\rho = \frac{e^2}{\hbar c}\left[A\,\Delta\phi + B\left(\frac{\hbar}{mc}\right)^2\Delta\Delta\phi\right]$$

($\Delta =$ Laplacian). Whereas the coefficient B has a finite numerical value, A is logarithmically infinite; however, by a suitable cut-off ($k_c \sim 137mc/\hbar$), A becomes a number of order unity. Dirac observed that $(-\Delta\phi/4\pi)$ is the 'external' charge density ρ_0 producing the potential ϕ; hence the first term ($\sim A$) in $\delta\rho$ means that a small fraction ($\sim 1/137$) of the external charge is 'neutralized' (at least in the static case). In Heisenberg's (1934) version of the theory, the term $\sim A\,\Delta\phi$ is automatically subtracted; this amounts to what we would call today a re-normalization of the charge. (The idea of charge re-normalization was vaguely anticipated in the papers, already quoted, by Peierls (1934), and by Furry and Oppenheimer (1934).) Then $\delta\rho$ becomes proportional to $(-\Delta\rho_0)$, or, more strictly speaking, to a spatial average of $(-\Delta\rho_0)$, taken with a certain weight function over a sphere of radius $\sim \hbar/mc$ (Uehling, 1935; Serber, 1935). The potential ϕ is correspondingly modified $(\rightarrow \phi + \delta\phi)$, thus altering slightly the laws of electrostatics. Observable effects of $\delta\phi$, for instance in the energies of bound electrons, were analysed by Uehling (1935); the results were disappointing, for a reason clear today: it is true that the vacuum polarization contributes to the Lamb shift, but only about $(-)2\cdot2$ per cent of the total. Its reality is now guaranteed by the precision of the measurements.

Within the same approximation (first order in $e^2/\hbar c$), no new difficulties appeared in the more general case of time-dependent electromagnetic fields: the charge and current densities induced are given by similar formulae, with the Laplacian Δ replaced by the d'Alembertian (Heisenberg, 1934; Serber, 1935; Pauli and Rose, 1936).

If one goes to terms of higher order in $e^2/\hbar c$, one meets with the most fascinating feature of the hole theory: Maxwell's equations are to be corrected by small terms non-linear (e.g. of the third order) in the field strengths and their derivatives. The superposition principle of electrodynamics and optics is no longer strictly valid. For instance, photons can be scattered by photons, or by electrostatic fields. This had already been suspected by Halpern (1933) and Delbrück (1933) who argued that such processes can be mediated by virtual electron–positron pairs. However, Heisenberg's subtraction procedure was needed to give reasonably low values to the cross-sections for these scattering processes, in particular in the limit of low frequencies. Actual computations of these cross-sections (without the benefit of the Feynman diagram technique!) were extremely laborious, even when leaving aside all but the simplest cases, namely, low frequencies and small scattering angles (see, for example, Euler, 1936). It was then discovered (Euler and Kockel, 1935; Kemmer, 1937) that, as far as the calculations went, all results were the same as though the vacuum field Lagrangian contained additional fourth-order terms:

$$L = \tfrac{1}{2}(\mathbf{E}^2 - \mathbf{H}^2) + \frac{1}{360\pi^2} \frac{e^4\hbar}{m^4c^7} \{(\mathbf{E}^2 - \mathbf{H}^2)^2 + 7(\mathbf{E}.\mathbf{H})^2\} + \cdots$$

(Heaviside units). A closed expression for this Lagrangian, valid to all orders of e but for long wavelengths $(\gg \hbar/mc)$ only, was derived by Heisenberg and Euler (1936), and by Weisskopf (1936), through the study of special fields combined with invariance arguments, in the Hartree approximation.

As a result of all these developments, the general picture, in the later 30s, looked as follows: apart from self-energy divergences and related difficulties ('radiative corrections', see Dancoff, 1939), the positron theory appeared to furnish well defined and plausible rules for a quantitative prediction of observable phenomena. However, experimental methods for testing the finer details of the theory (vacuum polarization) were not yet available. From the aesthetic point of view, the subtraction devices seemed too artificial to be generally appealing. Pauli, in spite of being actively interested in the theory (see Pauli and Rose, 1936), revealed his misgivings by using the deprecatory term 'subtraction physics', and another typical quotation from the same paper reads: 'The formalism of the positron theory which is accepted at present and which unfortunately is not yet substituted by a more satisfactory one. . . .'—As seen from our present view-point, the theory has proved correct in all aspects it was able to handle.

3. OTHER FIELDS, HIGHER SPINS

In the early attempts to generalize Schrödinger's wave equation so as to make it relativistically invariant, the 'scalar wave equation'

$$\sum_a \partial^2 Q / \partial x_a{}^2 = \mu^2 Q$$

with $\mu = mc/\hbar$, seemed a natural starting point (Schrödinger, 1926; Gordon, 1926; Klein, 1927), in conformity with L. de Broglie's original ideas regarding wave particle relationships. This approach was, however, criticized by Dirac (1928) who argued that the general interpretation of quantum mechanics requires linearity in $\partial/\partial t$ of the wave equation and, led by this argument (which proved to be wrong), discovered his relativistic wave equation for the spin electron. The interest in the scalar (relativistic) field subsided until Pauli and Weisskopf (1934) showed that a consistent and physically reasonable theory of the scalar field can be constructed just by applying to it the canonical rules of field quantization as set up in 1929 by Heisenberg and Pauli, in their first paper on quantum electrodynamics. In this formalism, it is the state vector Ψ of the quantized system which obeys the first-order (in $\partial/\partial t$) differential equation

$$i\hbar \, \partial\Psi/\partial t = H\Psi,$$

and the physical interpretation in terms of Ψ meets with no difficulty. The corresponding particles carry, of course, no spin, and identification with elementary particles occurring in reality was impossible in 1934. Indeed, the topic remained academic until the π meson was discovered and found to have zero spin, in the late 40s and early 50s.

Today, the 'charged scalar' theory is a standard example for illustrating field quantization methods, in particular the 'canonical' method used by Pauli and Weisskopf, so it will be unnecessary to describe it in detail (see G. Wentzel, sections 8 and 11 of the book quoted previously). Pauli and Weisskopf emphasized, as a gratifying feature, the fact that the field energy appears, without any *ad hoc* subtraction, as a positive-definite quantity, allowing of a corpuscular interpretation, whereas the electric charge is non-definite: the particles carry either positive or negative charges. The quantum nature of the charge (the eigenvalues are integral multiples of the elementary charge) follows from the formalism. Owing to the commutation rules supposed, the particles obey Bose–Einstein statistics, whereas anticommutation rules would lead to difficulties (see below). In other respects, the results were surprisingly similar to those derived from the hole theory of the positron. For instance, photons of energy $> 2mc^2$ will, in a static Coulomb field, produce positive–negative pairs, and the cross-section for this process, as calculated by Pauli and Weisskopf, agrees in order of magnitude with that calculated by Bethe and Heitler for electron–positron pair production (*ceteris paribus*). There is also a vacuum polarization due to virtual boson pairs, with a logarithmic infinity demanding charge renormalization. A quadratic divergence ($\sim k_c{}^2$) appears in the electromagnetic self-energy of a charged boson (Weisskopf, 1939).

In 1937, the interest in quantized fields of a more general nature received a tremendous uplift by the discovery of the cosmic ray 'mesotrons' and the subsequent boom of the 'meson theory of nuclear forces' which will form the main topic of the last part of this report. In this present section we want to concentrate on some of the more purely mathematical questions regarding the structure of fields describing particles of a specified spin (questions which strongly attracted Pauli's personal attention).

In a systematic approach, it was natural to subdivide the question into a classical and a quantum-theoretical one: how should one generalize the classical relativistic field equations, so that after proper quantization the observable quantities can be interpreted in terms of particles of spin s, charged or uncharged, with rest mass or without? The classical (or 'c number') theories

3*

themselves could not be expected to describe single particles in a
straightforward manner since even for $s=0$ and $s=1/2$ this had
not been possible (for $s=0$, the probability density is not a
positive-definite quantity, and for $s=1/2$ one has the negative
energy states). But it could be hoped that a subsequent quantization (with hole-theoretical amendments in the case of half-odd
spins) would lead to a consistent theory.

A general classical theory, mainly for force-free particles, was
first set up by Dirac (1936), through a study of first-order differential equations similar in form to his wave equation for spin
$1/2$. The spinor notation of Van der Waerden (1929) proved a
valuable tool. The structure of these theories was much clarified
by Fierz (1939) (who acknowledged guidance by Pauli). In the
simpler case of integral spins, the classical field is a tensor of rank
s $(Q_{a_1} \cdots a_s; a_r = 1 \cdots 4)$, symmetric in all index pairs, with zero
trace, with vanishing divergence, and obeying the Schrödinger–
Klein–Gordon wave equation. For a plane wave, assuming
$m \neq 0$, all these conditions leave only $(2s+1)$ amplitude components independent, as is most easily seen in the 'rest frame'
$[Q_{a_1} \cdots = \exp(-i\mu t) \times \text{const.}]$; under spatial rotations these independent components transform according to the irreducible
representation $\mathscr{D}_s$, and the corresponding single particle states are
the $(2s+1)$ orientations of a spin s. Alternatively, all this can be
written in spinor notation, and generalized so as to include the
case of half-odd spin. (Instead, the half-odd spin can also be
considered as a result of adding a spin $1/2$ to an integral spin;
this is the description developed by Rarita and Schwinger, 1940.)
Possible expressions for energy–momentum and charge–current
densities were discussed by Fierz; there is considerable ambiguity,
although the total energy and the total charge are essentially
uniquely defined. The energy is positive in the case of integral
spin, but has either sign in the case of half-odd spin. This result
is decisive for what kind of quantization is possible: commutation
rules, or Bose–Einstein statistics, for integral spin; and anticommutation rules, or Pauli's exclusion principle and Fermi–Dirac
statistics, for half-odd spin. Fierz (1939 and 1950) derived a
general formula for these (anti-) commutation relations.

Whereas the exclusion principle is obviously indispensable if
there are negative energy states, it is much less obvious why the
quantization according to the exclusion principle should be ruled
out for integral spin. For Pauli, this was understandably a
question of deep concern (see Pauli, 1936; Fierz, 1939; Pauli,
1940). Essential here is the postulate 'that measurements at

two space points with a space-like distance can never disturb each other, since no signals can be transmitted with velocities greater than that of light'. This postulate forbids the appearance of the 'D_1 function' in the Lorentz invariant anticommutation relations, and one arrives at a mathematical contradiction if s is an integer. (See also the article by R. Jost in this volume.)

The case of zero rest mass is of particular interest since it applies to the electromagnetic field ($s = 1$) and to the (linearized) gravitational field of Einstein's general relativity theory ($s = 2$). In both of these physical problems, there exists a group of gauge transformations

$$Q_\alpha \to Q_\alpha + \partial\chi/\partial x_\alpha$$
$$Q_{\alpha\beta} \to Q_{\alpha\beta} + \partial\varphi_\alpha/\partial x_\beta + \partial\varphi_\beta/\partial x_\alpha - \tfrac{1}{2}\delta_{\alpha\beta} \sum_\gamma \partial\varphi_\gamma/\partial x_\gamma$$

(possible only if $m = 0$) such that all observable quantities are gauge invariant (in general relativity theory, the gauge transformation is equivalent to an infinitesimal coordinate transformation). It is then natural, for *any* spin value s, if $m = 0$, to assume that any two solutions are physically equivalent if they can be transformed into each other by a gauge transformation. In application to a plane wave, this reduces (for $s \geqslant 1$) the number of independent polarizations to *two*, as is well known for light waves and gravitational waves (for $m = 0$, there is no 'rest frame'). In the quantized theory, s can still be associated with the 'spin' or intrinsic angular momentum of one particle (e.g. of one photon or graviton): its component in the direction of propagation has the eigenvalues $\pm s$. Fierz (1940) has given explicit proof that the total angular momentum of a single particle state, according to this theory, is $\geqslant s$.

The existence of a gauge group in the case $m = 0$, and its absence for $m \neq 0$, entails some typical differences in the formal structure of the quantized theory in the two cases. The historic example is the (real) vector field ($s = 1$), with Maxwell's and Proca's (1936) field equations respectively. (Serving as a model for 'vector mesons', the quantized Proca theory was discussed in numerous papers (1938); see references quoted in section 4.) The canonical quantization procedure, which is straightforward when applied to the three independent amplitudes of a plane wave for $m \neq 0$, does not automatically permit the limiting process $m \to 0$. In particular, the 'Lorentz condition'

$$\sum_a \partial Q_\alpha/\partial x_\alpha = 0$$

which, in the canonical theory, is considered as an identity linking the four components Q_α, degenerates and becomes non-sensical for $m=0$. Indeed, this is the essence of the difficulty encountered by Heisenberg and Pauli in 1929, in their first attempts to formulate quantum electrodynamics. Fermi's proposal to replace the Lorentz condition, as an identity, by corresponding subsidiary conditions on the state vector Ψ provides the approach adequate for $m=0$. Stueckelberg (1938) invented another version of the vector meson theory (involving a redundant scalar field Q and a constraint on Ψ) which formally also covers the case $m=0$ (then $Q \equiv 0$), but this is no true union of the two theories. (For more recent studies on this question, see Belinfante, 1949; Coester, 1951.)

In all cases considered, the classical field equations are derivable from a variational principle involving a Lagrangian (density). The invariance properties of the Lagrangian (in the absence of external forces) can be used to construct conservative quantities and the corresponding densities which obey 'continuity equations' like

$$\sum_a \partial T_{\alpha\beta} / \partial x_\alpha = 0$$

for the energy–momentum–stress tensor $T_{\alpha\beta}$ ($= T_{\beta\alpha}$), or

$$\sum_a \partial M_{\alpha\beta\gamma} / \partial x_\alpha = 0$$

for the 'angular momentum' tensor $M_{\alpha\beta\gamma}$ ($= -M_{\alpha\gamma\beta}$). General expressions for $T_{\alpha\beta}$ and $M_{\alpha\beta\gamma}$ were first derived by Belinfante (1939) (with acknowledgments to Kramers and Podolanski) by exploiting the invariance of the Lagrangian under infinitesimal Lorentz transformations. Independently, Rosenfeld (1940) used the invariance under arbitrary infinitesimal coordinate transformations in general relativity theory for the same purpose, and the result agrees with Belinfante's in the limit of the special relativity metric. If *complex* fields $Q_{\alpha_1} \ldots$ are involved, the Lagrangian may be invariant under a (constant) change of phase of these fields ($Q_{\alpha_1} \ldots \to Q_{\alpha_1} \ldots e^{i\epsilon}$), and, for an infinitesimal ϵ, this leads immediately to a continuity equation

$$\sum_a \partial J_\alpha / \partial x_\alpha = 0$$

where J_α is now to be interpreted as the charge–current density. The physical significance attributed to these densities is, of course, that they are supposed to determine the manner in which the Q fields, or the corresponding particles, interact with gravitational and electromagnetic fields, respectively. In this context,

Belinfante (1940) emphasized the fact that the Lagrangian L of a field is in general non-uniquely defined; any substitution

$$L \to L + \sum_a \partial \Lambda_a / \partial x_a$$

leaves the field equations invariant, and whenever a four-vector Λ_a (phase invariant for complex fields) can be constructed in terms of $Q_{a_1} \ldots$ (the first derivatives $\partial Q_{a_1} \ldots / \partial x_\beta$ may also occur in Λ_a provided the second derivatives cancel out in $\sum_a \partial \Lambda_a / \partial x_a$) there is then some freedom in the choice of L, and a corresponding lack of uniqueness in the definitions of $T_{a\beta}$ and J_a (which, however, does not affect the total energy–momentum, $\int d^3x T_{4\beta}$, nor the total charge, $\int d^3x J_4$). For instance, in J_a, an additional term of the form $\sum_\beta \partial P_{a\beta} / \partial x_\beta$, where $P_{a\beta}$ $(= -P_{\beta a})$ is related to the spin polarization [e.g. for $s = 1$, $P_{a\beta} = i(Q_a{}^\star Q_\beta - Q_\beta{}^\star Q_a) \times$ const.] may appear with an arbitrary factor; in the rest frame, this amounts to altering the magnetic moment of the particle. Hence, one has to expect that the wave equation for the charged particle in an external electromagnetic field can be written in such a way as to give its spin magnetic moment an arbitrary value (except, of course, for $s = 0$). For the vector meson, an analysis by Corben and Schwinger (1940) showed this to be correct, and even earlier had it been known that Dirac's wave equation for $s = 1/2$ can be modified by a 'Pauli term' so as to give the electron an anomalous magnetic moment (see equation 91 in Pauli, 1941).

The general problem of constructing wave equations and Lagrangians for charged particles of spin s in an external field (Fierz and Pauli, 1939) turned out to be very difficult for $s > 1$. The usual device of substituting $\partial / \partial x_a - i(e/\hbar c) \phi_a$ for $\partial / \partial x_a$ must be used with great caution to avoid inconsistencies. Fierz and Pauli tackled the problem by admitting, besides the leading tensor or spinor, tensors or spinors of lower rank (e.g. for $s = 2$, a scalar) which, however, are made to vanish identically in the field-free case, due to a judicious choice of the Lagrangian. Roughly speaking one allows admixtures of spins $s - 1$, $s - 2 \cdots$, in the presence of the field, but in such a manner that, when switching off the field, one comes back to a particle of pure spin s. The theory was presented in some detail only for $s = 2$ and $s = 3/2$; for integral spin $\geqslant 3$, the admixtures needed were merely enumerated, with the queer result that the scheme is essentially unique only for $s \leqslant 4$.

Another question is whether particles with several spin states (e.g. one ground state and one excited) can be naturally described

within the field-theoretical formalism. For instance, spins 0 and
1 can be jointly described in terms of an algebra of 16×16
matrices which, however, is reducible into representations
corresponding to the spins 0 and 1 separately, without affecting
the properties of these particles (Duffin, 1938; Kemmer, 1939; see
also part II, 4, of Pauli, 1941). The existence of irreducible wave
equations, allowing a physical interpretation in terms of an
'elementary particle' with two different mass and spin states, has
been proved by Bhabha (1952). He gives an example of a wave
equation involving an irreducible set of 20×20 matrices, with
eigenstates $s = 3/2$ and $s = 1/2$ having different masses. Because
the charge density is positive-definite, quantization according to
the exclusion principle (hole theory) is possible. The eigenfunctions representing the particle in either state are here, of
course, quite different from the Dirac or Fierz–Pauli wave
functions of pure spin particles.

All theories involving spins $s > 1$ are intrinsically complicated
and, with the exception of the gravitational field, have not
attracted widespread interest because, as it appears today, the
'simpler' cases are favoured in reality. Nevertheless, the finding
that the field-theoretical formalism is far more comprehensive
than reality (as we know it) is of basic importance in that it
indicates that entirely new ideas will be needed to explain why the
particles observed in nature have their very specific properties.

4. FIELD THEORY APPLIED TO NUCLEAR
PHYSICS PROBLEMS

Once more, let us return to the late 20s and early 30s. Although, by then, we had learned that the emission and absorption
of photons is perfectly described by interpreting the electromagnetic field amplitudes as quantum-mechanical operators, it
was not commonly realized that a similar description might
fittingly be applied to other creation and annihilation processes,
or that even the words 'creation' or 'annihilation' of particles
afforded a proper way of speaking about occurrences like the β
decay. In this respect, a break-through came with the Pauli–
Fermi theory of the β decay, and to illustrate the change in thinking
we give here a translation of some of the introductory paragraphs
of Fermi's (1933) paper. After having referred to Pauli's explanation of the continuous β velocity spectrum in terms of a
'neutrino' which escapes unobserved carrying away part of the
energy liberated (see the article by C. S. Wu), Fermi goes on to say:

Besides the difficulty of the continuous energy distribution, a theory of the β rays faces still another essential difficulty in the fact that the present theories of the light particles do not explain in a satisfactory manner how these particles could be bound in a stable or quasi-stable manner inside a nucleus, considering the smallness of its volume.

The simplest way for the construction of a theory which permits a quantitative discussion of the phenomena involving nuclear electrons, seems then to examine the hypothesis that the electrons do not exist as such in the nucleus before the β emission occurs, but that they, so to say, acquire their existence at the very moment when they are emitted; in the same manner as a quantum of light, emitted by an atom in a quantum jump, can in no way be considered as pre-existing in the atom prior to the emission process. In this theory, then, the total number of the electrons and of the neutrinos (like the total number of light quanta in the theory of radiation) will not necessarily be constant, since there might be processes of creation or destruction of those light particles.

According to the ideas of Heisenberg, we will consider the heavy particles, neutron and proton, as two quantum states connected with two possible values of an internal coordinate ρ of the heavy particle. We assign to it the value $+1$ if the particle is a neutron, and -1 if the particle is a proton.

We will then seek an expression for the energy of interaction between the light and heavy particles which allows transitions between the values $+1$ and -1 of the coordinate ρ, that is to say, transformations of neutrons into protons or *vice-versa*; in such a way, however, that the transformation of a neutron into a proton is necessarily connected with the creation of an electron which is observed as a β particle, and of a neutrino; whereas the inverse transformation of a proton into a neutron is connected with the disappearance of an electron and a neutrino; . . . .

The simplest formulation for a theory in which the number of the particles (electrons and neutrinos) is not necessarily constant is available in the method of Dirac–Jordan–Klein of the 'quantized probability amplitudes'. In this formalism, the probability amplitudes ψ of the electrons and φ of the neutrinos, and their complex conjugates $\psi^\star$ and $\varphi^\star$, are considered as non-commutative operators acting on functions of the occupation numbers of the quantum states of the electrons and neutrinos. . . .

Fermi goes on to write down in field-theoretical notation his famous β interaction (incidentally, his special choice was what is called today the 'vector' interaction). We cannot follow here the subsequent, often devious, development of β theory, except for mentioning briefly the short-lived, but historically important, 'β theory of nuclear forces'. This is the idea (Tamm, 1934; Iwanenko, 1934) that, according to second-order perturbation theory, a proton and neutron can interact by virtually emitting and re-absorbing an electron–neutrino pair. Numerically, this interaction is extremely weak, except for being strongly singular at zero distance and allowing an adaptable cut-off. Several variants of this theory (e.g. involving electron–positron pairs) were subsequently proposed, and the discussion continued even after the discovery of the 'mesotron'.

Meanwhile, Yukawa (1935) had published his ingenious hypothesis that the nuclear forces are mediated by a boson field, that is to say, by *single* particles rather than pairs, in close analogy with the electromagnetic forces, with the important difference, however, that the particles must have a non-vanishing *rest mass* such that their Compton wavelength determines the range of the nuclear forces, as indicated by the static solution ($e^{-\mu r}/r$, with $\mu = mc/\hbar$) of the 'scalar wave equation'. Yukawa estimated the rest mass of the boson as 200 electron masses. The charge of the mediating bosons determines the 'exchange character' of the resulting forces. It is interesting to note that Yukawa also suggested the boson might be β unstable so that the nuclear β decay would be explainable as a two-step process mediated by a virtual boson. (Recently, this view has become fashionable again, with the difference that a *new* hypothetical boson is needed. A different multi-step mechanism for β decay and nuclear forces, involving bosons heavier than nucleons such that the mass difference would determine the force range, was tentatively proposed by Wentzel, 1936.)

Yukawa's (1935) paper was not received, wherever it became known, with immediate consent or sympathy. However two years later it suddenly became the focus of universal attention when charged particles heavier than electrons but lighter than protons were detected, with increasing certainty, in cosmic ray experiments: Yukawa had predicted their existence! Later they were even found to decay into electrons (and presumably neutrinos). The confusion which resulted from this erroneous identification of the 'μ meson' with the 'nuclear field meson' lasted more than ten years, and it had some adverse effects, though not very serious ones, on the development of meson theory.

Meanwhile, the main guidance had come from the advancing knowledge of the properties of the nuclear forces. Their spin dependence seemed to demand a *vector* meson, rather than a scalar one, and the quantized Proca field, as well as its possible interactions with nucleons, became the subject of numerous investigations (Yukawa, Sakata and Taketani, 1938; Stueckelberg, 1938; Fröhlich, Heitler and Kemmer, 1938; Bhabha, 1938). Kemmer (1938) was the first to consider also the case of a *pseudoscalar* field which was to become so important, later, for the description of the π meson. Kemmer pointed out that, although scalar and pseudo-scalar particles behave alike when free or subject to electro-magnetic forces, their interactions with nucleons are typically different, because of the difference in parity of the boson field operators. Another important contribution of Kemmer's (1938a) was the introduction of the *isotopic spin* formalism into meson field theory; the results would then automatically be charge-symmetric, and the nuclear forces would be 'charge-independent' (in *any* approximation), as empirical data (e.g. proton–proton scattering) already then seemed to indicate.

Although the shortcomings of the perturbation method were well recognized (see, e.g. Stueckelberg and Patry, 1939–40), the second-order results were commonly used for comparison with the experimental data. Besides the two-nucleon data, the stability of heavy nuclei ('saturation') served as an important criterion. While, at first, the vector theory seemed strongly favoured, it ran into difficulties when the sign of the 'tensor force' became known from measurements (by Rabi and co-workers) of the electric quadrupole moment of the deuteron, and during the early 40s increasing interest was bestowed upon the pseudoscalar theory. Singular ($\sim r^{-3}$) terms in the static tensor force could be cancelled out by introducing a vector field beside the pseudoscalar one (Møller and Rosenfeld, 1940; Schwinger, 1942; the struggle to make this type of theory agree with the deuteron data is reviewed in section 1 of Wentzel, 1947).

Another, much discussed, problem was the anomaly in the magnetic moments of the proton and neutron, attributed to the 'bound meson cloud'. The idea was the same as in an earlier proposal by Wick (1935) based on the β field theory, but the stronger meson–nucleon coupling seemed to promise more satisfying results, even though one still had to put up with an arbitrary cut-off. This optimism, however, could not long be maintained; indeed, these and related questions have remained baffling up to the present day.

In view of the actual strength of the nuclear forces, it soon became an urgent desire to get away from perturbation or similar weak coupling methods. The Bloch–Nordsieck method of quantum electrodynamics, though pointing in the right direction, could not be taken over because the characteristic spin and/or isotopic spin dependence of the meson–nucleon interaction introduces essential complications (see, for instance, Stueckelberg, 1938a). If, however, the coupling parameter g was assumed very *large*, so that an expansion into *falling* powers of g is indicated, it was then possible to make a separation of the meson field into a field bound to the (static and finite size) nucleons, and a free field which, in a higher approximation, is scattered by the compound nucleons. This 'strong coupling theory' was first carried through for the simplest non-trivial case: Yukawa's charged scalar theory (Wentzel, 1940). The most striking result was the appearance of 'nucleon isobars', i.e. excited states of the compound nucleon carrying higher charges Z, with an excitation energy proportional to $Z(Z-1)/g^2$. (The value of the coefficient, as also the 'strong coupling condition', was corrected in Wentzel, 1941; see also Oppenheimer and Schwinger, 1941.) To be applicable to pseudoscalar and vector fields, the method had to be generalized so as to allow mesons to be bound in p, rather than s, states; there are per nucleon 3 such p states in the neutral, 9 in the charge-symmetric pseudoscalar theory (Serber and Dancoff, 1943; Pauli and Dancoff, 1942). In the charge-symmetric pseudoscalar theory (also for certain vector and mixture theories: Pauli and Kusaka, 1943; Wentzel, 1943), the isobar energy is similar to the rotational energy of a spherical top, with eigenvalues proportional to $j(j+1)$, where j (half-odd) is both the spin and the isotopic spin of the isobar state; for a given j, there are $(2j+1)$ spin orientations and $(2j+1)$ charge states $(Z = -j+\frac{1}{2}, \cdots, j+\frac{1}{2})$. The ground states $j = 1/2$ are then to be identified with the ordinary neutron and proton states, while the first excited states, $j = 3/2$, have precisely the same properties as the now well known resonant $p(3/2, 3/2)$ states, observed in π meson–nucleon scattering, which have an excitation energy of about 300 MeV (Brueckner, 1952). It is amusing to find this same value quoted already in a paper by Villars (1946), where the effect of isobar admixtures on the proton–neutron system (deuteron and low energy scattering) is analysed: agreement of the strong coupling theory with the experimental data requires that the excitation energy be at least about 300 MeV (an unexpectedly high value!).

In their attempt to adapt the parameters of their mixture theory, including a cut-off k_c, to fit the experiments, Pauli and Kusaka considered it as imperative that the high energy meson–nucleon scattering cross-section be very small so as to conform to the cosmic ray observations, and this could actually be achieved by choosing k_c large enough (Oppenheimer and Schwinger, 1941). In this regard, we were all led astray by the mistaken identity of the cosmic ray mesons! Ironically, the apparent weakness of their nuclear interaction was one of the major motivations for work on the strong coupling theory, as well as for other contemporaneous speculations. Only very rarely was the suspicion expressed that there might be several kinds of mesons (Sakata and Tanikawa are quoted by Tomonaga, in a 1942 paper reprinted in the Supplement of the *Progress of Theoretical Physics*, Number 2, 1955, p. 80).

While it was thought that the isobar excitation energy might be of the order 50 MeV or even less, one had to worry whether the presence of higher isobar states in heavy nuclei might not upset the saturation. It was found (Pauli and Kusaka, 1943; Coester, 1944) that the saturation is maintained in the charge symmetric theory although the equilibrium value for the charge (more precisely: Z/A) might tend to become too low because the Coulomb energy favours negatively charged isobars (Fierz, 1941). This defect of the theory is, of course, removed with the higher value of the excitation energy. Pauli's other objection against the strong coupling theory was its complete failure to account for the magnetic moments of the proton and the neutron; their ratio becomes -1 in the strong coupling limit, and no sufficient remedy is brought by the next correction terms (Houriet, 1945). Moreover, the neutron–proton mass difference has the wrong sign. (These difficulties of the strong coupling theory are surveyed in section 2 of Wentzel, 1947.)

The suspicion that in reality the coupling might be neither 'strong' nor 'weak' prompted various attempts to deal with the 'intermediate coupling' case. Tomonaga (1947, and earlier work quoted there) invented an ingenious variational method which, e.g. for the charged scalar theory, allows an interpolation between the weak and strong coupling limits, for the static case (extended nucleon at rest). (Many papers by Tomonaga and his co-workers, dating back as far as 1941, which treat various versions of the theory in strong and intermediate coupling approximations, were reprinted in the Supplement of the *Progress of Theoretical Physics*, Number 2, 1955.) Another approach was made on classical or semi-classical lines, in the sense that the motions of the nuclear spin or charge coordinates were analysed in terms of classical gyrations, with emphasis on damping (reaction) effects in meson–nucleon scattering, often hopefully with regard to the alleged smallness of the cross-section (Heisenberg, 1939; Iwanenko and Sokolow, 1940; Bhabha, 1941; Fierz, 1941a; Pauli, 1946). Heitler (1941) developed a quantum theory of radiation damping which he applied to meson–nucleon scattering.

Could one be at all sure that the meson–nucleon interaction is of the type proposed by Yukawa? The idea of the older pair theories, namely, that the nucleons interact with *pairs* of particles (the interaction being quadratic in the field amplitudes), was taken up again and applied to meson pairs (Marshak, 1940). The scalar pair theory (Wentzel, 1942) has retained some mathematical interest as one of the few rigorously soluble field-theoretical problems. Spin-dependent pair interactions were treated in a strong coupling approximation by Pauli and Hu (1945) (earlier work on pair theories is quoted there), and by Blatt (1946).

Since about 1950, the rapidly accumulating experimental information has placed the development of meson theory on much firmer ground; but a major part of what is called 'theory' today is really half-empirical, and meson field theory, as a deductive scheme, has not been conspicuously successful. For some time it was believed, and many people still seem to believe, that a pseudoscalar field with a non-derivative (γ_5) coupling to nucleons accounts correctly for all facts related to π mesons and nucleons. Actually, there is very little to substantiate this claim, once one takes the crudest features, dominated by the $p(3/2, 3/2)$ resonance, for granted. This, then, leads on to the more general question which has often been raised (see, e.g. Heisenberg, 1946) whether our customary field-theoretical procedure is at all adequate; namely, to start from free fields describing 'bare' particles, and then to add an interaction term in the Lagrangian which causes the particles to become 'dressed' or 'compound', thereby degrading the original bare particles to unobservable entities. It is true that this approach, combined with re-normalization prescriptions, has resulted in a workable scheme for quantum electrodynamics, but this may be so only because, or as far as, the expansions in powers of $e^2/\hbar c$ converge rapidly. As to meson theory, and other more comprehensive field theories involving stronger interactions, the question is wide open.

REFERENCES

Section 1

Ehrenfest, P. (1906) *Phys. Z.* **7**, 528
Debye, P. (1910) *Ann. Phys. Lpz.* 4 **33**, 1427
Einstein, A. (1905) *Ann. Phys. Lpz.* 4 **17**, 132
Bose, S. N. (1924) *Z. Phys.* **26**, 178
Born, M., Heisenberg, W. and Jordan, P. (1926) *Z. Phys.* **35**, 557
Dirac, P. A. M. (1927a) *Proc. Roy. Soc. A* **114**, 243
Dirac, P. A. M. (1927b) *Proc. Roy. Soc. A* **114**, 710
Kramers, H. A. and Heisenberg, W. (1925) *Z. Phys.* **31**, 681
Weisskopf, V. and Wigner, E. (1930) *Z. Phys.* **63**, 54
Heitler, W. (1954) *Quantum Theory of Radiation*, 3rd ed. Clarendon Press
Heisenberg, W. (1931) *Ann. Phys. Lpz.* 5 **9**, 338
Jordan, P. and Pauli, W. (1928) *Z. Phys.* **47**, 151
Bohr, N. and Rosenfeld, L. (1933) *K. danske vidensk. Selsk., Math.-Fys. Medd.* XII, 8

Dirac, P. A. M. (1928) *Proc. Roy. Soc. A* **117**, 610
Heisenberg, W. and Pauli, W. (1929) *Z. Phys.* **56**, 1
Rosenfeld, L. (1930) *Z. Phys.* **63**, 574
Heisenberg, W. and Pauli, W. (1930) *Z. Phys.* **59**, 168
Waller, I. (1930) *Z. Phys.* **62**, 673
Oppenheimer, J. R. (1930) *Phys. Rev.* **35**, 461
Fermi, E. (1929–30) *R. C. Accad. Lincei* **9**, 881, and **12**, 431
Dirac, P. A. M., Fock, V. A. and Podolsky, B. (1932) *Phys. Z. Sowjet.* **2**, 468
Bloch, F. (1934) *Phys. Z. Sowjet.* **5**, 301
Tomonaga, S. (1946) *Progr. theor. Phys., Osaka* **1**, 27
Schwinger, J. (1948) *Phys. Rev.* **74**, 1439
Wentzel, G. (1933) *Z. Phys.* **86**, 479 and 635; **87**, 726
Dirac, P. A. M. (1939) *Ann. Inst. Poincaré* **9**, 13
Dirac, P. A. M. (1938) *Proc. Roy. Soc. A* **167**, 148
Dirac, P. A. M. (1942) *Proc. Roy. Soc. A* **180**, 1
Pauli, W. (1943) *Rev. mod. Phys.* **15**, 175
Pauli, W. (1933) *Handbuch der Physik Geiger-Scheel*, vol. 24, part 1, pp. 255–6
Bloch, F. and Nordsieck, A. (1937) *Phys. Rev.* **52**, 54
Pauli, W. and Fierz, M. (1938) *Nuovo Cim.* **15**, 167

Section 2

Jordan, P. (1927) *Z. Phys.* **44**, 473
Dirac, P. A. M. (1927) *Proc. Roy. Soc. A* **114**, 243
Jordan, P. and Klein, O. (1927) *Z. Phys.* **45**, 751
Jordan, P. and Wigner, E. (1928) *Z. Phys.* **47**, 631
Dirac, P. A. M. (1930) *Proc. Roy. Soc. A* **126**, 360
Oppenheimer, J. R. (1930) *Phys. Rev.* **35**, 562
Bhabha, H. J. (1936) *Proc. Roy. Soc. A* **154**, 195
Peierls, R. (1934) *Proc. Roy. Soc. A* **146**, 420
Furry, W. H. and Oppenheimer, J. R. (1934) *Phys. Rev.* **45**, 260
Dirac, P. A. M. (1934) *Proc. Camb. phil. Soc.* **30**, 150
Heisenberg, W. (1934) *Z. Phys.* **90**, 209
Weisskopf, V. (1934) *Z. Phys.* **89**, 27 and **90**, 817
Weisskopf, V. F. (1939) *Phys. Rev.* **56**, 72
Dirac, P. A. M. (1933) *Rapport du 7me Conseil Solvay de Physique*, p. 203
Uehling, E. A. (1935) *Phys. Rev.* **48**, 55
Serber, R. (1935) *Phys. Rev.* **48**, 49
Pauli, W. and Rose, M. (1936) *Phys. Rev.* **49**, 462
Halpern, O. (1933) *Phys. Rev.* **44**, 855
Delbrück, M. (1933) *Z. Phys.* **84**, 144
Euler, H. (1936) *Ann. Phys. Lpz.* 5 **26**, 398
Euler, H. and Kockel, B. (1935) *Naturwissenschaften* **23**, 246
Kemmer, N. (1937) *Helv. phys. Acta.* **10**, 112
Heisenberg, W. and Euler, H. (1936) *Z. Phys.* **98**, 714
Weisskopf, V. (1936) *K. danske vidensk. Selsk., Math.-Fys. Medd.* **14**, 6
Dancoff, S. M. (1939) *Phys. Rev.* **55**, 959

Section 3

Schrödinger, E. (1926) *Ann. Phys. Lpz.* 4 **81**, 109
Gordon, W. (1926) *Z. Phys.* **40**, 117
Klein, O. (1927) *Z. Phys.* **41**, 407
Dirac, P. A. M. (1928) *Proc. Roy. Soc. A* **117**, 610
Pauli, W. and Weisskopf, V. (1934) *Helv. phys. Acta* **7**, 709
Weisskopf, V. F. (1939) *Phys. Rev.* **56**, 72
Dirac, P. A. M. (1936) *Proc. Roy. Soc. A* **155**, 447

van der Waerden, B. L. (1929) *Nachr. Ges. Wiss. Göttingen*, p. 100
Fierz, M. (1939) *Helv. phys. Acta* **12**, 3
Rarita, W. and Schwinger, J. (1940) *Phys. Rev.* **60**, 61
Fierz, M. (1950) *Helv. phys. Acta* **23**, 416
Pauli, W. (1936) *Ann. Inst. Poincaré* **6**, 137
Pauli, W. (1940) *Phys. Rev.* **58**, 716
Fierz, M. (1940) *Helv. phys. Acta* **13**, 45
Proca, A. (1936) *J. Phys. Radium* **7**, 347
Stueckelberg, E. C. G. (1938) *Helv. phys. Acta* **11**, 225 and 299
Belinfante, F. J. (1949) *Phys. Rev.* **76**, 66
Coester, F. (1951) *Phys. Rev.* **83**, 798
Belinfante, F. J. (1939) *Physica* **6**, 887
Rosenfeld, L. (1940) *Mém. Acad. R. Belg.* **18**, Fascicule 6
Belinfante, F. J. (1940) *Physica* **7**, 449
Corben, H. C. and Schwinger, J. (1940) *Phys. Rev.* **58**, 953
Pauli, W. (1941) *Rev. mod. Phys.* **13**, 203
Fierz, M. and Pauli, W. (1939) *Proc. Roy. Soc. A* **173**, 211
Duffin, R. J. (1938) *Phys. Rev.* **54**, 1114
Kemmer, N. (1939) *Proc. Roy. Soc. A* **173**, 91
Bhabha, H. J. (1952) *Phil. Mag.* **43**, 33

Section 4

Fermi, E. (1933) *Ric. sci.* **2**, No. 12
Tamm, Ig. and Iwanenko, D. (1934) *Nature, Lond.* **133**, 981
Yukawa, H. (1935) *Proc. phys.-math. Soc. Japan* **17**, 48
Wentzel, G. (1936) *Z. Phys.* **104**, 34
Yukawa, H., Sakata, S. and Taketani, M. (1938) *Proc. phys.-math. Soc. Japan.* **20**, 319
Stueckelberg, E. C. G. (1938) *Helv. phys. Acta* **11**, 299
Fröhlich, H., Heitler, W. and Kemmer, N. (1938) *Proc. Roy. Soc. A* **166**, 154
Bhabha, H. J. (1938) *Proc. Roy. Soc. A* **166**, 501
Kemmer, N. (1938) *Proc. Roy. Soc. A* **166**, 127
Kemmer, N. (1938a) *Proc. Camb. phil. Soc.* **34**, 354
Stueckelberg, E. C. G. and Patry, J. F. C. (1939–40) *Helv. phys. Acta* **12**, 300; **13**, 167
Møller, C. and Rosenfeld, L. (1940) *K. danske vidensk. Selsk. Math.-Fys. Medd.* **17**, 8
Schwinger, J. (1942) *Phys. Rev.* **61**, 387
Wentzel, G. (1947) *Rev. mod. Phys.* **19**, 1
Wick, G. (1935) *R. C. Accad. Lincei* **21**, 170
Stueckelberg, E. C. G. (1938a) *Phys. Rev.* **54**, 889
Wentzel, G. (1940) *Helv. phys. Acta* **13**, 269
Wentzel, G. (1941) *Helv. phys. Acta* **14**, 633
Oppenheimer, J. R. and Schwinger, J. (1941) *Phys. Rev.* **60**, 150
Serber, R. and Dancoff, S. M. (1943) *Phys. Rev.* **63**, 143
Pauli, W. and Dancoff, S. M. (1942) *Phys. Rev.* **62**, 85
Pauli, W. and Kusaka, S. (1943) *Phys. Rev.* **63**, 400
Wentzel, G. (1943) *Helv. phys. Acta* **16**, 222 and 551
Brueckner, K. A. (1952) *Phys. Rev.* **86**, 106
Villars, F. (1946) *Helv. phys. Acta* **19**, 323
Coester, F. (1944) *Helv. phys. Acta* **17**, 35
Fierz, M. (1941) *Helv. phys. Acta* **14**, 105
Houriet, A. (1945) *Helv. phys. Acta* **18**, 473
Tomonaga, S. (1947) *Prog. theor. phys. Osaka* **2**, 6
Heisenberg, W. (1939) *Z. Phys.* **113**, 61
Iwanenko, D. and Sokolow, A. (1940) *J. Phys. Moscow* **3**, 57 and 417

Bhabha, H. J. (1941) *Proc. Roy. Soc. A* **178**, 324
Fierz, M. (1941a) *Helv. phys. Acta* **14**, 257
Pauli, W. (1946) *Meson theory of nuclear forces*, chap. III. New York; Interscience
Heitler, W. (1941) *Proc. Camb. phil. Soc.* **37**, 291
Marshak, R. E. (1940) *Phys. Rev.* **57**, 1101
Wentzel, G. (1942) *Helv. phys. Acta* **15**, 111
Pauli, W. and Hu, N. (1945) *Rev. mod. Phys.* **17**, 267
Blatt, J. M. (1946) *Phys. Rev.* **69**, 285
Heisenberg, W. (1946) *Z. Naturf.* **1**, 609

REGULARIZATION AND NON-SINGULAR INTERACTIONS IN QUANTUM FIELD THEORY

F. VILLARS

For over two decades Pauli has taken an active interest in the problem of divergence difficulties in the quantum theory of fields. In this review we try to sketch various phases of this problem, emphasizing his views and contributions towards possible solutions. For coherence, it will be necessary to embed details into a more general background; no attempt has been made, however, to do justice to every significant contribution in this wide area. It is hoped that this report will stand as a modest document of Pauli's critical concern with a fascinating problem.

1. INTRODUCTION

The divergencies of quantum field theory are a problem of long standing. We shall not review here the complete history of the attempts to come to terms with it; for background information we refer to the preceding article by G. Wentzel. Here we shall only sketch a few steps and points of view which will lead us to the period during which Pauli took part in attempts to clarify our understanding of this question.

The problem has been approached first on a level which might be called semi-classical, in which the picture of discrete, given sources interacting through quantized fields is used. The self-energy problem of the sources has still a close relation to the corresponding classical problem, and classical methods like the λ process of Wentzel[1] and Dirac[2] have been applied with equal success to the quantum problem. We recall that the λ process rests on the observation that the Coulomb potential $U(\mathbf{x} - \mathbf{x}_1, t - t_1)$ of a point charge at $\mathbf{x}_1(t_1)$ derives from the invariant Jordan–Pauli D-function

$$D(\mathbf{x}, t) = \frac{1}{4\pi |x|} \left[\delta(|x| - ct) - \delta(|x| + ct) \right] \qquad \ldots \ldots (1.1)$$

through the relation

$$U(\mathbf{x} - \mathbf{x}_1, t - t_1) = \frac{c}{2} \int_{-\infty}^{t} d\tau \, D(\mathbf{x} - \mathbf{x}_1, \tau - t_1)$$

$$- \frac{c}{2} \int_{t}^{\infty} d\tau \, D(\mathbf{x} - \mathbf{x}_1, \tau - t_1) \quad \ldots\ldots(1.2)$$

(See Wentzel,[3] §§ 18 and 19.)

U is *zero* unless $|\mathbf{x} - \mathbf{x}_1| > c|t - t_1|$; hence $U(0) = 0$ if this limit is defined as $\lim_{x \to 0} U(\mathbf{x})$, keeping $\mathbf{x}$ time-like. This is exploited in the λ process, by replacing the Jordan–Pauli function $D(x - x')$ by

$$D_\gamma(x - x') = \tfrac{1}{2}[D(x - x' + \lambda) + D(x - x' - \lambda)] \quad \ldots\ldots(1.3)$$

$\lambda = (\boldsymbol{\lambda}, \lambda_0)$ being a time-like four-vector, and the limit $\lambda^2 \to 0$ is understood to be taken in the end. It follows that this eliminates the Coulomb self-energy of the source, and leaves a transverse invariant self-mass λ^{-2}, which may be eliminated by renormalization.

It is interesting to compare the results of this method with the more primitive device of using extended sources, that is, a non-covariant momentum cut-off for virtual processes. As an example, a scalar meson field coupled to a nucleon at $\mathbf{x}_p$ is given by an interaction

$$H = g \int d\mathbf{x} \, v(\mathbf{x} - \mathbf{x}_p)\varphi(\mathbf{x}, t) = g \sum_k v(\mathbf{k}) \, e^{i\mathbf{k} \cdot \mathbf{x}_p}\varphi(\mathbf{k}, t)$$

Pauli, who first applied the λ process to meson theory,[4] pointed out that the substitution $D \to D_\lambda$ (1.3) is formally equivalent to introducing a form factor $v(k) = [\cos(\mathbf{k} \cdot \boldsymbol{\lambda} - k_0\lambda_0)]^{1/2}$. Seen in this light, the λ process appears as a very drastic method indeed, as it replaces the positive-definite cut-off $v(\mathbf{k})v^\star(\mathbf{k})$ of a virtual emission and re-absorption process by the indefinite function $\cos(\boldsymbol{\lambda} \cdot \mathbf{k} - \lambda_0 k_0)$. A calculation by Jauch[5] showed that the λ process led to the incorrect sign of the anomalous magnetic moments of nucleons, in contrast to the well known success of a calculation with a suitable form factor $v(k)$.[6]

The method also failed as a truly quantum-mechanical limiting process. The early work of Weisskopf[7] on the electron self-energy in hole theory had shown the profound modification which the polarizability of the electron–positron field vacuum introduced into the self-energy problem. With the possibility of creating virtual pairs, a many particle problem arose; Pauli[8] pointed out that the λ process would be of no help in this situation. Indeed, in the one-electron picture, the Coulomb self-field of the electron is defined as the limit obtained by approaching the position of the electron from a time-like direction, and found to be zero. In the hole theory, however, the situation is radically changed through the appearance of virtual pairs at space-like positions relative to the original particle. The associated Coulomb energy is not eliminated by the λ process. It is clearly evident then, that a discussion of divergence problems on the level of a classical description of sources has historical interest only. The quantization of the sources creates an entirely new problem.

What gives the divergence problem its peculiar aspect is the inter-relation of the purely physical problem of *formulating* the basic equations with the more subtle mathematical question arising in *solving* them. The field equations are after all extrapolated from classical dynamics, and the question as to what approximation to 'reality' they represent, if taken as a basis of quantum dynamics, is naturally raised. This has led to tampering with the solutions themselves, as for instance in the Heitler cut-off procedure,[9] or with the equations, as in Stueckelberg's attempts to formulate a divergence-free S matrix theory,[10] or to the introduction of additional fields into the equations (Pais f-fields[11]), or finally to a stretching of the conceptual basis of quantum mechanics itself, as with the introduction of a non-positive metric in Hilbert space. All these attempts emphasize the fact that the physicist's problem lies not just in the solution of a given set of equations, but rather in the elaboration of a code, by means of which a one to one correspondence between observations and a certain mathematical scheme may be established. It is quite conceivable that in present-day quantum dynamics this connection between reality and formalism is still too close; in other words, that the theory is still too 'naive'.

The urge for tampering derives a certain motivation from the fact that the divergence difficulties appear to be securely rooted in a set of basic assumptions of the currently accepted formalism: Lorentz invariance, local couplings (miscroscopic causality) and a positive metric in Hilbert space. Lorentz invariance implies the admission of a space-time continuum and associated kinematics; no new concepts, such as the idea of a universal length, have yet successfully supplanted this admittedly 'naive' basis for the description of events in space-time, and nothing will be said about it here. On the other hand, Pauli's name is again associated both with attempts to formulate a theory with non-local couplings, and with the investigation of the possibility of admitting quantum states of non-positive norm. Parts 4 and 5 will contain some comments on these questions.

The advent of formally covariant perturbation theory in 1947 made the divergence problem appear in a new light. Despite the success of formal renormalization in quantum electrodynamics, the problem of divergences (or of the values of renormalization constants) has not lost its interest. First, it is by no means clear that the unrenormalized values of charge and mass do not make their appearance in observable effects. In particular, recent work, especially by Schwinger,[12] emphasizes the fact that in the limit of very high momentum transfer, processes are governed by the unrenormalized values of the interaction strength. Another argument is the observation that renormalization has not been applicable with equal success to other field theories; but most important is perhaps the existence of groups of elementary particles with generic relationships among each other (Baryons, light fermions, etc.). A completely successful renormalization theory would probably preclude any interpretation of the actual mass ratios, etc. in these groups—in other words, there are meaningful questions waiting to be answered that may lie beyond the scope of the renormalization approach which was so successful in electrodynamics.

In the next section (2), the idea of regularization will be presented. This is evidently a method with a relatively modest aim, and conceived as a device to ensure that one deals only with mathematically well defined expressions. As such, it does not lead out of the framework of covariant perturbation theory. In section 3 some applications of this method will be discussed.

2. REGULARIZATION

When in 1948, the work of Tomonaga,[13] Schwinger,[14] Feynman,[15] and later of Dyson[16] become known in Zürich, it rapidly established itself as the subject of main interest. As with everything else, these methods had their roots in the past. We mention here only the work of Stueckelberg,[17] which anticipated many of the new features, in particular the expression of the S matrix in terms of the so-called 'casual' Green's functions S_F and D_F, which were to be characteristic of Feynman's theory. But Stueckelberg had centred his interest around the problem of constructing a finite S matrix theory, following Heisenberg's lead.[18] (For a review of these attempts, see Wentzel.[19]) In contrast to this, the work of the above-mentioned authors presented, in a forceful way, the good news that one might not need to be as radical as Heisenberg, at least for the time being. The new techniques made it definitely clear that the infinities encountered in electrodynamics were associated with a Lorentz invariant infinite electromagnetic mass of the electron and an infinite polarization charge. It was just this novel feature of Lorentz invariant perturbation theory which made it possible to single out these infinities, and to separate them from finite radiative corrections, to which a physical meaning could be attributed. It also made clear that the incompatibility of a non-zero photon self-energy with gauge invariance could be systematically exploited to discard ambiguous, but formally invariant, terms by insisting on a gauge invariant result.

It must be clearly stated that the scope of the new approach was by no means well understood and it is interesting to see, in retrospect, how a gradual clarification of this point was achieved, and to recall some of the confusions that existed about it and also some of the wild hopes it temporarily raised. As an example, we may mention here the expectation that the cancellation of divergences in the expression for the self-charge of the electron might give us a numerical value for the fine-structure constant—a hope that was quickly dispelled. Jost and Luttinger[20] pointed out that the square of the ratio between renormalized and unrenormalized charge may be written as

$$\frac{e^2}{e_0{}^2} = \frac{1}{1+C}$$

C being a series of divergent terms: $C = e_0{}^2 c_1 + e_0{}^4 c_2 + \cdots$ They found the signs of c_1 and c_2 to be equal, and later Schwinger[21] proved in general that $C > 0$.

But in general we recall that Pauli's attitude with respect to the possibilities opened up by the new approach was characteristically one of critical optimism. His criticism was primarily focused on the claim of the unambiguity of the physical predictions of the theory (after isolation of the infinities); his optimism and vivid interest due to the hope that something might actually be learned from facing the remaining difficulties, rather than by claiming total success before it was actually achieved.

It was evident that the source of such ambiguities was in the singular structure of the Green's function $D(x-x')$ and $S(x-x')$, describing the propagation of the electromagnetic and of the electron–positron field, respectively. He ventured the statement that such singularities should eventually be absent in a future version of field dynamics. The only and obvious step to be taken in this direction was to replace the single mass associated with each field by a suitable mass spectrum $\rho(m)$. Thus, instead of the Green's function

$$\Delta(x) = (2\pi)^{-4} \int_C d^4k \, e^{ik \cdot x} \frac{1}{k^2 + m^2} \qquad \ldots (2.1)$$

(C being a suitable contour in the k_0 plane), we associate with a boson field the non-singular propagator

$$\Delta^{(r)}(x) = (2\pi)^{-4} \int_C d^4k \, e^{ik \cdot x} \int d\mu^2 \frac{\rho(\mu^2)}{k^2 + \mu^2} \qquad \ldots (2.2)$$

The function $\Delta^{(r)}$ is regular on the light cone provided

$$\int d\mu^2 \, \rho(\mu^2) = 0, \qquad \int d\mu^2 \, \mu^2 \rho(\mu^2) = 0 \qquad \ldots (2.3)$$

The case of a finite number of discrete masses proved particularly instructive:

$$\rho(\mu^2) = \sum_i \eta_i \delta(\mu^2 - M_i^2) \qquad \ldots (2.4a)$$

The minimum number of masses to satisfy

$$\sum \eta_i = 0, \qquad \sum M_i^2 \eta_i = 0 \qquad \ldots (2.4b)$$

is three, and in this case the Fourier transform

$$\int d\mu^2 \, \rho(\mu^2)(k^2 + \mu^2)^{-1}$$

of the regularized Green's function becomes equal to

$$\sum_i \frac{\eta_i}{k^2 + M_i^2} = \frac{\text{const.}}{(k^2 + M_1^2)(k^2 + M_2^2)(k^2 + M_3^2)} \qquad \ldots (2.5)$$

Considering $\Delta^{(r)}(x)$ as the actual Green's function of a boson field $\varphi(x)$, this latter is thus seen to satisfy a field equation

$$\prod_i (\Box^2 - M_i^2)\varphi(x) = s(x) \qquad \ldots (2.6)$$

($s(x)$ being a source density). As Pais and Uhlenbeck [22] were to show in 1950, a multi-mass equation like (2.6) implies an indefinite metric in Hilbert space. Since this point is of a certain relevance, let us briefly indicate how this may be seen. Using the definition of the Green's function $\Delta_+(x)$ for example,

$$\Delta_+(x) = \langle 0|\varphi(x+x')\varphi(x')|0\rangle$$
$$= \sum_{nk} \langle 0|\varphi(x+x')|nk\rangle\langle nk|\varphi(x')|0\rangle \qquad \ldots (2.7)$$

it follows [23] that the weight factor $\rho(\mu^2)$ of equation (2.2) is given by

$$\int d\mu^2\, \rho(\mu^2)\delta(k^2+\mu^2) = \sum_n \langle 0|\varphi(0)|nk\rangle\langle nk|\varphi(0)|0\rangle \quad \ldots (2.8)$$

and hence is non-negative. This is at variance with the property (4a,b) of $\rho(\mu^2)$, unless the states $|nk\rangle$ are assumed to have an indefinite norm:

$$\langle nk|n'k'\rangle = g_{nn'}\delta(k-k')$$

$g_{nn'}$ being hermitian, non-positive and non-singular. In this case clearly the right-hand side of (2.8) is to be replaced by

$$\sum_{nn'} g^{-1}{}_{nn'}\langle 0|\varphi(0)|nk\rangle\langle n'k|\varphi(0)|0\rangle$$

and is not positive-definite any longer.

This situation made it obvious that a self-contained dynamics, in which propagators were non-singular, was not to be obtained without raising a host of new problems. We need to mention here only two: first some means must be found to deal with the 'non-physical' states of non-positive norm. The experience with such a situation in the Bleuler–Gupta [24] method for treating longitudinal and scalar photons offers only little help here. In that case the gauge group guarantees that non-physical states do not enter into the description of physical phenomena. But in general, the submatrix $\tilde{S}$ of the scattering matrix S, connecting 'physical' states only, will not be unitary by itself. Of course one might think of other ways of connecting a physical interpretation with the matrix elements of S, as has been attempted recently by Bogoliubov; [25] but this is done at the risk of even losing the property of macroscopic causality, [26] and is therefore not an obvious solution of the problem.

It must be re-stated that in those days of 1948–49 such thoughts were in nobody's mind. Pauli was rightly concerned with finding a consistent prescription for dealing with otherwise undefined mathematical expressions, as arose in various problems through confluence of singularities in products of Green's functions. To avoid those, a propagator

$$\frac{1}{k^2+M^2}$$

was to be replaced by expression (2.5) (left side!), using $M_1 = M$, $\eta_1 = 1$, together with conditions (2.4b). Such a method could be viewed simply as a mathematical limiting process, the physical result being defined as the limit $M_i(i > 1) \to \infty$.   It is this device that became known as 'formal regularization'.[27]

However this method had its pitfalls.   A similar prescription had independently been introduced by Stueckelberg and Rivier;[28] these authors reached the conclusion that the finite results obtained in this way (as example they gave the nucleon magnetic moment) were still undetermined.   This had its reason in the simple fact that their expression for the magnetic moment was written in terms of the functions Δ_1 and $\bar{\Delta}$ separately; they adopted a prescription which consisted of replacing the functions $\bar{\Delta}$ by a 'regularized' counterpart.   The result was then found to depend on the way the limit $(M_1 \to \infty)$ was taken.

Similar difficulties presented themselves in the case of vacuum polarization, and in the case of the stress tensor $T_{\mu\nu}$ of a fermion field.   The latter, as well as the polarization tensor $K_{\mu\nu}$, defined by

$$\langle 0|j_\mu(x)|0 \rangle = \int dx' \, K_{\mu\nu}(x-x')A_\nu(x')$$

must have zero divergence, and a formal regularization prescription for individual propagators would not guarantee this. In both cases a satisfactory prescription of formal regularization was found to exist, but in both cases this prescription assumes the nature of a pseudophysical theory.   The coupling to the auxiliary (non-physical) quanta must be derivable from a gauge invariant Lagrangian, which includes these auxiliary fields. This for instance excludes the appearance of individually regularized electron Green's functions

$$S^{(r)}(p) = \sum_i \eta_i \frac{i\gamma.p + M_i}{p^2 + M_i{}^2}$$

in any expression involving virtual electron pairs.   Only products of propagators forming a closed loop may be regularized (as a whole), whereas propagators connected with external electron lines appear unaffected.

These facts are suggestive of an actual modification of the Lagrangian, that is, of a modification of the field dynamics. Viewed as such, there is of course no reason to pass to the limit $M_i \to \infty$ for all masses of the 'unphysical' quanta.   This raises the question of the existence of any experimental evidence against such quanta of finite mass.   This question has recently been studied by Drell[29] and his collaborators, in connection with a study of proposed high energy experiments.   It turns out that radiative correction like the Lamb shift in the H atom and the anomaly in the electron g factor are remarkably insensitive to the value of the auxiliary masses M_t, as long as they are sufficiently large, of the order of the nucleon mass. A regularized photon

$$\frac{1}{k^2} - \frac{1}{k^2 + M_2^2}$$

propagator for instance decreases the Lamb shift ΔE_L by a fraction

$$\left(\frac{m_e}{M_2}\right)^2 \log\left(\frac{m_e}{M_2}\right)\Big/\log C$$

m_e being the electron mass, $\log C = 7.6$. The electron magnetic moment anomaly $(\alpha/2\pi)$ decreases by the fraction $\frac{2}{3}(m_e/M_2)^2$. For an M_2 of the order of the nucleon mass such changes are entirely negligible and well within the experimental accuracy of the results.

In the next section, a somewhat more detailed discussion of the case of vacuum polarization and of electron self-energy will be presented.

3A. ONE ELECTRON PROPERTIES

The formally covariant methods brought about a new insight into the properties of the physical single particle, and its inertial and electromagnetic properties. Historically, already the investigation of the e^2 electrodynamic corrections to the one electron states were full of interesting information, some of which we shall review in this section. More recently, a much more thorough approach has been made (Källén,[30] Schwinger[31]) to formulate the properties of the physical electron—as an eigenstate of the coupled electron–positron and electromagnetic field—outside the framework of perturbation theory.

The first formally covariant calculations of the electron's self-energy (in the e^2 approximation) are due to Schwinger[14] and Feynman.[15] Schwinger's method initially consisted of a covariant form of canonical transformation, by means of which the electron is decoupled from the radiation field. This method therefore represented a familiar technique, which had been widely used in previous years, especially in connection with meson theory,[32] but mostly in the form of time-independent perturbation theory. Schwinger made use of Tomonaga's[13] version of the time-dependent Schroedinger equation

$$\delta\Phi(\sigma)/\delta\sigma(x) = H_{\text{int}}(x)\Phi(\sigma) \qquad \ldots(3.1)$$

σ being a space-like surface and $\delta/\delta\sigma(x)$ representing a local variation of σ at point x. By a contact transformation $e^{iS(\sigma)}$, H_{int} was eliminated and a term

$$\frac{i}{2}[S(\sigma), H_{\text{int}}(x)] \qquad \ldots\ldots(3.2)$$

left, containing the e^2 electron self-energy. By using the covariant commutator and vacuum expectation values, the one electron part of (3.2) was shown to have the form $\delta m \bar{\psi}\psi$, with δm a formally invariant (σ-independent), but divergent integral.

Feyman's approach was based on the programme of constructing Green's function describing the propagation in space-time of the electron field operator $\psi(xt)$ in the presence of a radiative coupling. A characteristic feature of this approach was the way the so-called 'causal' Green's functions S_F and D_F (for electron–positron and electromagnetic field, respectively) appeared, in place of the retarded functions one would use in classical theory. Let us recall that $S_F(\mathbf{x}, t)$ and $D_F(\mathbf{x}, t)$ are characterized by the boundary condition that only positive frequencies occur for $t > 0$, only negatives for $t < 0$. The appearance of S_F and D_F as an expression of 'causality' in quantum field theory had already previously been emphasized by Stueckelberg;[17] it was later discussed anew in a paper by Fierz.[33] Dyson subsequently showed how all elements S_{fi} of the scattering matrix for a system of coupled relativistic fields may be expressed in terms of the 'causal' Green's functions for the constituent fields.

The boundary conditions for the causal Green's function are expressed in the definition

$$iS_{F\alpha\beta}(x, x') = \begin{cases} \langle 0|\psi_\alpha(x)\bar{\psi}_\beta(x')|0\rangle & (t > t') \\ -\langle 0|\bar{\psi}_\beta(x')\psi_\alpha(x)|0\rangle & (t < t') \end{cases} \qquad \ldots\ldots(3.3)$$

$\psi(x)$ being the free electron field operator and $|0\rangle$ the free vacuum state. In the presence of a coupling to the photon field, (3.3) defines Green's function $G_{\alpha\beta}(x, x')$ of the physical electron, if $\psi, \bar{\psi}$ stand for the Heisenberg operators of the electron field, and $|0\rangle$ defines the 'physical' vacuum state. An expansion in powers of the coupling e gives G in terms of the bare particle propagator S_F and the mass operator $M = e^2 M_1 + e^4 M_2 + \cdots$

$$G(x, x') = S_F(x - x') + \iint S_F(x - x'')M(x'', y'')G(y'', x') \qquad \ldots\ldots(3.4)$$

It follows that $G(x, x')$ satisfies the equation

$$\left(\gamma_\mu \frac{\partial}{\partial x_\mu} + m\right)G(x, x') + \int \{e^2 M_1(xx'') + \cdots\}G(x'', x') = -\delta(x - x')$$

4+P.M.V.

The one electron matrix elements $\langle 1|\psi(x)|0\rangle$ then satisfy the corresponding homogeneous equation. The structure of M_1 is best seen in momentum space, and displayed in the following way:

$$e^2 M_1(p) = \frac{ie^2}{(2\pi)^4} \int d^4k\, \gamma_\lambda S_F(p-k)\gamma_\lambda D_F(k) \quad \ldots\ldots(3.5)$$

which has the structure

$$e^2 M_1 = A + B(i\gamma.p+m) + (i\gamma.p+m)C(p^2)(i\gamma.p+m) \quad \ldots\ldots(3.6)$$

Due to the singularities in S_F and D_F, the constants A and B are divergent. Since $(i\gamma.p+m)\psi(p)=0$ the electromagnetic mass δm is given by $\delta m = A$. A regularized photon propagator

$$D_F^{(r)}(x) = D_F(x) + \sum_i{}' \eta_i D_F(x; M_i) \quad \left(\sum_i{}' \eta_i = -1\right) \quad \ldots\ldots(3.7)$$

leads to a finite expression

$$\delta m = -\frac{3\alpha}{2\pi} m\left[\sum_i{}' \eta_i \log\left(\frac{M_i}{m}\right) + \text{const.}\right] \quad \ldots\ldots(3.8)$$

With a single auxiliary field, δm may be made finite and even with an M_1 of the order of the nucleonic mass, we find that $\delta m \ll m$.

A more complete investigation of the electromagnetic mass phenomenon however turned up an unsatisfactory aspect. Pais and Epstein[34] pointed out that a self-mass, made finite by any formal invariant cut-off procedure, is not sufficient to make total energy and momentum of the physical electron transform as a four vector, due to a non-vanishing self-stress, S. This situation is well known in the classical self-energy problem (for a review of this question, see Pais[35]). S is the expectation value, for an electron at rest, of

$$\frac{1}{3}\int dx\left(\sum_{\mu=1}^4 T_{\mu\nu} - T_{44}\right) = \frac{1}{3}(H - m\int \bar{\psi}\psi\, dx) = \frac{1}{3}\left(H - m\frac{\partial H}{\partial m}\right)$$
$$\ldots\ldots(3.9)$$

$T_{\mu\nu}$ being the energy tensor, and H the Hamiltonian of the electron–photon system. It is now easily seen that with (3.8) we obtain

$$S = \frac{1}{3}\left(\delta m - m\frac{\partial}{\partial m}\delta m\right) = \frac{\alpha}{2\pi} m \quad \ldots\ldots(3.10)$$

It was subsequently shown by Rohrlich[36] and by the author[37] that S will vanish if the 'auxiliary fields' $\phi_\lambda^{(1)}$ contributing to the regularized photon propagator (3.7) are given a physical reality, and in particular their contribution to the energy tensor included in $T_{\mu\nu}$. This leads, instead of (3.9), to the operator

$$\frac{1}{3}\left(H - m\frac{\partial H}{\partial m} - \sum_i{}' M_i\frac{\partial H}{\partial M_i}\right)$$

and consequently to

$$S = \frac{1}{3}\left(1 - m\frac{\partial}{\partial m} - \sum_i{}' M_i\frac{\partial}{\partial M_i}\right)\delta m$$

which is easily seen to be zero by (3.8). (It can easily be shown that this last argument is in fact not restricted to the e^2 approximation (3.8) to δm.) The interest of this result lies in the fact that it points out that the identification of the infinite self-energy as an invariant mass term is not yet an entirely satisfactory solution, and that the 'renormalization' of infinities is no guarantee of consistency.

3B. VACUUM POLARIZATION

The problem of vacuum polarization in positron theory has already been mentioned in the preceding section. We shall present here only an outline of the situation as viewed in the light of covariant methods developed since 1946. These covariant techniques have fully substantiated the finite polarization effects on a point charge calculated by Uehling,[38] and Pauli–Rose,[39] as well as the non-linear correction terms to Maxwell's equations calculated by Heisenberg–Euler[40] and Weisskopf[41] by means of the original Heisenberg subtraction method. (For reference see the previous article by G. Wentzel.)

In the new approach, the central quantity is the invariant Green's function $G(x; x')$ of the electron–positron field

$$G_{\alpha\beta}(x, x') = \begin{cases} -i\langle 0|\psi_\alpha(x)\bar{\psi}_\beta(x')|0\rangle & (t > t') \\ +i\langle 0|\bar{\psi}_\beta(x')\psi_\alpha(x)|0\rangle & (t < t') \end{cases} \quad \dots\,(3.11)$$

$|0\rangle$ being the vacuum state. In the presence of an external classical field $A_\mu{}^{\text{ext}}(x)$, G satisfies the inhomogeneous Dirac equation

$$\left\{\gamma_\mu\left(\frac{\partial}{\partial x_\mu} - ieA_\mu(x)\right) + m\right\}G(x, x') = -\delta(x - x') \quad \dots\,(3.12)$$

for $A_\mu \to 0$, it reduces to Feynman's function $S_F(x - x')$. From the definition of G it follows that the symmetrized current operator

$$j_\mu(x) = \frac{-ie}{2} (\gamma_\mu)_{\beta\alpha}[\psi_\alpha(x)_1\bar\psi_\beta(x)] \qquad \ldots(3.13)$$

has a vacuum expectation value

$$\langle 0|j(x)|0\rangle = e \text{ trace } (\gamma_\mu G(x, x'))|_{x'=x} \qquad \ldots(3.14)$$

provided the limit $x' \to x$ is taken symmetrically from the two time-like directions. The vacuum current $\langle 0|j_\mu|0\rangle$ depends in a non-linear way on the external field A; the linear terms describe the polarizability of the vacuum, whereas the higher terms give non-linear correction to the electromagnetic field equations. From the integral equation satisfied by G:

$$G(x, x') = S_F(x-x') - ie \int dx'' S_F(x-x'')(\gamma.A(x''))G(x'', x') \qquad \ldots(3.15)$$

it follows that the vacuum current linear in A is given by

$$\langle 0|j_\mu(x)|0\rangle = -ie^2 \int dx'' \text{ trace } \{\gamma_\mu S_F(x-x'')\gamma_\lambda S_F(x''-x')\}_{x'=x} A_\lambda(x'')$$
$$= \int dx'' K_{\mu\lambda}(x'')A_\lambda(x'') \qquad \ldots(3.16)$$

It is now easily seen that this expression $K_{\mu\nu}$ as it stands does *not* satisfy the condition $\partial K_{\mu\nu}/\partial x_\nu = 0$, required for a gauge invariant polarization current $\langle 0|j|0\rangle$. The divergence of $K_{\mu\nu}$ is indeed given by

$$\frac{\partial K_{\mu\nu}}{\partial x_\nu} = -8ie^2 \frac{\partial \Delta_F(x)}{\partial x_\mu} \delta(x) \qquad \ldots(3.17)$$

This expression is indeterminate, since in the neighbourhood of $x = 0$, one has

$$\frac{\partial \Delta_F(x)}{\partial x_\mu} = \frac{-x_\mu}{2\pi} \left\{\frac{d}{d\lambda} - \frac{m^2}{4}\right\}\left(\delta(\lambda) + \frac{1}{i\pi\lambda}\right) + \cdots \qquad \ldots(3.18)$$

λ being given by $\lambda = -\sum x_\mu^2 = -\mathbf{x}^2 + c^2t^2$. The right-hand side of (3.17) is therefore not zero, but the formal gauge invariance of the theory gave justification for the hope that a consistent limiting process for handling undetermined expressions might be found. Historically first came the observation by Umezawa[42] and collaborators (1948) and by Rayski[43] (1949) that the vacuum current due to charged bosons of mass m gave a result for $\partial K_{\mu\nu}/\partial x_\nu$ which is $-1/2$ of that for fermions (3.17). It follows that the total polarization tensor

$$\sum_F K_{\mu\nu}^F + \sum_B K_{\mu\nu}^B$$

due to a set of fermion and boson pairs has a divergence:

$$4ic^2\delta(x)\left\{\sum_{i=1}^{N}\frac{\partial\Delta_F(x,M_i)}{\partial x_\mu}-2\sum_{j=1}^{M}\frac{\partial\Delta_F(x,m_j)}{\partial x_\mu}\right\} \quad \ldots\ldots(3.19)$$

and that this expression is identically zero, on account of (3.18), if suitable relations between the numbers N and of boson- and fermion-fields were satisfied. These relations are:

$$N = 2n, \quad \sum_{}^{N} M_i^2 = 2\sum_{}^{M} m_j^2 \qquad \ldots\ldots(3.20)$$

This result was generalized later by Umezawa and Kawabe[44] (1949) to include the effects of vector mesons. This result has historical interest only; but it represents a first attempt to enforce consistency only within a formalism encompassing *all* existing fields. It is not to be expected, however, that masses of bosons and fermions would just satisfy relation (3.20); nor does this method take into account radiative corrections to $K_{\mu\nu}$, for which similar simple relations do not hold any more. Pauli's views on the subject, as we recall them, were clearly pre-occupied with the search for a modification of the existing structure of the theory. He expressed the view that the commutators of field variables and Green's functions of field equation would have to be non-singular in a future version of the theory; and that as a means to achieve this the concept of a well defined *mass* associated with a given field would eventually have to be abandoned. In the meantime, he proposed that formal regularization, in suitable form, be used to give a well defined mathematical meaning to the tensor $K_{\mu\nu}$. From (3.18) it is obvious that the substitution

$$K_{\mu\nu}(x;m) \to \tilde{K}_{\mu\nu}(x) = \int_0^\infty d\mu^2 \, \rho(\mu^2) K_{\mu\nu}(x;\mu) \quad \ldots\ldots(3.21)$$

would assure gauge invariance of $\tilde{K}_{\mu\nu}$, provided

$$\int d\mu^2 \, \rho(\mu^2) = 0, \qquad \int d\mu^2 \, \mu^2\rho(\mu^2) = 0 \qquad \ldots\ldots(3.22)$$

It was important, at this point, to investigate to what extent physically observable parts of the polarization current are affected by this 'regularization'. The tensor $\tilde{K}_{\mu\nu}$ has a well defined Fourier transform, whose structure, from gauge-invariance and dimensional arguments, is

$$\tilde{K}_{\mu\nu}(p) = (p_\mu p_\nu - p^2\delta_{\mu\nu})\int d\mu^2 \, \rho(\mu^2) K(p^2/\mu^2) \quad \ldots\ldots(3.23)$$

Since

$$(p_\mu p_\nu - p^2\delta_{\mu\nu})A_\nu(p) = -J_\mu^{\text{ext}}(p)$$

the external current,

$$\tilde{K} = \int d\mu^2 \, \rho(\mu^2) K(0)$$

gives the part of $\langle 0|j_\mu|0 \rangle$ proportional to J_μ^{ext}, and defines the renormalization of charge. The regularization condition (3.22) reduces this renormalization to zero. The remaining terms are observable in principle; as they contain only positive powers of p^2/μ^2, a weight function

$$\rho(\mu^2) = \delta(\mu^2 - m_e^2) + \rho'(\mu^2)$$

will leave this physical result unaffected, provided ρ' is zero except for $\mu^2 \gg m_e^2$. The result thus obtained agrees entirely with the results previously found by Uehling[38] and Pauli and Rose.[39]

This is also the place to add a remark concerning the photon self-energy. The actual evaluation of $K_{\mu\nu}$ from (3.16) leads to the following structure for $K_{\mu\nu}$:

$$K_{\mu\nu}(p) = (p_\mu p_\nu - p^2 \delta_{\mu\nu}) K(p^2/m_e^2) + I m_e^2 \delta_{\mu\nu}$$

I being an ambiguous constant arising from the indeterminacy of (3.19), and required to be zero by gauge invariance. In $\tilde{K}_{\mu\nu}$, this leads to an additional term

$$I\delta_{\mu\nu} \int d\mu^2 \mu^2 \rho(\mu^2) = \kappa^2 \delta_{\mu\nu} \qquad \ldots (3.24)$$

This term is made identically zero by the stronger condition (3.22). If this term is not eliminated, then one gets a modification of the propagation of an electromagnetic wave in free space. Indeed from

$$(p_\mu p_\nu - p^2 \delta_{\mu\nu}) A_\nu(p) = -\langle 0|j_\mu(p)|0 \rangle$$

it follows with (3.24) that A_μ satisfies the equation

$$\{(p_\mu p_\nu - p^2 \delta_{\mu\nu})(1 + \tilde{K}) + \kappa^2 \delta_{\mu\nu}\} A_\nu = 0 \qquad \ldots (3.25)$$

In violation of gauge invariance, the (classical) electromagnetic field is here endowed with a mass term. In a quantized electromagnetic field this term appears as the self-energy (or mass) of the photon. It is seen that the regularization condition (3.22) ensures that $\kappa \equiv 0$; without regularization, an ambiguous result follows depending on the method of calculation. Wentzel's result[45] is an illustration of this situation.

From the point of view of a mathematical device to ensure unambiguous observable results, the method described here has been superseded by a more elegant method developed by Schwinger.[46] Schwinger introduced for $G(x; x')$ the integral representation:

$$G(x, x') = -\left(x\left|\frac{1}{i\gamma\cdot\pi+m-i\epsilon}\right|x'\right) = -i\int_0^\infty \mathrm{d}s(x|e^{-is(i\gamma\cdot\pi+m)}|x')$$
$$\ldots\ldots(3.26)$$

[π being the operator $p-eA$, which is written here in the x-representation: $(x|\pi_\mu|x') = (-i\,\partial/\partial x_\mu - eA_\mu(x))\delta(x-x')$].

With (3.14) and the observation that $-ie\gamma_\mu\delta A_\mu(x) = \delta(i\gamma\cdot\pi+m)$, it is made apparent that the polarization current follows from the variation of an action integral:

$$\int \mathrm{d}x\, \delta A_\mu(x)\langle 0|j_\mu(x)|0\rangle = i\int \mathrm{d}x\, \text{trace }(\delta(i\gamma\cdot\pi+m)G)$$
$$= i\delta\int_0^\infty \frac{\mathrm{d}s}{s}\int \mathrm{d}x\, \text{trace }(x|e^{-is(i\gamma\cdot\pi+m)}|x)$$
$$= \delta\int \mathrm{d}x\, \mathscr{L}^{(1)}(x) = \delta W^{(1)}$$

Gauge invariance now requires that $\mathscr{L}^{(1)}(x)$ has this property. $\mathscr{L}^{(1)}(x)$ has the structure of an integral over an invariant parameter

$$\mathscr{L}^{(1)}(x) = \int_0^\infty \frac{\mathrm{d}s}{s}\Omega(x; s)$$

All divergences are due to the non-convergence of the invariant s-integration at the lower limit $s\to 0$; $\Omega(x, s)$ is free of them, and being gauge invariant, may be written in terms of the fields $F_{\mu\nu}$ rather than in terms of the potentials A_μ. For constant (slowly varying) fields, $\mathscr{L}^{(1)}$ may be evaluated in closed form; this method then reproduces exactly the earlier results of Heisenberg and Euler and of Weisskopf, but it displays explicitly the divergent term in $\mathscr{L}^{(1)}$ as a multiple of the free field Lagrangian $\mathscr{L}^{(0)} = \frac{1}{2}(E^2-B^2)$

$$\mathscr{L}^{(1)} = \left(\frac{e^2}{12\pi^2}\int_0^\infty \frac{\mathrm{d}s}{s}\, e^{-m^2 s}\right)\mathscr{L}^{(0)} + \text{finite terms}$$

This first term is then eliminated by a renormalization, that is a change of *scale* of both fields and electric charge. For rapidly varying fields, such as the Coulomb field of the nucleus, $W^{(1)}$ can be evaluated by perturbation methods; the bilinear terms in the field are then of the form

$$W = \frac{1}{2}\iint \mathrm{d}x\mathrm{d}x'\, A_\mu(x)\, K_{\mu\nu}(x-x')\, A_\nu(x')$$

In Schwinger's method, $K_{\mu\nu}$ appears now in the form of a Fourier integral with respect to s:

$$K_{\mu\nu}(x) = \int_0^\infty \mathrm{d}s \, e^{-im^2s} \mathcal{K}_{\mu\nu}(x; s)$$

To compare this with the regularization procedure, we observe that the regularized $\tilde{K}_{\mu\nu}$ of Pauli may be written as

$$\tilde{K}_{\mu\nu}(x) = \int_0^\infty \mathrm{d}s \, R(s) \mathcal{K}_{\mu\nu}(x; s)$$

where the regularization conditions (3.22) enforce that

$$R(0) = \frac{\mathrm{d}R}{\mathrm{d}s}\bigg|_{s=0} = 0$$

This shows again that in Schwinger's method, the divergencies are all due to the divergence of the final s-integral at $s = 0$, and by operating with the s-integrand, one manipulates only well defined finite, gauge invariant, quantities.

Schwinger's elegant solution of the gauge problem proved to be something of an anticlimax to the expectation that an investigation of the divergence difficulties in quantum electrodynamics might reveal some clue to the question of how to formulate an intrinsically finite theory.

It is now evident that, accepting the 'renormalization philosophy', finite results can be unambiguously extracted from the formalism. There remain stubborn problems of convergence of renormalized perturbation series, and of the values of the renormalization parameters, about which the final word has probably not yet been said.

4. FORM FACTORS AND NON-LOCAL INTERACTIONS

The qualitative success of non-relativistic cut-off procedures (as for instance in the meson–nucleon coupling) is well known. Many attempts have been made to find a relativistic generalization of the cut-off method. In order to illustrate the difficulties this led to, assume a local coupling of the type $g \int \mathrm{d}x \, \varphi(\mathbf{x})\rho(\mathbf{x})$, φ being a boson field, $\rho(x)$ a source of some type, so that this term describes absorption and emission of single quanta at point $\mathbf{x}$. A possible corresponding non-local coupling is then

$$g \int \varphi'(\mathbf{x})\rho(\mathbf{x}) \, \mathrm{d}\mathbf{x}, \qquad \varphi'(\mathbf{x}t) \equiv \int \mathrm{d}\mathbf{x}'\mathrm{d}t' \, F(\mathbf{x} - \mathbf{x}', t - t')\varphi(\mathbf{x}'t')$$

$$\ldots\ldots(4.1)$$

The form factor F contains a characteristic length r_0; the Fourier transform $g(k)$ of $F(x)$ may for instance have the form

$$g(k) = \frac{r_0^{-4}}{(k^2)^2 + r_0^{-4}} \qquad \ldots (4.2)$$

In 1948 McManus and Peierls[47] developed a classical electro-dynamics with a coupling of type (4.1). The equations of motion for the electron become integro-differential equations, which for small accelerations $(d/dt \ll c/r_0)$ may be expanded in powers of r_0. The self-force leads then to a finite electromagnetic mass and to the usual radiation damping term, whereas the external force is given in terms of an average of the external field with the structure factor F.

What interests us here is the question, to what extent is a causal behaviour of the system maintained, and also, to what extent do the above results hold in quantum theory. With regard to the first question, only the preservation of macroscopic causality is under discussion. To satisfy it, the form factor $F(x)$ must be of finite 'range'. That such functions may successfully be con-structed has been shown by McManus, and subsequently, in the context of quantum theory, by Bloch[48] and by Chrétien and Peierls.[49] A general pre-requisite is that the invariant function $F(x)$ should *not* have the character of a 'propagation function'; in other words, F should be unable to transport any part of a wave packet $\varphi(\mathbf{x}, t)$ over macroscopic distances. Propagators are characterized as meromorphic functions in k space: $\sim 1/(k^2 + M_i^2)$ with the poles of $-k^2$ on the real axis at positions M_i^2 corres-ponding to the masses of quanta they transport. Acceptable form factors, as was shown by Chrétien and Peierls, may be meromorphic functions with poles for complex values of $-k^2$, as for example the function $g(k)$ in (4.2), or else entire functions of k^2, or combinations of both. More general types of form factors suggest themselves in quantum theory, where the charge density ρ has the structure $\bar{\psi}(x)\psi(x)$, and $\varphi(x)\rho(x)$ may be generalized into

$$\int d^4y \, d^4y' \, F(x, y, y') \varphi(x) \bar{\psi}(y) \psi(y') \qquad \ldots (4.3)$$

Such three-point form factors were investigated by Bloch, and Kristensen and Møller.[50]

The introduction of such form factors into quantum field theory poses a non-trivial problem of the definition of field operators. One possibility is to use the formalism developed by Yang and Feldman[51] and by Källén[52] in which one works directly with the operator equations of motion, that is, one uses the Heisenberg

4*

picture of field operators. The field equations are written as integral equations with boundary conditions imposed at $t = \pm\infty$. Thus for instance the equation

$$(\square^2 - \mu^2)\varphi(x) = -g\rho(x) = -g \int dy \, dy' \, F(xyy')\bar{\psi}(y)\psi(y') \quad \ldots\ldots(4.4)$$

will be written in the two ways:

$$\varphi(x) = \varphi_{\text{in}}(x) - \int_{-\infty}^{t} dx' \, \Delta_{\text{ret}}(x-x')\rho(x') \quad \ldots\ldots(4.5a)$$

$$\varphi(x) = \varphi_{\text{out}}(x) - \int_{t}^{\infty} dx' \, \Delta_{\text{av}}(x-x')\rho(x') \quad \ldots\ldots(4.5b)$$

The same procedure is applied to the field equations for $\psi(x)$ and $\bar{\psi}(x)$. The in- and out-fields satisfy the homogeneous field equations, and their commutators (anticommutators) are those of uncoupled fields. The set of equations (4, 5a,b) (and the corresponding equations for ψ and $\bar{\psi}$) may be solved by iteration, and relations between the in- and the out-fields may be established to any order in the interaction, by successive approximation. Finally, observing that the φ_{in}, φ_{out} represent the asymptotic fields at $t = -\infty$ and $t = +\infty$ respectively, they may be used to define initial and final states of a scattering process:

$$\Psi_i = \varphi_{\text{in}}^{(-)}(k_1)\cdots\psi_{\text{in}}^{(-)}(p_1)\cdots|0\rangle$$
$$\Psi_f = \varphi_{\text{out}}^{(-)}(k_1')\cdots\psi_{\text{out}}^{(-)}(p_1')\cdots|0\rangle$$

In terms of these states, the scattering matrix S_{fi} is then given by

$$S_{fi} = \langle \Psi_f | \Psi_i \rangle \quad \ldots\ldots(4.6)$$

and evaluated by the usual techniques.

These methods clearly apply to non-local interactions as well, provided again that the form factor be of finite 'range' in the sense defined above. The main question is then whether such a theory is now indeed finite, that is, free of divergences. This question is not fully answered. As a partial result we state that electron and nucleon self-energies in e^2 (g^2) are finite, but not automatically in higher order. An additional prescription introduced by Bloch to ensure covergence of the electron self-energy to all orders violates the macroscopic causality condition, as was pointed out by Pauli.[53]

In 1953 Pauli took up the question of the equivalence of a theory with non-local interaction with a Hamiltonian theory, that is the question of the existence of canonical variables. In this work, Pauli first showed explicitly how the integrals of motion representing total energy, momentum and charge may be constructed in a theory with non-local coupling; these integrals contain the field variables at different times, a situation which is the principal difficulty for introducing quantization in a conventional way. At this point a sharp distinction must also be drawn between 'normal' and 'pathological' form factors. The first class of form factors is defined by the property of the equations to have the same manifold of solution as in the absence of coupling. In this case, canonical variables are shown to exist for the classical field equation. For quantum fields, a complication arises due to the necessity of observing the ordering of operators, and the existence of canonical fields was shown only to the first order in the interaction.

We mention here, finally, that the introduction of even normal factors brings up the question of gauge invariance, if these couplings are applied to electrodynamics. While such gauge invariance can be enforced by suitable correction terms, e.g. a factor $\exp\left[ie\int_{x}^{x'} \mathrm{d}\xi \cdot A(s)\right]$ for a two-point form factor $F(x-x')$, one may question whether this additional complication is in the spirit of the whole approach. As Pais and Uhlenbeck have shown (loc. cit.), gauge invariance in the average may be preserved without these extra terms; that is, a weaker relation:

$$\int_{D} \frac{\partial j_{\mu}(x)}{\partial x_{\mu}}\,\mathrm{d}^4x = 0$$

(D being a small space-time volume element covering the range of F) may still hold.

We conclude this part with a remark on 'normal' and other form factors, as this will lead to the subject of the next and last section. Pais and Uhlenbeck consider a Lagrangian of type

$$\mathcal{L} = \tfrac{1}{2}\varphi K(-\Box^2)\varphi + \rho(x)\varphi$$

The critical point is then the number and locations of the zeros $M_i{}^2$ of $K(k^2)=0$. In the case of one single zero, $M_0{}^2$, we have

$$K = (-\Box^2 + M_0{}^2)\mathrm{e}^{f(-\Box^2)}$$

f being an entire function. It is then possible to introduce

$$\varphi = \mathrm{e}^{-f(-\Box^2)/2}\varphi' = \int \mathrm{d}^4x'\ F(x-x')\varphi'(x')$$

Thus

$$L = \tfrac{1}{2}\varphi'(-\Box^2 + M_0{}^2)\varphi' + \rho(x)\int \mathrm{d}x'\ F(x-x')\varphi'$$

and describes a non-local theory. If, on the other hand, $K = 0$ has several roots M_i, we have a multi-mass equation of the type mentioned in section 2. We notice that a one-mass equation for φ' could formally be gained by the substitution:

$$\varphi = \prod_{i>0} \left(\frac{1}{M_i{}^2 - \square^2}\right)^{1/2} \mathrm{e}^{-f(-\square^2)/2}\varphi' \qquad \ldots \ldots (4.7)$$

This would lead to a 'pathological' form factor. What is actually done here is the elimination of additional degrees of freedom contained in φ (namely the quanta of masses M_i), which corresponds to imposing boundary conditions on the system between initial and final states. As a consequence, the 'truncated' system cannot be cast into Hamiltonian form. The possibility of using such truncated systems was recently investigated by Bogoliubov, Medvedev and Polivanov.[25] Its attraction naturally stems from the efficiency of this method to assure convergence, since the eliminated quanta are partly of negative energy, and the denominators in (4.7) serve as 'regulators'. A special case arises if the roots $M_i{}^2$ of $K(-\square^2) = 0$ are multiple or appear only in complex conjugate pairs. More will be said about this in the next section.

5. INDEFINITE METRIC

Concept of Indefinite Metric

One of the results most clearly crystallized from non-relativistic quantum theory is the description of quantum kinematics by the motion of a unit vector ψ in a space with unitary metric (Hilbert space). In a measurement, a coordinate system formed by the eigenvectors $|n\rangle$ of the operator Q to be measured is laid out, and ψ expanded in the form $\psi = \sum_n a_n |n\rangle$; the unitary metric guarantees then that $(\psi, \psi) = \sum_n |a_n|^2$ and that the average $\bar{Q}$ of Q is expressed as $\bar{Q} = \sum_n Q_n |a_n|^2$, relations which allow a consistent probabilistic interpretation of measurement.

This scheme is also upheld in relativistic quantum theory. The reason why it has time and again been tampered with lies in the fact that the unitary metric is so closely linked with the divergence difficulties. This does not mean that in these attempts the usual scheme of interpretation is given up. The argument is rather that for the case of description, the physical Hilbert space H_1 is embedded in a wider space, $H = H_1 + H_2$, of which it forms a subspace with unitary metric. To have any effect on the dynamics, H_1 may not be an invariant subspace, and hence there is no guarantee that ψ_1, the projection of ψ on H_1, preserves its norm.

There have been various attempts to handle this difficulty: Heisenberg[54] attempted to show that by postulating suitably pathological properties of the states of H_2, one has at least the asymptotic relation that

$$\psi(t = -\infty)\epsilon H_1$$

leads to

$$\psi(t = +\infty)\epsilon H_1$$

which would guarantee the unitarity of the scattering matrix for physical states.

Another proposal is due to Bogoliubov,[25] who pointed out that the reaction matrix K has in any case a hermitian submatrix K_1 in H_1. He proposes an *ad hoc* prescription, which is to calculate K in H, extract K_1 and *define* a unitary S_1 by the usual relation

$$S_1 = \frac{1 + i\pi K_1}{1 - i\pi K_1}$$

The concept of an indefinite metric was first deliberately introduced by Dirac[55] in 1942, as a means of removing the infinite electromagnetic self-energy of the electron. The method is easily illustrated for the case of a harmonic oscillator

$$H = \frac{\omega}{2}(p^2 + q^2), \quad i[p, q] = 1 \qquad \ldots(5.1)$$

The usual procedure is to introduce the operators

$$a = (p - iq)/2^{1/2} \quad a^+ = (p + iq)/2^{1/2} \qquad \ldots(5.2)$$

whence it follows that

$$H = \frac{\omega}{2}(a^+a + aa^+), \quad [a, a^+] = 1 \qquad \ldots(5.3)$$

Eigenstates $|m\rangle$ of H are now constructed by defining a ground state $|0\rangle$ by $a|0\rangle = 0$, and excited states $|n\rangle$ by

$$|n\rangle = (n!)^{-1/2}(a^+)^n|0\rangle$$

The adjoint states $\langle n|$, defined by $\langle an|m\rangle = \langle n|a^+m\rangle$ together with $\langle 0|0\rangle = 1$ determine then the scalar product $\langle n|m\rangle$, which by means of the commutator (5.3) is $\langle n|m\rangle = \delta_{nm}$. In this way, an explicit matrix representation of the operators a, a^+ satisfying (5.3) is gained, which gives

$$a^+|n\rangle = (n+1)^{1/2}|n+1\rangle \quad H|n\rangle = (n+\tfrac{1}{2})\omega|n\rangle$$
$$a|n\rangle = n^{1/2}|n-1\rangle$$

An alternative matrix representation follows from the postulate $a^+|0\rangle = 0$. Let us call, in that case, $a^+ = b$, and $a = b^+$, so that $[b, b^+] = -1$, $H = (\omega/2)(bb^+ + b^+b)$. Following the same steps as before, in particular

$$\langle nb|m\rangle = \langle n|b^+m\rangle$$

the scalar product now turns out to be $\langle n|m\rangle = (-1)^n \delta_{nm}$. In this fashion a new matrix representation of the operators p and q is gained with

$$b^+|n\rangle = (n+1)^{1/2}|n+1\rangle, \; b|n\rangle = -n^{1/2}|n-1\rangle, \; H|n\rangle = -(n+\tfrac{1}{2})\omega|n\rangle$$

In this new representation we have an indefinite metric.

Dirac introduced such an indefinite metric into the radiation field $A(x)$, replacing the absorption operator

$$a_k e^{i\mathbf{k}\cdot\mathbf{x}-i\omega t} \quad \text{by} \quad \frac{1}{2^{1/2}}(a_k e^{i\mathbf{k}\cdot\mathbf{x}-i\omega t} + b_{-k} e^{i\mathbf{k}\cdot\mathbf{x}-i\omega t})$$

(Notice that this leaves the commutation relation $[A(\mathbf{x}), \dot{A}(\mathbf{x}')]$ unchanged.) We recall that the λ process led to an invariant electron self-energy, which still diverged for $\lambda \to 0$ as λ^{-2}. With the indefinite metric added, this residual self-energy turned out to be identically zero. This has now strictly historical interest only, since Pauli's investigation in 1943 showed that this scheme did not work at all in hole theory, with or without λ process.

In the work of Pais and Uhlenbeck, the indefinite metric is introduced in a way different from Dirac's. The multi-mass field has a Hamiltonian equivalent to that of a system of oscillators with energies

$$\pm \sum_k \frac{\omega_k}{2}(p_k{}^2 + q_k{}^2)$$

Using the alternative quantization for the negative energy oscillators, the eigenvalues of the multiple mass field are kept positive. In this way, the vacuum $|0\rangle$ is truly a 'ground' state, but this is achieved at the expense of having transitions into states with odd numbers of b-quanta occur with negative probabilities.

Special Cases : Two-mass Fields

The difficulties of interpretation arising with the existence of quanta of negative probability could be avoided if the appearance of these quanta could be restricted to virtual processes. In this case, a unitary S matrix might be possible. Heisenberg[56] has pointed out in his analysis of the Lee model that this might be achieved by means of a degenerate mass doublet (confluence of the mass of the normal V particle and the ghost state). Later Pauli[57] investigated the possibility of using a field with two complex conjugate masses for the same purpose. We shall give here a brief sketch of this two-mass case, in order to show on which argument this possibility rests. As was shown by Pais and Uhlenbeck,[22] the real field φ, satisfying an equation

$$(\Box^2 - \mu_1{}^2)(\Box^2 - \mu_2{}^2)\varphi(x) = \rho(x) \qquad \ldots (5.4)$$

is dynamically equivalent to two fields φ_a and φ_b with oscillator Hamiltonians :

$$H = \sum_k \omega_k a_k{}^+ a_k + \sum_k \Omega_k b_k{}^+ b_k + \int \rho\varphi \, dx \qquad \ldots (5.5)$$

$$(\omega_k = (\mu_1{}^2 + k^2)^{1/2}, \quad \Omega_k = (\mu_2{}^2 + k^2)^{1/2})$$

the field $\varphi(x)$ being given (for $\mu_2 > \mu_1$) by

$$\varphi = (\mu_2{}^2 - \mu_1{}^2)^{-1/2} \sum_k e^{i\mathbf{k} \cdot \mathbf{x}} \times$$

$$\left\{ \left(\frac{1}{2V\omega_k}\right)^{1/2}(q_k + q_k{}^+) - \left(\frac{1}{2V\Omega_k}\right)^{1/2}(b_k + b_{-k}{}^+) \right\} \qquad \ldots (5.6)$$

In view of the negative sign, we introduce an indefinite metric for the states of the second oscillator : $[b, b^+] = -1$. In the limit

$$\mu_2{}^2 - \mu_1{}^2 = \Delta \to 0$$

the matrix element φ between the vacuum and the states $a^+|0\rangle$, $b^+|0\rangle$ becomes infinite, as may be seen from (5.6). A different representation is then indicated :

Introduce operators A_k, B_k by

$$2^{1/2}A_k = \left(\frac{\omega_k}{\epsilon_k}\right)^{1/2}(a_k - b_k), \qquad 2^{1/2}B_k = \left(\frac{\epsilon_k}{\omega_k}\right)^{1/2}(a_k + b_k)$$

$(\epsilon_k = \Omega_k - \omega_k)$. Written in terms of the new operators, the limit $\epsilon \to 0$ (that is $\Delta \to 0$) can be carried out to give

$$H \rightarrow \sum \omega_k (A_k{}^+ B_k + B_k{}^+ A_k - \tfrac{1}{2} B_k{}^+ B_k) + \int \rho \varphi \, dx \quad \ldots (5.7)$$

and

$$\varphi = \sum_k e^{i\mathbf{k} \cdot \mathbf{x}} \left(\frac{1}{2V \omega_k{}^3} \right)^{1/2} (A_k + A_{-k}{}^+) + \tfrac{1}{4}(B_k + B_{-k}{}^+) \quad \ldots (5.8)$$

The non-vanishing commutators are

$$[A_k, B_k{}^+] = [B_k, A_k{}^+] = 1$$

As a consequence, there are two types of one quantum states for the free Hamiltonian H^0:

(a) the 'normal' state $B_k{}^+ |0\rangle = \psi_B$ satisfying

$$H^0 \psi_B = \omega \psi_B \quad \langle \psi_B | \psi_B \rangle = 0$$

(b) the 'dipole state' $A_k{}^+ |0\rangle = \psi_A$. This is *not* an eigenstate of H^0 at all, but satisfies

$$H^0 \psi_A = \omega \psi_A - \tfrac{1}{2} \omega \psi_B \qquad \ldots (5.9)$$

Its norm is zero, too, but it is not orthogonal to the normal state: $\langle \psi_B | \psi_A \rangle = 1$. Heisenberg now proceeds to exploit this dipole-limit systematically. As a consequence of (5.9), matrix elements of $\varphi(\mathbf{x}t)$ with respect to states ψ_A have a pathological time-dependence

$$\langle \psi_A | \varphi(\mathbf{x}t) | 0 \rangle \sim e^{-i\omega t}(1 - 2i\omega t)$$

Heisenberg argues that on account of this property, all S matrix elements between normal and dipole states are zero; hence the submatrix of S, connecting normal states alone, is then unitary. At the same time one has the advantage of the less singular Green's function $(k^2 + \mu^2)^{-2}$ in the limit $\Delta \rightarrow 0$.

Lee Model

This model [58] of a completely 'soluble' field theory has played an important part in the development of the ideas associated with the use of an indefinite metric. This resulted from the startling result of an investigation by Pauli and Källén on the mathematical structure of the Lee model.[59] Lee, in his original version of the model (which describes the coupling between two 'nucleons' N and V, though a light boson θ, of such a type as to allow $V \leftrightarrows N + \theta$, but to forbid $N \leftrightarrows V + \theta$), had already formulated the relation between the renormalized and unrenormalized coupling constants, g and g_0, to be

$$g^2 = g_0{}^2 / (1 + g_0{}^2 C)$$

C being the divergent integral $(2V)^{-1} \sum_k \omega_k^{-3}$. It follows that $g = 0$ for any finite g_0. Pauli and Källén therefore introduced a nucleon form factor $f(k)$, giving C a finite value $C = g_c^{-2}$, leading to

$$g^2 = g_0^2 g_c^2 / (g_0^2 + g_c^2)$$

Notice that $g < g_c$ for positive g_0^2. Pauli and Källén, and later Heisenberg, investigated the case where g^2 is positive but larger than g_c^2, as it would be *for any finite value* of g^2 in the limit of a point coupling. In that case $g_0^2 < 0$; as a result of this, the Hamiltonian ceases to be hermitian. This inconsistency may be removed by introducing an indefinite metric, giving the state with n bare V particles the norm $(-1)^n$. In this fashion, the Hamiltonian remains at least self-adjoint. As is well known, in this case $(g^2 > g_c^2)$ also a second discrete root appears in the equation for the physical ('dressed') V particle; this state (the 'ghost') turns out to have negative norm. The scattering process

$$V + \theta \to V_g + \theta'$$

then occurs with negative probability, and the S matrix is not unitary. The only exception to this arises in the dipole limit, where the masses of physical and ghost-particles coincide. This situation was sketched in the previous section.

This situation has somewhat more than academic interest in view of the fact that in conventional field theories too a finite unrenormalized coupling probably leads to zero effective coupling constant, and to assume for it a finite (empirical) value may be inconsistent with the original field equations. Källén[60] and Landau[61] in particular have emphasized this point.

Heisenberg's Non-linear Theory[62]

Heisenberg's recent work is the most radical attempt to cut the knot of divergence difficulties and consistency problems. In his view, the renormalization approach has to be abandoned altogether. If a theory (after consistent renormalization) is in fact finite, why not analyse the possible structures of a renormalized theory, and present it in a manifestly finite form? This is clearly a question as to which set of equations is to be considered 'basic'. Schwinger, for instance, has indeed presented a formally renormalized quantum field theory in the form of coupled integral equations for boson and fermion Green's functions, and for the vertex operator.[12] But these equations show also that the unrenormalized mass and charge parameters are not altogether eliminated from the theory, and appear in processes with very high energy–momentum transfer. Heisenberg carried out a similar programme for the Lee model,[46] constructing explicitly the renormalized field equations which turn out to be integro-differential equations. As $g^2 > 0$ in this case, the quanta of the renormalized V particle field generate an indefinite metric.

In order to avoid the renormalization programme, the concept of the bare particles (appearing in the same number and variety as the physical particles one wants to describe) has to be abandoned, too. Heisenberg therefore introduces a single, self-coupled spinor field; an indefinite metric is assumed to guarantee the finiteness of the theory. One problem in proposing such a scheme is to build into it the invariance properties that may serve to define electric charge, nucleon number, isotopic spin, and will also solve the mysterious question of violation of conservation laws by selected interactions. Again Pauli[63] took part in these endeavours, but from the point of view of the main theme of this review, the second question appears more important. How is, with an assumed indefinite metric, a physical interpretation of the formalism made possible? To this end it is interesting to see how the indefinite metric is introduced. To have a finite theory, it must be a consequence of the non-linearity that the function

$$S_{\alpha\beta}(x, x') = i\langle 0|\{\psi_\alpha(x),\, \bar{\psi}_\beta(x')\}|0\rangle$$

has no δ and δ' function singularities on the light cone. Assuming that the dominating (singular) part of the anticommutator near the light cone is a c number, this latter is seen to satisfy a non-linear equation, from the study of which the singularities can be investigated. Indeed, they turn out to be infinite oscillations, rather than δ functions and derivatives thereof. By a previously given argument, this implies an indefinite metric. Heisenberg then proceeds to construct a *model* for S (not showing oscillations, but rather giving their limit, zero, on the light cone), in which the 'regularization' of S is achieved by means of a 'dipole ghost', as described in the second part of this section.

Unfortunately, at this stage of development, the intrinsic consistency of this whole programme is still open to question, and the mathematical methods to handle it crude. Characteristically, Pauli felt that it was premature—to say the least—to try to extract verifiable information from this scheme. He pressed for further clarification of conceptual points by means of simple models. As much as he was in sympathy with radically new formulations of quantum field theory, he showed again that his main concern was with clarity; for its sake he would feel strongly critical of new ideas in their amorphous development stage, whatever their intuitive appeal might be.

REFERENCES

Section 1

1. Wentzel, G. *Z. Phys.* **86**, 479, 1933 and **87**, 726, 1934
2. Dirac, P. A. M. *Proc. Roy. Soc. A* **167**, 1938
3. Wentzel, G. *Quantum Theory of Wave Fields*, §§18 and 19. New York; Interscience
4. Pauli, W. *Phys. Rev.* **64**, 332, 1943
5. Jauch, J. M. *Phys. Rev.* **63**, 334, 1943
6. Fröhlich, H., Heitler, W. and Kemmer, N. *Proc. Roy. Soc. A* **166**, 154, 1938
7. Weisskopf, V. F. *Z. Phys.* **89**, 27, 1934 and **90**, 817, 1934; *Phys. Rev.* **56**, 72, 1939
8. Pauli, W. *Rev. mod. Phys.* **15**, 175, 1943
9. Heitler, W. and Peng, H. W. *Proc. Camb. phil Soc.* **38**, 296, 1942
10. Stueckelberg, E. C. G. *Helv. phys. Acta* **18**, 195, 1945; **19**, 242, 1946
11. Pais, A. *Verh. Akad. Wet. Amst.* **19**, No. 1, 1947
12. Schwinger, J. *Differential Equations of Quantum Field Theory.* 1956. Menlo Park, California; Stanford Research Institute

Section 2

13. Tomonaga, S. *Progr. theor. Phys., Osaka* **1**, 27, 1946; *Phys. Rev.* **74**, 224, 1948
14. Schwinger, J. *Phys. Rev.* **74**, 1439, 1948; **75**, 651, 1949; and **76**, 790, 1949
15. Feynman, R. P. *Phys. Rev.* **76**, 749 and 769, 1949
16. Dyson, F. *Phys. Rev.* **75**, 486 and 1736, 1949
17. Rivier, D. *Helv. phys. Acta* **22**, 265, 1949. This paper contains a summary of Stueckelberg's work
18. Heisenberg, W. *Z. Phys.* **120**, 513 and 673, 1943.
19. Wentzel, G. *Rev. mod. Phys.* **19**, 1, 1947
20. Jost, R. and Luttinger, J. M. *Helv. phys. Acta* **23**, 201, 1950
21. Schwinger, J. Unpublished remark, 1949
22. Pais, A. and Uhlenbeck, G. E. *Phys. Rev.* **79**, 145, 1950
23. Lehmann, H. *Nuovo Cim.* **11** (Ser. 9), 542, 1954
24. Bleuler, K. *Helv. phys. Acta* **23**, 567, 1950; Gupta, S. N. *Proc. phys. Soc.* **63**, 681, 1950 and **64**, 850, 1951
25. Bogoliubov, N. N. *1958 Annual International Conference on High Energy Physics at CERN.* Geneva
26. See ref. 25. Discussion remarks by Pauli, W. and Glaser, V.
27. Pauli, W. and Villars, F. *Rev. mod. Phys.* **21**, 434, 1949
28. Rivier, D. and Stueckelberg, E. C. G. *Phys. Rev.* **74**, 218, 1949
29. Drell, S. A. *Ann. Phys.* **4**, 75, 1959

Section 3

30. Källén, G. *Lecture Notes on Quantum Electrodynamics.* 1956. Geneva; CERN
31. Schwinger, J. *Proc. nat. Acad. Sci. Wash.* **37**, 379, 1951
32. Stuckelberg, E. C. G. and Patry, J. F. C. *Helv. phys. Acta* **13**, 167, 1940; Pauli, W. *Phys. Rev.* **64**, 332, 1943

33. Fierz, M. *Helv. phys. Acta* **23**, 731, 1950
34. Pais, A. and Epstein, S. T., *Rev. mod. Phys.* **21**, 445, 1949
35. Pais, A. *Developments in the Theory of the Electron.* 1948. Princeton, N.J.; Institute for Advanced Study
36. Rohrlich, F. *Phys. Rev.* **77**, 357, 1950
37. Villars, F. *Phys. Rev.* **79**, 122, 1950
38. Uehling, E. *Phys. Rev.* **48**, 55, 1935
39. Pauli, W. and Rose, M. E. *Phys. Rev.* **49**, 462, 1936
40. Heisenberg, W. and Euler, H. *Z. Phys.* **98**, 714, 1936
41. Weisskopf, V. F. *K. danske. videnske. Selsk. Math.-Fys. Medd.* **14**, No. 6, 1936
42. Umezawa, H., Yukawa, J. and Yamada, E. *Prog. theor. Phys., Osaka* **3**, 317, 1948; **4**, 25, 1949
43. Jost, R. and Rayski, J. *Helv. phys. Acta* **22**, 457, 1949
44. Umezawa, H. and Kawabe, R. *Progr. theor. Phys., Osaka*, **4**, 423, 1949; **4**, 443, 1949; **5**, 769, 1950
45. Wentzel, G. *Phys. Rev.* **74**, 1070, 1948
46. Schwinger, J. *Phys. Rev.* **82**, 664, 1951

Section 4

47. McManus, H. *Proc. Roy. Soc. A.* **195**, 323, 1948
48. Bloch, C. *K. danske. videnske. Selsk. Math.-Fys. Medd.* **26**, No. 1, 1950 and **27**, No. 8, 1952
49. Chrétien, M. and Peierls, R. *Nuovo Cim.* **10**, (Ser. 10) 668, 1953
50. Kristensen, P. and Møller, C. *K. danske. videnske. Selsk. Math.-Fys. Medd.* **27**, No. 7, 1952
51. Yang, C. N. and Feldman, D. *Phys. Rev.* **76**, 972, 1952
52. Källén, G. *Ark. Fys.* **2**, 371, 1951
53. Pauli, W. *Nuovo Cim.* **10**, (Ser. 10) 648, 1953
54. Heisenberg, W. *Rev. mod. Phys.* **29**, 269, 1957
55. Dirac, P. A. M. *Proc. Roy. Soc. A* **180**, 1, 1942
56. Heisenberg, W. *Nuclear Phys.* **4**, 532, 1957
57. Pauli, W. *1958 Annual International Conference on High Energy Physics at CERN.* Geneva
58. Lee, T. D. *Phys. Rev.* **95**, 1329, 1954
59. Källén, G. and Pauli, W. *K. danske. videnske. Selsk. Math.-Fys. Medd.* **30**, No. 7, 1955
60. Källén, G. *Helv. phys. Acta* **25**, 417, 1952; *K. danske. videnske. Selsk. Math.-Fys. Medd.* **27**, No. 12, 1958
61. Landau, L. D. in *Niels Bohr and the Development of Physics.* 1955. New York; McGraw-Hill
62. Heisenberg, W. *Nachr. Akad. Wiss. Göttingen* **27**, 111, 1953; *Z. Naturf. A* **9**, 292, 1954; Heisenberg, W., Kortel, F. and Mitter, H. *Z. Naturf. A* **10**, 425, 1955; Ascoli, R. and Heisenberg, W. *Z. Naturf. A* **12**, 177, 1957; Duerr, H. P., Heisenberg, W., Mitter, H., Schlieder, S. and Yamazaki, K. *Z. Naturf.* in press
63. Heisenberg, W. and Pauli, W. Unpublished manuscript

DAS PAULI-PRINZIP UND DIE LORENTZ-GRUPPE

RES JOST

HISTORISCHER TEIL

Einleitung

Seitdem es eine quantisierte Feldtheorie gibt, bildet diese ein Hauptarbeitsgebiet von Pauli. Die Entwicklung dieser Theorie hat er nicht nur durch seine eigenen Arbeiten in sehr entscheidender Weise gefördert, sondern er hat auch ständig und intensiv die Arbeiten anderer Forscher sich durch Studium erworben und durch seine Kritik beeinflusst. Es ist nicht übertrieben, in Pauli das personifizierte Gewissen der Feldtheorie zu sehen.

Ein besonderes Anliegen musste es für ihn sein, die Forderungen der speziellen Relativitätstheorie und der Quantentheorie miteinander zu konfrontieren. Die Verschmelzung dieser Forderungen in einer widerspruchsfreien Theorie ist (in 4 Dimensionen) bekanntlich ein Problem, dessen Lösung nicht einmal in einem Modell in nicht trivialer Weise gelungen ist. Trotzdem reifte in der mühsamen Beschäftigung mit dieser Frage, ganz unerwartet, für Pauli eine Frucht, die eine Beziehung zu dem grossen Resultat aus dem Jahre 1925, dem Ausschlussprinzip, schaffte. Wir meinen den Zusammenhang zwischen *Spin und Statistik*: Dass nämlich in einer relativistischen Theorie, die den üblichen Annahmen der Quantentheorie genügt, Teilchen mit halbzahligem Spin sich nach dem Ausschlussprinzip, solche mit ganzzahligem Spin sich aber nach der Bose–Einstein Statistik verhalten.

Wir werden in diesem historischen Teil Pauli's frühe Arbeiten zur Feldtheorie auf dieses Ziel hin durchgehen. Dann werden wir die beträchtliche Zahl von Arbeiten, die den Satz selbst zum Gegenstand haben, besprechen, um zum Schluss noch eine verwandte Fragestellung (CTP Theorem) zu berühren.

1. Pauli's Arbeiten bis zur Entdeckung des Positrons

In diese Periode fallen die zwei grossen Arbeiten mit Heisenberg,[1] die die systematische Feldtheorie erst eigentlich kristallisieren.

Was war in der Entwicklung vorausgegangen: Dirac[2] hatte
1927 erstmals und mit Erfolg die Prinzipien der Quantentheorie
auf das Maxwell'sche Feld angewendet und so das erste und
wichtigste Modell einer quantisierten Feldtheorie gefunden. Die
Feldquanten (Photonen) gehorchten dabei der Bose–Einstein
Statistik. Die Anwendung analoger Quantisierungsvorschriften
auf die Schroedinger'sche Wellengleichung für ein Elektron war
deswegen unbefriedigend, weil sie ebenfalls für die Elektronen zur
Bose–Einstein Statistik führte.

Hier setzen nun Arbeiten von Jordan[3] und Jordan und Wigner[4]
ein, die zeigen, dass eine passende Abänderung der Vertauschungsrelationen für die Fourierkoeffizienten des Feldes zu
Teilchen führt, die dem Ausschlussprinzip folgen. Und zwar
besteht die Abänderung darin, dass man die Kommutatoren
durch Antikommutatoren ersetzt.

Damit war der formale Apparat soweit entwickelt, dass man
die Frage nach einem Zusammenhang zwischen dem Transformationscharakter eines Feldes und der Statistik der durch
Quantisierung eingeführten Teilchen stellen konnte.

Von besonderer Wichtigkeit für uns aber ist die etwa 6 Wochen
vor der Jordan–Wigner'schen Arbeit fertiggestellte Abhandlung
von Jordan und Pauli[5] *zur Quantenelektrodynamik ladungsfreier
Felder.* In ihr wird zuerst am Standpunkt der Lorentzinvarianz
auch bei der Quantisierung folgerichtig festgehalten. Für die
Vertauschungsrelationen der Feldstärken wird schliesslich die
Gleichung abgeleitet:

$$[F_{\mu\nu}(x), F_{\sigma\eta}(y)] = iD_{\mu\nu,\sigma\eta}(x-y) \qquad \ldots(1.1)$$

wo

$$D_{\mu\nu,\sigma\eta}(\xi) = (g_{\nu\sigma}\partial_\mu\partial_\eta + g_{\mu\eta}\partial_\nu\partial_\sigma - g_{\mu\sigma}\partial_\nu\partial_\eta - g_{\nu\eta}\partial_\mu\partial_\sigma)D(\xi) \qquad \ldots(1.2)$$

und

$$D(\xi) = (2\pi)^{-3} \int \frac{d^3k}{|\mathbf{k}|} \sin k\xi^0 \cdot e^{i(\mathbf{k}\xi)} \qquad \ldots(1.3)$$

die invariante Funktion von Jordan und Pauli ist. ∂_μ steht für
$\partial/\partial\xi^\mu$. Die wesentlichen Eigenschaften dieser Funktion sind:

$$D(-\xi) = -D(\xi) \qquad \ldots(1.4)$$

und

$$\Box D(\xi) = g^{\mu\nu}\partial_\mu\partial_\nu D = 0 \qquad \ldots(1.5)$$

Durch (1.4) and (1.5) und die Forderung, dass D bezüglich der
eigentlichen Lorentzgruppe $L_+^\uparrow$ invariant sei:

$$D(\Lambda\xi) = D(\xi), \quad \Lambda \in L_+^\uparrow \qquad \ldots(1.6)$$

ist D bis auf einen Faktor festgelegt. Aus (1.4) und (1.6) allein folgt aber auch

$$D(\xi) = 0 \quad \text{für} \quad \xi^2 < 0 \qquad \ldots (1.7)$$

also das Verschwinden des Kommutators (1.1) für raumartige Separationen $x-y$. (Dies deswegen, weil $L_+^\uparrow$ die Punkte eines Hyperboloides $\xi^2 = -\alpha^2 < 0$ transitiv transformiert, eine invariante Funktion auf einem solchen also einen konstanten Wert haben muss. Dieser Wert ist wegen (1.4) notwendig Null.) Es ist merkwürdig, dass diese letzte Feststellung in der Arbeit nicht besonders betont wird, obschon Heisenberg's[6] Arbeit über die Unschärferelation schon in einem früheren Bande derselben Zeitschrift erschienen war; die Interpretation von (1.7) und (1.1) im Sinne dieses Prinzips also scheinbar auf der Hand lag.

Wir wollen trotzdem im Geiste der zitierten Arbeit noch etwas weiter schliessen und uns fragen, was man aus Invarianzgründen allein über die Grösse

$$\langle [F_{\mu\nu}(x), F_{\sigma\eta}(y)]\rangle_0 = i\Delta_{\mu\nu,\sigma\eta}(x-y) \qquad \ldots (1.8)$$

sagen kann. Der Ausdruck links stellt einen Vakuumserwartungswert dar. Vorausgesetzt wird (neben der Existenz dieses Vakuums) die Invarianz der Theorie gegenüber der eigentlichen inhomogenen Lorentzgruppe.*

Weiter ist

$$F_{\mu\nu}(x) + F_{\nu\mu}(x) = 0 \qquad \ldots (1.9)$$

Aus (1.9) ergibt sich leicht als allgemeinster Ausdruck für die rechte Seite von (1.8):

$$\begin{aligned}
\Delta_{\mu\nu,\sigma\eta}(\xi) = {} & (g_{\nu\sigma}\partial_\mu\partial_\eta + g_{\mu\eta}\partial_\nu\partial_\sigma - g_{\mu\sigma}\partial_\nu\partial_\eta - g_{\nu\eta}\partial_\mu\partial_\sigma)A \\
& + (g_{\nu\sigma}g_{\mu\eta} - g_{\mu\sigma}g_{\nu\eta})B \\
& + (\epsilon_{\mu\nu\sigma\rho}\partial_\eta + \epsilon_{\mu\nu\rho\eta}\partial_\sigma - \epsilon_{\sigma\eta\mu\rho}\partial_\nu - \epsilon_{\sigma\eta\rho\nu}\partial_\mu)\partial^\rho C \\
& + \epsilon_{\mu\nu\sigma\eta}D
\end{aligned} \qquad \ldots (1.10)$$

Dabei sind A, B, C und D wieder bezüglich $L_+^\uparrow$ invariante Funktionen von ξ. Aber aus der Definition von $\Delta_{\mu\nu,\sigma\eta}(\xi)$ folgt die Symmetrie

$$\Delta_{\mu\nu,\sigma\eta}(\xi) = -\Delta_{\sigma\eta,\mu\nu}(-\xi) \qquad \ldots (1.11)$$

und diese bedeutet nach (1.10) für die Funktionen A, B, C, D:

---

* Die Frage, ob in einer Theorie, welche Teilchen der Masse Null enthält, das Vakuum ein sinnvoller Begriff ist, soll hier nicht berührt werden.

$$A(-\xi) = -A(\xi), \quad B(-\xi) = -B(\xi), \quad D(-\xi) = -D(\xi)$$
$$\dots(1.12)$$

aber

$$C(-\xi) = C(\xi) \qquad \dots(1.13)$$

A, B und D verschwinden also für $\xi^2 < 0$, nicht aber notwendigerweise auch C. Diese Folgerung lässt sich nicht verschärfen, auch wenn man die Feldgleichungen

$$\partial_\sigma F_{\mu\nu} + \partial_\mu F_{\nu\sigma} + \partial_\nu F_{\sigma\mu} = 0 \qquad \dots(1.14)$$

berücksichtigt. Diese implizieren $D = 0$ und $\square C = 0$. Es ist aber äusserst unwahrscheinlich, dass jemand 1927 den Ansatz (1.10) überhaupt ernst genommen hätte, denn die rechte Seite ist ein Gemisch von Tensoren und Pseudotensoren 4. Ranges. Die Terme der rechten Seite transformieren also bei der Spiegelung

$$TP: \quad \xi^{\nu'} = -\xi^\nu \qquad \dots(1.15)$$

durchaus nicht gleich. Es erscheint in der Tat äusserst vernünftig, die Gleichung

$$\langle[F_{\mu\nu}(-x), F_{\sigma\eta}(-y)]\rangle_0 = -\langle[F_{\mu\nu}(x), F_{\sigma\eta}(y)]\rangle_0 \qquad \dots(1.16)$$

oder

$$\Delta_{\mu\nu,\sigma\eta}(-\xi) = -\Delta_{\mu\nu,\sigma\eta}(\xi) \qquad \dots(1.16')$$

zu verlangen. Dann werden C und D notwendig verschwinden und wir haben

$$\Delta_{\mu\nu,\sigma\eta}(\xi) = 0 \quad \text{für} \quad \xi^2 < 0 \qquad \dots(1.17)$$

Dieser merkwürdige Zusammenhang zwischen einer Spieglungsinvarianz und dem Verschwinden des Vakuumerwartungswertes eines Kommutators ist ein Spezialfall des CTP Theorems. Doch täuscht unsere Diskussion insofern, als für das volle CTP Theorem noch eine wesentlich neue Voraussetzung (nämlich die Stabilität des Vakuums) notwendig ist.

Mit der Frage ob sich das Maxwell Feld auch nach dem Ausschlussprinzip quantisieren lasse, hat sich wohl zuerst Jordan[7] in einem eher gemeinverständlichen Artikel befasst. Diese Tatsache erschwert naturgemäss das Verständnis der betreffenden Bemerkungen.

Das hier entscheidende Argument gegen diesen Ansatz findet sich wohl zuerst im Handbuchartikel von Pauli:[8]

Da im klassischen Grenzfall $F_{\mu\nu}(x)$ messbar ist, muss der Kommutator (1.1) für raumartige Separationen verschwinden, denn eine Messung von $F_{\mu\nu}$ im Punkte x kann die Messung im Dunkte y nur beeinflussen, falls $(x-y)^2 > 0$ ist. Der betreffende

Passus, der die Situation besser beschreibt als mir das möglich wäre, lautet:

'Der Umstand, dass im klassischen Grenzfall die Feldstärke E und H hinsichtlich ihres raumzeitlichen Verlaufes, also auch ihre Phasen messbare Grössen sind, hat notwendig zur Folge, dass die Lichtquanten symmetrische Zustände haben (der Einstein–Bose Statistik gehorchen) müssen. Anders ist es bei der Materie, wo die ψ-Funktionen keine messbaren Grössen sind und wo der Fall der symmetrischen und der der antisymmetrischen Zustände mehrerer gleichartiger Teilchen vom Korrespondenzstandpunkt aus gleichwertig sind.' ... (Die) 'Phase' (der ψ-Funktion) 'geht weder in den Hamiltonoperator noch in eine andere messbare physikalische Grösse ein, die ψ-Funktion ist unmessbar'.

Die zwei grossen Arbeiten von Heisenberg und Pauli[1] geben zum ersten Male eine systematische Theorie der Feldquantisierung und bauen auch die Quantenelektrodynamik in diesen allgemeinen Rahmen ein. Eines der Hauptziele ist der Beweis für die Lorentzinvarianz des Quantisierungsverfahrens (kanonische Quantisierung) selbst. Der vierdimensionale Standpunkt, wie er in der Arbeit mit Jordan vorherrschte, wurde aus sehr begreiflichen Gründen zu Gunsten des dreidimensionalen verlassen. Es ist bekannt, dass die Betonung des kanonischen Formalismus und die damit verbundene Auszeichnung der Zeit die Ausbildung einer relativistisch invarianten Störungsrechnung verhinderte und damit den Fortschritt der Feldtheorie möglicherweise verzögerte.

2. Die Arbeiten bis 1940

In dieser Situation wirkte die Entdeckung des Positrons durch C. D. Anderson und damit die Bestätigung der kühnen Dirac'schen Löchertheorie befreiend.

Nun war es klar, dass die Dirac Elektronen nach dem Ausschlussprinzip quantisiert werden mussten, falls überhaupt die Definition eines Vakuums möglich sein sollte.

Weiter war die Analyse der verwendeten Begriffe durch die Arbeit von Bohr und Rosenfeld[9] wesentlich fortgeschritten. Diese Arbeit gibt Gedankenexperimente an, die genau mit den aus (1.1) folgenden Unschärferelationen verträgliche Messungen der Feldstärken $F_{\mu\nu}(x)$ erlauben. Sie stand damit im Gegensatz zu früher geäusserten Vermutungen.[10]

Dadurch wurde das oben für das Maxwell Feld verwendete Kausalitäts-oder Lokalitäts-Argument wesentlich gestärkt und es war sehr zu vermuten, dass auch die Ladungsdichte sich innerhalb der Theorie widerspruchsfrei lokalisieren lasse.* Diese Vermutung passt nun sehr wohl zur Löchertheorie, in welcher die Ladungsdichte eine sinnvolle lokale Observable ist. Dagegen gilt dies nicht mehr für die Teilchendichte.

Diese Feststellung, mit welcher das ursprüngliche Dirac'sche Argument gegen die skalare relativistische Wellengleichung und für die vierkomponentige Gleichung entfällt, bildet den Ausgangspunkt der Arbeit von Pauli und Weisskopf[11] über die Quantisierung der skalaren relativistischen Wellengleichung. Diese beschreibt hier geladene Teilchen vom Spin 0. Die Wellenfunktion $\psi(x)$ ist komplex und ihre Phase, wegen des Bestehens einer Eichgruppe, grundsätzlich nicht beobachtbar. Das Lokalisierungsargument, das im Falle des Maxwell Feldes verwendet werden durfte, darf also auf das Feld ψ nicht unbesehen angewendet werden. Wohl aber wird man die Existenz einer lokalisierbaren Ladungsdichte annehmen dürfen. Diese ist wie alle andern wichtigen Observablen bilinear in ψ und $\psi^\star$ und lautet für die kräftefreie Theorie

$$\rho = ie[(\partial_0\psi^\star)\psi - \psi^\star\partial_0\psi] \qquad \ldots\ldots(2.1)$$

Nun gilt offenbar

$$[\rho(x), \rho(y)] = 0 \quad \text{für} \quad (x-y)^2 < 0 \qquad \ldots\ldots(2.2)$$

falls $\psi(x)$ mit $\psi(x')$ kommutiert und

$$[\psi^\star(x), \psi(y)] = 0 \quad \text{für} \quad (x-y)^2 < 0 \qquad \ldots\ldots(2.3)$$

Aber dasselbe würde auch gelten, wenn $\psi(x)$ mit $\psi(x')$ antikommutierte und

$$[\psi^\star(x), \psi(y)]_+ = 0 \quad \text{für} \quad (x-y)^2 < 0 \qquad \ldots\ldots(2.4)$$

so dass man aus der Lokalisierbarkeit von $\rho(x)$ sicher nicht auf (2.3) schliessen darf. Die Gleichung (2.3) entspricht der kanonischen Quantisierung, also der Bose–Einstein Statistik. Die Gleichung (2.4) aber entspricht nicht der Quantisierung nach dem Ausschlussprinzip, sondern sie stellt eine Ungereimtheit dar. In der Tat, falls wir voraussetzen (was in der kräftefreien, nach Ausschlussprinzip quantisierten Theorie richtig ist), dass die linke Seite von (2.4) eine c-Zahl ist, so folgt aus (2.4), weil

$$[\psi^\star(x), \psi(y)]_+ = F(x-y) \qquad \ldots\ldots(2.5)$$

der Wellengleichung

$$[\partial^\mu\partial_\mu + m^2]F(\xi) = 0 \qquad \ldots\ldots(2.6)$$

---

* Genau genommen müssen alle lokalen Operatoren noch mit geeigneten Gewichten über Raum und Zeit gemittelt werden.

genügt und lorentzinvariant ist, dass $F(x)$ notwendig ungerade ist. Also gilt für beliebiges x und y

$$\psi^\star(x)\psi(y) + \psi^\star(y)\psi(x) + \psi(y)\psi^\star(x) + \psi(x)\psi^\star(y) = 0 \quad \ldots (2.7)$$

was offensichtlich nur mit $\psi = 0$ verträglich ist.

Das ist eines der Argumente, die in der zitierten Arbeit gegen die Quantisierung nach dem Ausschlussprinzip gegeben werden. In einer weiteren Abhandlung [12] wird gezeigt, dass sich auch dann keine Lokalität für die Ladungsdichte ergibt, wenn man für diese gewisse in den Feldern nicht lokale Ausdrücke zulässt.

Damit hatte man in den wichtigsten Fällen: Spin 0, Spin 1/2 und Photonen eine befriedigende Erklärung des Zusammenhanges zwischen Spin und Statistik. Bevor aber der Fall des beliebigen Spins behandelt werden konnte, musste zuerst die Theorie der kräftefreien Felder zu einer beliebigen endlichen Darstellung der Lorentzgruppe geschaffen werden. Dies geschah im Anschluss an Dirac [13] durch Fierz. [14] Hier erweist es sich nun, dass ganz allgemein vor der Quantisierung bei zweideutigen Darstellungen (halbzahligem Spin) die totale Energie indefinit, die Ladung aber definit wird. Um ein stabiles Vakuum zu erhalten, muss man also nach dem Ausschlussprinzip quantisieren. Dann erhält man Teilchen beider Ladungen in symmetrischer Weise. Bei eindeutigen Darstellungen (ganzzahligem Spin) ist die totale Energie definit und die Ladung indefinit. Die Quantisierung nach Bose–Einstein ist daher möglich, diejenige nach dem Ausschlussprinzip aber mit einer lokalen Ladungsdichte unverträglich. Das Argument ist dabei durchaus analog zu den Schlüssen, die von (2.4) zum Widerspruch (2.7) führen.

Natürlich müssen die Argumente für ein reelles Tensorfeld etwas modifiziert werden: Hier wird man etwa wie das schon beim Maxwell Feld geschehen ist die Beobachtbarkeit des Feldes selbst voraussetzen. Eine analoge Bemerkung betrifft die zweideutigen Felder, die der Majorana'schen Realitätsbedingung unterworfen sind. Auch hier wird man die Lokalisierbarkeit einer bilinearen Grösse verlangen müssen.

Im Zusammenhang mit der Arbeit von Fierz müssen unbedingt noch diejenigen Arbeiten erwähnt werden, die auf der Wigner'schen Analyse der irreduziblen unitären Darstellungen der inhomogenen Lorentzgruppe aufbauen. [15] Sie zeigen, dass die Theorie von Fierz zu jeder Darstellung der inhomogenen Lorentzgruppe mit reeller, nicht verschwindender Masse (mindestens) eine Wellengleichung liefert. Für die Masse Null findet man nur Wellengleichungen zu Darstellungen, die sich aus denjenigen mit nicht verschwindender

Masse durch Grenzübergang ergeben. Die restlichen Darstellungen zur Masse Null, die statt der diskreten Spinvariablen eine kontinuierliche Variable enthalten, scheinen physikalisch keine Rolle zu spielen. Wir werden ihre Quantisierung nicht besprechen.

Die berühmte Arbeit von Pauli[16] mit dem Titel *The Connection Between Spin and Statistics* verallgemeinert zunächst das Fierz'sche Resultat auf nicht notwendigerweise irreduzible Spinorfelder. Pauli gibt dazu mit neuen und interessanten Methoden einen direkten Beweis dafür, dass in einer bezüglich der eigentlichen Lorentzgruppe invarianten (c-Zahl-) Theorie freier Felder die Ladungsdichte für eindeutige und die Energiedichte für zweideutige Darstellungen indefinit sind. Daran schliessen sich dann dieselben Folgerungen, die wir oben erwähnt haben, wobei allerdings die Existenz einer positiven Energie bei ganzzahligem Spin von Fierz übernommen werden muss.

Was nun die neuen mathematischen Methoden angeht, so bestehen diese einerseits aus einer Klassifikation der Spinoren in vier Klassen, andererseits in der Erkenntnis, dass die Wellengleichung der freien Felder bezüglich einer Spiegelung invariant ist, auch wenn man ursprünglich nur die Invarianz bezüglich der eigentlichen Lorentzgruppe voraussetzt.

Die Klassifikation der Spinorfelder geschieht mit Hilfe des Vorzeichenpaares $((-1)^m, (-1)^n)$. Dabei sind m und n die Anzahl der punktierten und der unpunktierten Indices des Spinors. Dieser *Charakter* nimmt für eindeutige Darstellungen die Werte $(+, +)$ und $(-, -)$ an. Ersteres für Tensoren geraden, letzteres für Tensoren ungeraden Ranges. Für zweideutige Darstellungen sind die Werte $(+, -)$ und $(-, +)$, wobei die symbolische Gleichung

$$\psi^\star_{(+,-)} = \varphi_{(-,+)} \qquad \dots (2.8)$$

gilt. Bei eindeutigen Darstellungen ändert sich der Charakter durch den Übergang zum Konjugiert-komplexen nicht.

Der Operator $i\partial_\nu = p_\nu$ gehört zum Charakter $(-, -)$. Die lineare Wellengleichung für eindeutige Felder wird also von der symbolischen Form

$$\begin{aligned} \sum p\psi_{(+,+)} &= \sum \psi_{(-,-)} \\ \sum p\psi_{(-,-)} &= \sum \psi_{(+,+)} \end{aligned} \qquad \dots (2.9)$$

sein. Sie bleibt daher bei der Transformation

$$\left.\begin{aligned} \psi_{(+,+)} \to \psi_{(+,+)}, \qquad \psi_{(-,-)} \to -\psi_{(-,-)} \\ p \to -p \end{aligned}\right\}(\theta)$$

invariant. Daraus folgt leicht, dass ein aus p, $\psi_{(+,+)}(x)$ und $\psi_{(-,-)}(x)$ (durch endlich oftmalige Multiplikation und Addition) gebildetes Tensorfeld ungeraden Ranges bei (θ) das Vorzeichen wechselt. Es gibt also keine definite Ladungsdichte.

Interessanter ist der Fall der zweideutigen Darstellungen. Hier lautet die Wellengleichung symbolisch

$$\sum p\psi_{(+,-)} = \sum \psi_{(-,+)}$$
$$\sum p\psi_{(-,+)} = \sum \psi_{(+,-)} \qquad \ldots\ldots(2.10)$$

Die Gleichung (2.10) ist nun wieder invariant bei einer Transformation, die p in $-p$ und $\psi_{(\sigma_1,\sigma_2)}$ in $\sigma_1\psi_{(\sigma_1,\sigma_2)}$ transformiert. *Aber diese Transformation ist mit* (2.8) *unverträglich.* Diese durchaus entscheidende Tatsache führt Pauli zu der folgenden Transformation

$$\psi_{(+,-)} \to i\psi_{(+,-)}, \qquad \psi_{(-,+)} \to (-i)\psi_{(-,+)} \Big\}_{(\theta')}$$
$$p \to -p$$

Jetzt aber folgt, dass jedes bilinear aus $\psi_{+,-}(x)$, $\psi_{-,+}(x)$ und deren Ableitungen (beliebiger Ordnung) aufgebaute Tensorfeld geraden Ranges bei (θ') das Vorzeichen wechselt. Also kann bei zweideutigen Feldern die Energie nicht positiv sein.

Die Existenz der Transformation θ, θ' beansprucht das grösste Interesse. Ihre eigentliche Bedeutung wird erst beim CTP-Theorem klar werden.

Mit dieser Untersuchung von Pauli kommt die Behandlung unseres Gegenstandes zu einem gewissen Abschluss. Für kräftefreie Teilchen war der Zusammenhang zwischen Spin und Statistik in befriedigender Weise geklärt. Man konnte darin 'eine der wichtigsten Anwendungen der speziellen Relativitätstheorie' sehen.

Fassen wir nochmals die Annahmen zusammen, die für die Herleitung des Zusammenhanges wesentlich waren:

(1) Invarianz bezüglich der eigentlichen Lorentzgruppe.

(2) Die Existenz eines energetisch tiefsten Zustandes, den wir normierbar und nicht entartet annehmen und den wir mit dem Vakuum identifizieren.

(3) Ein positives Skalarprodukt im linearen Raum der Zustände.

(4) Physikalische Grössen wie die Ladungsdichte sollen bei raumartiger Separation kommutieren. Die Felder selbst kommutieren oder antikommutieren bei raumartiger Separation (Lokalität).

3. Die neuen Arbeiten über Spin und Statistik.
Das CTP Theorem

Neuen Anlass zur Beschäftigung mit der nun schon klassischen Frage von Spin und Statistik bot die bedeutende Entwicklung der Quantenelektrodynamik durch die Arbeiten von J. Schwinger, R. P. Feynman und F. J. Dyson.

Zunächst forderten die neuen und erfrischenden Anschauungen von Feynman[18] zur Auseinandersetzung heraus. Im Rahmen dieses Formalismus ergab die falsche Statistik eine 1 übertreffende Wahrscheinlichkeit dafür, dass ein schwaches, äusseres elektromagnetisches Feld das Vakuum unverändert lässt. Die Analyse von Pauli[19] im konventionellen Formalismus führt zu einem Modell, in welchem die Forderungen 2.1, 2.2 und 2.4 erfüllt sind, 2.3 aber verletzt ist. Die Einführung einer nicht notwendig positiven aber doch reellen Metrik im Raum der Zustände wurde schon früher zu anderm Zweck von Dirac angeregt und von Pauli[20] eingehend diskutiert. In legitimer Weise spielt sie aber nur in der Quantenelektrodynamik eine beschränkte Rolle.[21]

Viel merkwürdiger war die eigenwillige Art mit welcher Schwinger[22] die richtige Statistik bei gegebenem Spin begründet. Diese folgt bei ihm aus der Invarianzforderung bei der simultanen Anwendung der Zeitumkehr T und der Teilchen-Antiteilchen Konjugation in Theorien, die gegenüber der Raumspiegelung P invariant sind.*

Unabhängig von Schwinger kam Lüders[24] zu dem sehr nah verwandten Resultat, dass unter sehr weiten Voraussetzungen eine P invariante Theorie, in welcher die normalen Vertauschungsrelationen bestehen, automatisch CT invariant ist.

Die endgültige und allgemeine Formulierung des hier zuständigen Theorems aber stammt wiederum von Pauli[25] und lautet CTP *Theorem*: Eine bezüglich der eigentlichen Lorentzgruppe invariante Feldtheorie mit normalen Vertauschungsrelationen ist auch CTP invariant.

Der Fortschritt der neuen Fassung besteht darin, dass (natürlich vor der Entdeckung der Paritätsverletzung) nur die Invarianz bezüglich der eigentlichen Lorentzgruppe vorausgesetzt wird. Ausserdem wird das Theorem für beliebigen Spin bewiesen,

---

* Wir wollen hier nur beiläufig erwähnen, dass die Zeitumkehr notwendig einer *antiunitären Transformation* (Wigner[23]) oder einem Automorphismus mit Umkehrung der Faktorenreihenfolge, einem Antiautomorphismus (Schwinger[22]) entspricht.

während Lüders sich auf die wichtigsten Spinwerte 0, 1/2 und 1 beschränkt.

Es war jetzt wohl klar, dass die Wurzel des Theorems im Umstand zu suchen war, dass TP in der *komplexen* Lorentzgruppe stetig mit der Einheit verbunden werden kann. So weist diese Arbeit in der Formulierung des Problems und der Resultate wesentlich über die verwendeten Beweismethoden hinaus.

Es ist nicht unsere Absicht, die nun einsetzende Reihe von neuen Arbeiten zu referieren. Das Interesse an diesen Fragen wurde natürlich geweckt durch die Erschütterung der gruppen-theoretischen Grundlagen der Physik, welche die Entdeckung der Paritätsverletzung mit sich brachte.

Zu der Frage: 'Kommutator oder Antikommutator für verschiedene Felder?' soll eine Arbeit von Lüders[26] erwähnt werden. Danach sind die normalen Vertauschungsrelationen, in denen Felder zu zweideutigen Darstellungen miteinander bei raumartiger Separation antikommutieren, mit solchen zu eindeutigen Darstellungen kommutieren und Felder zu eindeutigen Darstellungen untereinander kommutieren, mit lokalen Bewegungs-gleichungen immer verträglich. Je nach der zugrundegelegten Energiedichte können aber noch andere zulässige Möglichkeiten existieren, die aber durch eine passende, in einem Spezialfall von Klein[27] angegebene (natürlich nicht unitäre), Transformation der Felder wieder in den Normalfall übergeführt werden können.

Nun treten aber in neuerer Zeit Versuche auf, die Feldtheorie selbst in eine neue Form zu giessen. Am bekanntesten sind die beiden Richtungen von Lehmann, Symanzik und Zimmermann[28] einerseits und von Wightman[29] andererseits. An Nützlichkeit (wenn das Wort hier erlaubt ist) übertrifft die erste Form die zweite, allgemeinere, doch sind die gründlichsten und schwierigsten mathematischen Analysen zweifellos der Ausdauer und dem Mut von Wightman zu verdanken.

Man kann auch in diesen allgemeinen Rahmen die Frage nach der CTP-Invarianz stellen. Es zeigt sich, dass das Wightman'-sche Schema eine befriedigende Behandlung und ein Verständnis hiefür abgibt.[30]

Weniger befriedigend, aber vielleicht interessanter ist das Problem von Spin und Statistik in diesem Formalismus. Da die Wightman'schen Felder vorerst mit Teilchen nichts zu tun zu haben scheinen, lässt sich nur die Frage stellen, ob ein Feld mit dem konjugiert- komplexen kommutieren (oder antikommutieren) kann oder nicht. Das hängt wieder vom Transformationscharakter des Feldes in der gewohnten Weise ab. Man hat sich gewöhnt, auch diesen Zusammenhang mit der Bezeichnung 'Spin und Statistik' zu versehen. Die Behandlung dieses Problems verdankt man Burgoyne.[31]   Führt man Teilchen im Anschluss an Lehmann *et al.*[28] durch eine Forderung über das asymptotische Verhalten der Feldoperatoren ein, so folgt allerdings in einfachster Weise aus den falschen *schwachen* Vertauschungsrelationen das Verschwinden des betreffenden Feldes.

Die oben erwähnte Untersuchung von Lüders[26] ist bisher nicht in diesen allgemeinen Rahmen eingebaut worden.

Schliesslich muss noch auf eine Lücke hingewiesen werden: das elektromagnetische Feld in Wechselwirkung mit geladenen Teilchen fügt sich in den Wightmanschen Formalismus nicht ohne weiteres ein.   Es erfordert nämlich eine sehr spezielle indefinite Metrik im Raum der Zustände.[21]   Diese Tatsache dürfte zwar für das CTP Theorem (wo die definite Metrik nicht wesentlich gebraucht wird) und auch für die Statistik der Photonen nicht stören, wohl aber für die Statistik der geladenen Teilchen, weil diese durch nicht eichinvariante Felder beschrieben sind.

Am einleuchtendsten wäre vielleicht die konsequente Behandlung des Grenzfalles, der entsteht, wenn man, von einer kleinen Photonenmasse ausgehend, diese nach Null streben lässt.[32]

In dem folgenden systematischen Teil versuche ich, eine möglichst elementare aber vollständige Einführung in diejenigen Entwicklungen der Wightman'schen Theorie zu geben, die zur Untersuchung der CTP Invarianz und des Zusammenhanges von Spin und Statistik notwendig sind.

Der erste Abschnitt stellt Tatsachen über die reelle und die komplexe Lorentzgruppe zusammen, soweit wir diese später brauchen werden. Im zweiten Abschnitt werden kurz die Haupteigenschaften der W-Funktionen in Erinnerung gerufen. Für die exakte Begründung der Theorie der Vakuumerwartungswerte muss auf die Literatur verwiesen werden.[29]   Der dritte Abschnitt ist am anspruchsvollsten und enthält den Beweis für den (in unserem Zusammenhang fundamentalen) Satz, dass die Vakuumerwartungswerte bezüglich komplexer Lorentztransformationen invariant sind.   Im vierten Abschnitt werden die reellen Regularitätspunkte der W-Funktionen charakterisiert. Fünfter und sechster Abschnitt enthalten schliesslich die Anwendung der bereitgestellten Hilfsmittel auf die CTP-Invarianz und auf Spin und Statistik.

SYSTEMATISCHER TEIL

1. Die homogene Lorentzgruppe

Die *reelle* homogene Lorentzgruppe L besteht aus denjenigen reellen linearen Transformationen Λ des reellen Vektors $\xi = (\xi^0, \xi^1, \xi^2, \xi^3)$, welche die Form $\xi^2 = (\xi^0)^2 - \sum_{k=1}^{3} (\xi^k)^2$ invariant lassen.

Bezeichnet man mit Λ auch die Matrix der linearen Transformation und mit Λ^T die dazu transponierte, dann charakterisiert

$$\Lambda^T G \Lambda = G \quad \text{mit} \quad G = \begin{pmatrix} 1 & 0 & 0 & 0 \\ 0 & -1 & 0 & 0 \\ 0 & 0 & -1 & 0 \\ 0 & 0 & 0 & -1 \end{pmatrix}$$

die Lorentztransformationen. Daraus folgt, dass der Wert der Determinanten einer Lorentztransformation ± 1 ist. L zerfällt demnach in L_+ (det $\Lambda = +1$) und L_- (det $\Lambda = -1$), wobei L_+ selbst wieder eine Gruppe ist. Von Bedeutung sind für uns die folgenden invarianten Kegel:

(1) Der Kegel der zeitartigen Vektoren $\xi^2 > 0$. Dieser zerfällt in den *Vorkegel* V_+ ($\xi_0 > 0$ und $\xi^2 > 0$) und den *Nachkegel* V_- ($\xi_0 < 0$ und $\xi^2 > 0$).

(2) Der Kegel der Nullvektoren $\xi^2 = 0$ und $\xi \neq 0$; dieser zerfällt analog in N_+ ($\xi_0 > 0$ und $\xi^2 = 0$) und N_- ($\xi_0 < 0$ und $\xi^2 = 0$).

(3) Der Vektor Null $\xi = 0$.

(4) Der Nebenkegel, bestehend aus den raumartigen Vektoren $\xi^2 < 0$.

Weil nun $\Lambda \in L_+$ den Vorkegel entweder in sich oder dann in den Nachkegel transformiert, zerfällt L_+ selbst wieder in die *eigentliche Lorentzgruppe* $L_+^\uparrow$ ($\Lambda V_+ = V_+$) und in $L_+^\downarrow$ ($\Lambda V_+ = V_-$). Analog zerfällt L_-. Da man leicht zeigen kann, dass $L_+^\uparrow$ zusammenhängend ist, gibt es keine weitere geometrische Aufspaltung der Gruppe L. Die vier Komponenten von L lassen sich wie folgt schreiben

$$L = (L_+^\uparrow + PTL_+^\uparrow) + (PL_+^\uparrow + TL_+^\uparrow)$$
$$L = \quad\quad L_+ \quad\quad + \quad\quad L_- \quad\quad\quad \dots (1.1)$$

Dabei sind P und T die speziellen Lorentztransformationen

$$P: \begin{array}{l} \xi^{0\prime} = \xi^0 \\ \xi^{k\prime} = -\xi^k \end{array} \quad T: \begin{array}{l} \xi^{0\prime} = -\xi^0 \\ \xi^{k\prime} = \xi^k \end{array} \quad PT: \xi^{\nu\prime} = -\xi^\nu$$

$$\dots (1.2)$$

Die *komplexe* homogene Lorentzgruppe $L(C)$ besteht aus denjenigen komplexen linearen Transformationen Λ der komplexen Vektoren $\zeta = (\zeta^0, \zeta^1, \zeta^2, \zeta^3)$, welche die Form $\zeta^2 = (\zeta^0)^2 - \sum_{k=1}^{3} (\zeta^k)^2$ invariant lassen. Wieder gilt $\Lambda^T G \Lambda = G$. Daher zerfällt $L(C)$ in $L_+(C)$ (det $\Lambda = +1$) und $L_-(C)$ (det $\Lambda = -1$). Nun ist aber schon $L_+(C)$ zusammenhängend und man hat die Zerlegung

$$L(C) = L_+(C) + PL_+(C) \qquad \ldots (1.3)$$

$L_+(C)$ enthält als reelle Transformationen also $L_+^\uparrow$ und $PTL_+^\uparrow$. Insbesondere lässt sich in $L_+(C)$ das Einselement E mit dem Element PT durch einen Weg verbinden. Zum Beispiel durch den folgenden:

$$\Lambda(\varphi) = \begin{pmatrix} \cos\varphi & i\sin\varphi & 0 & 0 \\ i\sin\varphi & \cos\varphi & 0 & 0 \\ 0 & 0 & \cos\varphi & \sin\varphi \\ 0 & 0 & -\sin\varphi & \cos\varphi \end{pmatrix}, \quad 0 \leqslant \varphi \leqslant \pi \qquad \ldots (1.4)$$

Natürlich kann man auf viele verschiedene Weisen eine passende Umgebung des Einselementes der Lorentzgruppe analytisch parametrisieren. Besonders elementar ist die folgende Art:
Es sei

$$R = \begin{pmatrix} 0 & \lambda_4 & \lambda_5 & \lambda_6 \\ \lambda_4 & 0 & \lambda_3 & -\lambda_2 \\ \lambda_5 & -\lambda_3 & 0 & \lambda_1 \\ \lambda_6 & \lambda_2 & -\lambda_1 & 0 \end{pmatrix} \qquad \ldots (1.5)$$

dann stellt

$$\Lambda = (E+R)(E-R)^{-1} \qquad \ldots (1.6)$$

eine Lorentztransformation dar. Reellen λ's entsprechen reelle, komplexen λ's komplexe Transformationen.

In der Tat folgt aus (1.5) $R^T G + GR = 0$ und daraus

$$\Lambda^T G \Lambda = (E-R^T)^{-1}(E+R^T)G(E+R)(E-R)^{-1}$$
$$= (E-R^T)^{-1}(E-R^T)G(E-R)(E-R)^{-1} = G$$

Schliesslich lautet die Auflösung von (1.6)

$$R = (\Lambda-E)(\Lambda+E)^{-1} \qquad \ldots (1.7)$$

Diese ist möglich, sofern -1 nicht Eigenwert von Λ ist, jedenfalls aber in einer genügend kleinen Umgebung des Einselementes.

Diejenigen Lorentztransformationen (1.6), die zu einem rein imaginären R gehören, können selbst als rein imaginär bezeichnet werden. Sie haben die Eigenschaft, dass $\Lambda^{*T}\Lambda = \Lambda'\Lambda = E$ wird und sind dadurch unabhängig von einer Parametrisierung definiert.

Von besonderer Wichtigkeit ist für uns die folgende *Darstellung der Lorentzgruppe*: Man setze für reelle Vektoren ξ, $X = \xi^\nu \sigma_\nu$ und analog für komplexe Vektoren ζ, $Z = \zeta^\nu \sigma_\nu$ wobei

$$\sigma_0 = \begin{pmatrix} 1 & 0 \\ 0 & 1 \end{pmatrix} \quad \sigma_1 = \begin{pmatrix} 1 & 0 \\ 0 & -1 \end{pmatrix} \quad \sigma_2 = \begin{pmatrix} 0 & 1 \\ 1 & 0 \end{pmatrix} \quad \sigma_3 = \begin{pmatrix} 0 & -i \\ i & 0 \end{pmatrix}$$

Es ist $\xi^2 = \det X$ und $\zeta^2 = \det Z$. Ausserdem ist $X^\star = X$. Nun seien A und B zweireihige Matrizen für die det $A = \det B = 1$ ist. Dann stellt

$$X' = AXA^\star \qquad \ldots(1.8)$$

eine Lorentztransformation $\Lambda(A) \in L_+^\uparrow$ und

$$Z' = AZB^T \qquad \ldots(1.9)$$

eine solche $\Lambda(A, B) \in L_+(C)$ dar. Diese Darstellungen sind zweideutig, indem im ersten Fall $\Lambda(-A) = \Lambda(A)$ und im zweiten $\Lambda(-A, -B) = \Lambda(A, B)$ ist. Wieder ist es leicht einzusehen, dass sich jedes $\Lambda \in L_+$ gemäss (1.8) und jedes $\Lambda \in L_+^\uparrow(C)$ gemäss (1.9) darstellen lässt.

Die Darstellung (1.8) bildet bekanntlich die Grundlage des *Spinorkalküls*.[33] Die einfachsten Spinoren

$$\begin{pmatrix} u_1 \\ u_2 \end{pmatrix} \quad \text{und} \quad \begin{pmatrix} v_1 \\ v_2 \end{pmatrix}$$

transformieren sich gemäss $u' = Au$ und $v' = A'v$. Dabei ist A' die zu A konjugiert komplexe Matrix, also $A' = A^{\star T}$. Der allgemeine Spinor $a_{\alpha_1 \ldots \alpha_n, \beta_1 \ldots \beta_m}$ transformiert wie das Produkt $u_{\alpha_1} \ldots u_{\alpha_n} v_{\beta_1} \ldots v_{\beta_m}$. Er gehört zu einer endlichen Darstellung der Gruppe $L_+^\uparrow$. Diese ist irreduzibel, falls der Spinor in den Indices $\alpha_1 \cdots \alpha_m$ und $\beta_1 \cdots \beta_m$ symmetrisch ist und zu einer eindeutigen Darstellung, falls n und m dieselbe Parität haben. Alle endlichen irreduziblen Darstellungen werden so erhalten. Ausserdem ist jede endliche Darstellung von $L_+^\uparrow$ vollreduzibel. Der konjugiert komplexe Spinor $a^\star_{\alpha_1 \ldots \alpha_n, \beta_1 \ldots \beta_m}$ transformiert wie $b_{\beta_1 \ldots \beta_m, \alpha_1 \ldots \alpha_n}$. Verjüngungen eines Spinors können nur mit den invarianten Spinoren

$$\epsilon^{\alpha\beta} = \begin{pmatrix} 0 & 1 \\ -1 & 0 \end{pmatrix} \quad \text{und} \quad \epsilon^{\dot\alpha\dot\beta} = \begin{pmatrix} 0 & 1 \\ -1 & 0 \end{pmatrix}$$

vollzogen werden.

Nun lässt sich offenbar jede der erwähnten Darstellungen von $L_+^\uparrow$ zu einer Darstellung von $L_+(C)$ erweitern. Bei der Transformation $\Lambda(A, B)$ sollen sich u und v nach $u' = Au$ und $v' = Bv$

transformieren. Der Spinor $a_{\alpha_1\ldots\alpha_n,\,\beta_1\ldots\beta_m}$ transformiert sich weiterhin wie das Produkt $u_{\alpha_1}\ldots u_{\alpha_n}v_{\beta_1}\ldots v_{\beta_m}$. Diese Erweiterung hat für zweideutige Darstellungen eine sehr merkwürdige Konsequenz, auf die Pauli mit grossem Nachdruck hingewiesen hat: die Transformation PT, die etwa durch $A=-E$ und $B=E$ dargestellt sei, transformiert ein Paar von konjugiert komplexen, zweideutigen Spinoren nicht wieder in ein solches. In der Tat, es multipliziert sich $a_{\alpha_1\ldots\alpha_n,\,\beta_1\ldots\beta_m}$ offenbar mit $(-1)^n$ aber $a^{*}_{\alpha_1\ldots\alpha_n,\,\beta_1\ldots\beta_m}$ mit $(-1)^m$. n und m haben aber verschiedene Parität.

Bei eindeutigen Darstellungen tritt dieses Faktum nicht auf.

Der Pauli'sche Charakter einer Darstellung.[16] Darunter versteht man das Vorzeichenpaar $((-1)^n, (-1)^m)$, das der Darstellung $a_{\alpha_1\ldots\alpha_n,\,\beta_1\ldots\beta_m}$ zugeordnet ist. Das Produkt zweier Charaktere ist durch $(a, b)(a', b') = (aa', bb')$ erklärt. Dem direkten Produkt von Darstellungen entspricht das Produkt der Charaktere, und bei der Reduktion einer Darstellung treten immer nur Darstellungen desselben Charakters auf. Eindeutige Darstellungen gehören entweder zum Charakter $(1, 1)$ (Tensoren geraden Ranges). oder zu $(-1, -1)$ (Tensoren ungeraden Ranges). Die zweideutigen Darstellungen zerfallen in die beiden Klassen $(1, -1)$ und $(-1, 1)$.

Die Normalform einer komplexen Lorentztransformation. Wir definieren: zwei komplexe Lorentztransformationen Λ und $\check{\Lambda}$ aus $L_+(C)$ heissen bezüglich $L_+^\uparrow$ äquivalent, falls $\check{\Lambda}=\Lambda_1\Lambda\Lambda_2$ und $\Lambda_{1,2}\in L_+^\uparrow$.

Es handelt sich dann darum, innerhalb einer Äquivalenzklasse einen möglichst einfachen Repräsentanten zu finden. Darüber gibt der folgende Satz Auskunft.

Satz: Eine komplexe Lorentztransformation $\Lambda\in L_+(C)$ ist zu einer der beiden folgenden äquivalent

$$M(\varphi,\chi) = \begin{pmatrix} \cos\varphi & i\sin\varphi & 0 & 0 \\ i\sin\varphi & \cos\varphi & 0 & 0 \\ 0 & 0 & \operatorname{Ch}\chi & -i\operatorname{Sh}\chi \\ 0 & 0 & i\operatorname{Sh}\chi & \operatorname{Ch}\chi \end{pmatrix}, \quad \varphi,\chi \text{ reell} \qquad \ldots(1.10)$$

oder

$$M_1(\tau) = \pm\begin{pmatrix} 1-\tfrac{1}{2}\tau^2 & \tfrac{1}{2}\tau^2 & i\tau & 0 \\ -\tfrac{1}{2}\tau^2 & 1+\tfrac{1}{2}\tau^2 & i\tau & 0 \\ i\tau & -i\tau & 1 & 0 \\ 0 & 0 & 0 & 1 \end{pmatrix}, \quad \tau\neq 0, \text{ reell} \qquad \ldots(1.11)$$

Beweis: Wir verwenden für die Äquivalenz das Zeichen $\sim$ und diskutieren zunächst die Darstellung (1.9). Es sei also $\Lambda = \Lambda$ (A, B), dann gilt $(A, B) \sim (CAD, C'BD') \sim (D^{-1}B'^{-1}AD, E)$, letzteres indem man $C'BD' = E$ wählt. Es handelt sich nun noch darum, durch geeignete Wahl von D die Matrix $B'^{-1} A$ auf Normalform zu transformieren. Dabei ergeben sich bekanntlich die zwei Fälle, entweder

$$(A, B) \sim \left(\begin{pmatrix} \lambda^2 & 0 \\ 0 & \lambda^{-2} \end{pmatrix}, E \right) \sim \left(\begin{pmatrix} \lambda & 0 \\ 0 & \lambda^{-1} \end{pmatrix}, \begin{pmatrix} \lambda^{\star -1} & 0 \\ 0 & \lambda^{\star} \end{pmatrix} \right)$$

mit $\lambda^2 = e^{x + i\varphi}$
oder

$$(A, B) \sim \left(\pm \begin{pmatrix} 1 & 2i\tau \\ 0 & 1 \end{pmatrix}, E \right) \sim \left(\pm \begin{pmatrix} 1 & i\tau \\ 0 & 1 \end{pmatrix}, \begin{pmatrix} 1 & i\tau \\ 0 & 1 \end{pmatrix} \right)$$

mit beliebigem reellen $\tau \neq 0$.

Rechnet man die zugehörigen Lorentztransformationen gemäss (1.9) aus, so findet man die obenstehenden Normalformen.

Die Normalformen (1.10) und (1.11) sind die den bekannten Normalformen[15] einer reellen Lorentztransformation entsprechenden rein imaginären Transformationen. Die obige Herleitung ist insofern speziell, als sie sich auf die Darstellung (1.9) stützt. Ein analoges Resultat lässt sich aber für beliebige Dimensionszahlen direkt herleiten.[36]

2. Die Vakuumerwartungswerte [29]

Wir setzen nun eine relativistische Feldtheorie voraus. Diese sei durch eine endliche Anzahl von Spinorfeldern

$$\overset{(k)}{\psi_{\nu_k}}(x)$$

beschrieben. ν_k steht als Abkürzung für $\alpha_1 \cdots \alpha_{n_k}, \beta_1 \cdots \beta_{m_k}$. Es werden die üblichen Voraussetzungen gemacht, von denen wir die folgenden besonders hervorheben.

(1) Der Raum der Zustände sei ein *Hilbertraum*, dh. in ihm sei ein positives Skalarprodukt definiert. Die Feldoperatoren, gemittelt über geeignete Testfunktionen, wirken auf diesen.

(2) Zur Theorie gehöre eine unitäre Darstellung der inhomogenen Lorentzgruppe. (Λ, a) bedeute die Transformation $x' = \Lambda x + a$. Dabei ist $\Lambda \in L_+^{\uparrow}$. Die Darstellung sei mit $U(\Lambda, a)$ bezeichnet. Es gilt dann

$$U(\Lambda, a) \overset{(k)}{\psi_{\nu_k}}(x) U^{-1}(\Lambda, a) = \sum_{\mu_k} S_{\nu_k}{}^{\mu_k}(\Lambda^{-1}) \overset{(k)}{\psi_{\mu_k}}(\Lambda x + a) \quad \ldots (2.1)$$

wobei $S(\Lambda)$ eine der im vorigen Abschnitt besprochenen endlichen Darstellungen der Gruppe $L_+^\uparrow$ bedeutet. Es existiert also ein Energie-Impuls Vektor P_ν.

(3) Es existiere ein Vakuum, dh. ein nicht entarteter Zustand tiefster Energie. Dieser Zustand gehört zur Energie Null und ist invariant.

Eine Feldtheorie, wie wir sie ins Auge fassen, ist vollständig durch die Vakuumerwartungswerte der endlichen Produkte der Feldoperatoren definiert. Es sei

$$W_\nu(\xi_1\cdots,\xi_N) = \langle\overset{(0)}{\psi_{\nu_0}}(x_0)\overset{(1)}{\psi_{\nu_1}}(x_1)\cdots\overset{(N)}{\psi_{\nu_N}}(x_N)\rangle_0 \quad \ldots(2.2)$$

ein solcher. Dabei steht ν für die Indices $\nu_0\nu_1\cdots\nu_N$ und es ist $\xi_k = x_k - x_{k-1}$ gesetzt. Die aus 2. und 3. folgende Translationsinvarianz ist in (2.2) schon ausgenützt. Weiter folgt aus 2. und 3. für $\Lambda \in L_+^\uparrow$

$$W_\nu(\Lambda\xi_1\cdots,\Lambda\xi_N) = \sum_\mu S_\nu{}^\mu(\Lambda)W_\mu(\xi_1\cdots,\xi_N) \quad \ldots(2.3)$$

Da W_ν eine eindeutige Funktion der ξ's ist, verschwindet sie, falls $S(\Lambda)$ zu einer zweideutigen Darstellung gehört.

Von entscheidender Bedeutung für uns aber ist diejenige Folgerung aus 2. and 3., die besagt, dass die Fourier-Transformierte $\tilde{W}\nu(p_1\cdots,p_N)$ von $W\nu(\xi_1\cdots,\xi_N)$ verschwindet, falls nicht alle Vektoren $p_k \in V_+$ erfüllen. Daraus folgt, dass $W\nu$ $(\xi_1\cdots,\xi_N)$ Randwert einer analytischen Funktion $W\nu(\zeta_1\cdots,\zeta_N)$ ist. Diese ist durch das Fourier-Integral definiert und regulär analytisch falls $Im\zeta_k \in V_+$. Das so definierte Gebiet werde mit $\mathscr{R}_N$ bezeichnet. Für $\mathscr{R}_1$ werden wir einfach $\mathscr{R}$ schreiben. $\mathscr{R}_N$ enthält keine reellen Punkte, diese liegen nur am Rande. Schliesslich folgt aus der Definition der Funktion $W\nu(\zeta_1\cdots,\zeta_N)$ die Gleichung

$$W_\nu(\Lambda\zeta_1\cdots,\Lambda\zeta_N) = \sum_\mu S_\nu{}^\mu(\Lambda)W_\mu(\zeta_1\cdots,\zeta_N) \quad \ldots(2.4)$$

für $\Lambda \in L_+^\uparrow$.

Wir schliessen diesen Abschnitt mit zwei Bemerkungen:

(a) Die Voraussetzung 1. wurde bisher nur implizit verwendet, nämlich dort, wo die Existenz eines reellen Spektrums des Energieoperators angenommen wurde. Wir werden die Voraussetzung erst an später Stelle wieder verwenden und dann ausdrücklich auf diese Tatsache aufmerksam machen.

(b) Voraussetzungen über Vertauschungsrelationen oder über die Lokalität der Theorie wurden bis jetzt keine gemacht. Wir verschieben auch diese auf einen späteren Zeitpunkt.

3. Der Satz von Bargmann, Hall und Wightman [29]

Wir kommen nun zum wichtigsten (und schwierigsten) Hilfsmittel der weiteren Untersuchung, nämlich zu dem im Titel erwähnten Satz. Dieser lautet

Satz: Falls $W_\nu(\zeta_1 \cdots, \zeta_N)$ in $\mathcal{R}_N$ regulär und eindeutig ist und falls weiter für jedes $\Lambda \in L_+^\uparrow$

$$W_\nu(\zeta_1 \cdots, \zeta_N) = \sum_\mu S_{\nu\mu}(\Lambda) W_\mu(\Lambda^{-1}\zeta_1 \cdots, \Lambda^{-1}\zeta_N) \quad \ldots (3.1)$$

erfüllt ist, wobei $S(\Lambda)$ eine endliche (und notwendig eindeutige) Darstellung der eigentlichen Lorentzgruppe ist, dann gestattet $W_\nu(\zeta_1 \cdots, \zeta_N)$ eine *eindeutige* analytische Fortsetzung in ein Gebiet $\mathcal{R}_N'$, das die Vereinigungsmenge aller $\Lambda\mathcal{R}_N$ mit $\Lambda \in L_+(C)$ ist. Weiter gilt die Gleichung (3.1) für jedes $\Lambda \in L_+(C)$, wobei $S(\Lambda)$ die gemäss Abschnitt 1 eindeutig definierte Fortsetzung der ursprünglichen Darstellung in $L_+(C)$ ist.

Beweis: A. Der Satz sagt unter anderem aus, dass die Gleichung (3.1) mit $\Lambda \in L_+(C)$ verwendet werden kann, um $W_\nu(\zeta_1, \cdots, \zeta_N)$ in denjenigen Punkten von $\mathcal{R}_N'$ (das sind Punkte $(\zeta_1, \cdots, \zeta_N)$, welche durch eine komplexe Lorentztransformation Λ^{-1} auf Punkte in $\mathcal{R}_N$ abgebildet werden können), die nicht zu $\mathcal{R}_N$ gehören, zu definieren und dass diese Definition *eindeutig* ist. Für die Eindeutigkeit ist aber notwendig und hinreichend, dass (3.1) immer dann gilt, wenn zwar $(\zeta_1 \cdots, \zeta_N) \in \mathcal{R}_N$ und $(\Lambda^{-1}\zeta_1 \cdots, \Lambda^{-1}\zeta_N) \in \mathcal{R}_N$ aber $\Lambda \in L_+(C)$, falls also (3.1) mit $\Lambda \in L_+(C)$ nicht schon in $\mathcal{R}_N$ zu Mehrdeutigkeiten Anlass gibt. Das ergibt sich aus der Tatsache, dass $L_+(C)$ eine Gruppe ist.

Wenn dies einmal gezeigt sein wird, folgt der Rest leicht. Denn die durch (3.1) festgelegte Fortsetzung ist offenbar analytisch: man wähle Λ so, dass $(\Lambda^{-1}\zeta_1 \cdots, \Lambda^{-1}\zeta_N) \in \mathcal{R}_N$, halte Λ dann fest und lasse $(\zeta_1 \cdots, \zeta_N)$ in einer genügend kleinen Umgebung variieren.

Nun kann man aber dem somit aufgezeigten Hauptproblem eine etwas andere Wendung dadurch geben, dass man auf der rechten Seite von (3.1) $(\zeta_1 \cdots, \zeta_N)$ festhält, aber diese jetzt als Funktion $F(\Lambda)$ auf $L_+(C)$ auffasst. Natürlich ist diese Funktion zunächst nur dort definiert, wo $(\Lambda^{-1}\zeta_1 \cdots, \Lambda^{-1}\zeta_N)$ in $\mathcal{R}_N$ liegt. Dadurch ist ein von $(\zeta_1 \cdots, \zeta_N)$ abhängiges Gebiet in $L_+(C)$ festgelegt. Es bleibt zu zeigen, dass $F(\Lambda)$ in diesem konstant ist. Die Fortsetzung geschieht dadurch, dass man $F(\Lambda)$ auf der ganzen Gruppe gleich dieser (von $\zeta_1 \cdots, \zeta_N$ abhängigen) Konstanten setzt.

B. Hierüber gelangen wir nun leicht zu einem Teilresultat:

$$F(\Lambda) = \sum_{\mu} S_{\nu}{}^{\mu}(\Lambda) W_{\mu}(\Lambda^{-1}\zeta_1 \cdots, \Lambda^{-1}\zeta_N) \qquad \cdots (3.2)$$

ist nämlich in einer genügend kleinen Umgebung des Einselementes $\Lambda = E$ konstant auf $L_+(C)$. Dabei ist $(\zeta_1 \cdots, \zeta_N) \in \mathscr{R}_N$ angenommen. Um dies einzusehen, führen wir in der Gruppe $L_+(C)$ die im ersten Abschnitt erwähnten Parameter $\lambda_1 \cdots, \lambda_6$ ein. Weiter betrachten wir eine derart kleine Umgebung $|\lambda_k| < a$, dass dort

(1) $\Lambda(\lambda_1 \cdots, \lambda_6)$ und $\Lambda^{-1}(\lambda_1 \cdots, \lambda_6)$ regulär analytisch sind,

(2) $S_{\nu}{}^{\mu}(\Lambda(\lambda_1 \cdots, \lambda_6))$ regulär analytisch ist (dies ist eigentlich keine neue Einschränkung, da $S(\Lambda)$ als eindeutige Darstellung ein Polynom in Λ ist.)

(3) $(\Lambda^{-1}\zeta_1 \cdots, \Lambda^{-1}\zeta_N) \in \mathscr{R}_N$, dann ist $W_{\mu}(\Lambda^{-1}\zeta_1 \cdots, \Lambda^{-1}\zeta_N)$ als iterierte Funktion regulär analytisch in $\lambda_1 \cdots, \lambda_6$. Dasselbe gilt für

$$F(\Lambda(\lambda_1 \cdots, \lambda_6)) = F_1(\lambda_1 \cdots, \lambda_6)$$

Für *reelle* $\lambda_1 \cdots, \lambda_6$ ist $F_1(\lambda_1 \cdots, \lambda_6)$ *konstant*, denn ihnen entsprechen reelle Transformationen aus $L_+^{\uparrow}$, also ist F_1 in unserer Umgebung überhaupt konstant.

C. Die Schwierigkeit tritt erst auf, wenn wir zeigen wollen, dass $F(\Lambda)$ im ganzen Gebiet, dass durch $(\Lambda^{-1}\zeta_1 \cdots, \Lambda^{-1}\zeta_N) \in \mathscr{R}_N$ charakterisiert ist und das wir $\mathscr{J}$ nennen wollen, konstant ist. Wie wir aus B. wissen, ist das in einer Umgebung von E und allgemeiner in einer *passenden Umgebung irgend eines Punktes von* $\mathscr{J}$ der Fall. Das folgt leicht aus der Tatsache, dass $S(\Lambda)$ eine Darstellung und $L_+(C)$ eine Gruppe ist. Falls $\mathscr{J}$ zusammenhängend ist, folgt daraus die Konstanz von $F(\Lambda)$ auf $\mathscr{J}$. Wir werden also zeigen, dass jeder Punkt $\Lambda \in \mathscr{J}$ durch einen Weg, der ganz in $\mathscr{J}$ verläuft, mit E verbunden werden kann.

Das bedeutet (wenn wir jetzt Λ^{-1} durch Λ ersetzen), dass wir zu jedem $(\zeta_1 \cdots, \zeta_N) \in \mathscr{R}_N$ und jedem Λ, für welches $(\Lambda\zeta_1 \cdots, \Lambda\zeta_N) \in \mathscr{R}_N$ ist, einen Weg $\Lambda(t)$ mit $\Lambda(0) = E$ und $\Lambda(1) = \Lambda$ finden müssen, so dass ständig

$$(\Lambda(t)\zeta_1 \cdots, \Lambda(t)\zeta_N) \in \mathscr{R}_N \quad \text{für} \quad 0 \leqslant t \leqslant 1$$

D. Die letzte Aufgabe lässt sich vereinfachen. Es sei nämlich $\Lambda = \Lambda_1 M \Lambda_2$ und $\Lambda_{1,2} \in L_+^{\uparrow}$. M sei dabei die Normalform (1.10). Dann können wir den gesuchten Weg wie folgt zusammenstückeln:

(1) $\Lambda(t) = \Lambda_2(t)$ für $0 \leqslant t \leqslant \frac{1}{3}$, $\Lambda_2(0) = E$, $\Lambda_2(\frac{1}{3}) = \Lambda_2$

(2) $\Lambda(t) = M(t)\Lambda_2$ für $\frac{1}{3} \leqslant t \leqslant \frac{2}{3}$, $M(\frac{1}{3}) = E$, $M(\frac{2}{3}) = M$

(3) $\Lambda(t) = \Lambda_1(t)M\Lambda_2$ für $\tfrac{2}{3} \leqslant t \leqslant 1$, $\Lambda_1(\tfrac{2}{3}) = E$, $\Lambda_1(1) = \Lambda_1$

$$\dots (3.3)$$

Der erste und der dritte Weg sind offenbar gänzlich harmlos, da (1) ja in $L_+^\uparrow$ gilt, $L_+^\uparrow$ zusammenhängend ist und $\mathscr{R}_N$ bezüglich dieser Gruppe invariant ist. Die Existenz des zweiten Weges aber wird durch den folgenden Hilfssatz sichergestellt.

Hilfssatz: Es sei $\zeta(\varphi, \chi) = M(\varphi, \chi)\zeta$

$$M(\varphi, \chi) = \begin{pmatrix} \cos\varphi & i\sin\varphi & 0 & 0 \\ i\sin\varphi & \cos\varphi & 0 & 0 \\ 0 & 0 & \mathrm{Ch}\,\chi & -i\,\mathrm{Sh}\,\chi \\ 0 & 0 & i\,\mathrm{Sh}\,\chi & \mathrm{Ch}\,\chi \end{pmatrix}$$

$$\dots (3.4)$$

mit reellem $|\varphi| < \pi$ und χ. Ausserdem sei $\zeta \in \mathscr{R}$ und $\zeta(\varphi, \chi) \in \mathscr{R}$. Dann ist auch $\zeta(t\varphi, t\chi) \in \mathscr{R}$ für $0 \leqslant t \leqslant 1$.

Da der im Hilfssatz erwähnte Weg nur von φ und χ und nicht von ζ abhängt, liefert dieser auch im Fall mehrerer Vektoren unmittelbar den gesuchten Weg 2.

Bevor wir den Hilfssatz beweisen, wollen wir noch eine Lücke schliessen, die sich auf diejenigen $\Lambda \in \mathscr{J}$ bezieht, die zur Normalform (1.11) gehören. Diese Ausnahmen brauchen deswegen nicht behandelt zu werden, weil $\mathscr{J}$ offen ist und weil jede Umgebung einer solchen Transformation Transformationen enthält, die zur Normalform (1.10) gehören.

E. Beweis des Hilfssatzes. Wir setzen $\zeta(\varphi, \chi) = \xi(\varphi, \chi) + i\eta(\varphi, \chi)$ und finden

$$\eta^0(\varphi, \chi) = \eta^0 \cos\varphi + \xi^1 \sin\varphi > 0 \qquad \dots (3.5)$$

$$(\eta(\varphi, \chi))^2 = A - B > 0 \qquad \dots (3.6)$$

mit

$$A = (\eta^0 \cos\varphi + \xi^1 \sin\varphi)^2 - (\eta^1 \cos\varphi + \xi^0 \sin\varphi)^2 \qquad \dots (3.7)$$

und

$$B = (\eta^2 \,\mathrm{Ch}\,\chi - \xi^3 \,\mathrm{Sh}\,\chi)^2 + (\eta^3 \,\mathrm{Ch}\,\chi + \xi^2 \,\mathrm{Sh}\,\chi)^2 \qquad \dots (3.8)$$

Die Bedingung (3.5) und die aus (3.6) und (3.8) folgende Bedingung $A > 0$ bestimmen ein φ-Intervall in $|\varphi| < \pi$, das $\varphi = 0$ enthält, und dessen Länge kleiner ist als π. Es sei φ_0 der Mittelpunkt dieses Intervalles. Dann ist $|\varphi_0| < \pi/2$ und

$$A = \alpha^2 \cos^2(\varphi - \varphi_0) - \beta^2 \sin^2(\varphi - \varphi_0) \qquad \dots (3.9)$$

und es gilt $|\varphi - \varphi_0| < \pi/2$.

5*

Ganz analog lässt sich B auf Diagonalform transformieren:

$$B = \gamma^2 \, \mathrm{Ch}^2 \, (\chi - \chi_0) + \delta^2 \, \mathrm{Sh}^2 \, (\chi - \chi_0) \qquad \ldots (3.10)$$

wobei allerdings die Ausnahmefälle $\eta^2 = \epsilon \xi^3$, $\eta^3 = -\epsilon \xi^2$ mit $\epsilon = \pm 1$ auftreten. In diesen ist (3.8) von der Form

$$B = \gamma^2 e^{\pm 2\chi} \qquad \ldots (3.11)$$

Im Normalfall aber gilt nach den Voraussetzungen jetzt

$$F(t) = (\alpha^2 + \beta^2)^{1/2} \cos (t\varphi - \varphi_0)$$
$$- \{\beta^2 + \gamma^2 + (\gamma^2 + \delta^2) \, \mathrm{Sh}^2 \, (t\chi - \chi_0)\}^{1/2} > 0 \qquad \ldots (3.12)$$

für die Werte $t = 0$ und $t = 1$. Nun findet man aber, dass $F''(t) < 0$ ist, solange wenigstens $\cos (t\varphi - \varphi_0) > 0$ ist. Dies ist aber für $0 \leqslant t \leqslant 1$ der Fall, weil $|\varphi_0| < \pi/2$ und $|\varphi - \varphi_0| < \pi/2$ ist. Also ist $F(t)$ in $0 \leqslant t \leqslant 1$ konvex, und es gilt dort

$$F(t) \geqslant tF(0) + (1-t)F(1) \geqslant \mathrm{Min} \, (F(0), F(1)) > 0 \qquad \ldots (3.13)$$

Nun folgt aus (3.13), immer für $0 \leqslant t \leqslant 1$, unter Verwendung von (3.6), (3.9) und (3.10)

$$(\eta(t\varphi, t\chi))^2 > (F(t))^2 \qquad \ldots (3.14)$$

währenddem

$$\eta^0(t\varphi, t\chi) > 0 \qquad \ldots (3.15)$$

nach (3.5) automatisch garantiert ist.

Der Spezialfall (3.11) erledigt sich offenbar analog (oder durch ein Stetigkeitsargument).

4. Die reellen Punkte in $\mathscr{R}_N{}'$ [30]

Mit dem Satz des letzten Abschnittes ist die Hauptschwierigkeit überwunden. Der Rest der Untersuchung besteht aus elementaren Folgerungen aus diesem. Natürlich werden wir die Funktion $W_\nu(\zeta_1 \cdots, \zeta_N)$ des Satzes mit einem der Vakuumerwartungswerte des 2. Abschnittes identifizieren. Es ist dann zu erwarten, dass die reellen Punkte in $\mathscr{R}_N{}'$ (das sind diejenigen Punkte, in welchen der Vakuumerwartungswert (2.2) und nicht erst dessen analytische Fortsetzung, falls eine solche möglich ist, regulär ist) eine besondere physikalische Bedeutung haben. Das trifft auch zu. Wir wollen sie mit $(\rho_1 \cdots, \rho_N)$ bezeichnen. Sie werden im folgenden Satz charakterisiert.

Satz: Der reelle Punkt $(\rho_1 \cdots, \rho_N)$ gehört genau dann zu $\mathscr{R}_N{}'$, falls für jede Wahl von nicht negativen λ_k mit nicht verschwindender Summe der Vektor $\lambda_1 \rho_1 + \cdots + \lambda_N \rho_N$ raumartig ist.

Beweis: Die Bedingung ist offenbar *notwendig*. Falls nämlich $(\rho_1 \cdots, \rho_N) \in \mathscr{R}_N'$, dann existiert $\Lambda \in L_+(C)$ derart, dass $\rho_k = \Lambda \zeta_k$ und $(\zeta_1 \cdots, \zeta_N) \in \mathscr{R}_N$. Weiter wird dann $(\sum \lambda_k \zeta_k)^2 = \zeta^2$ reell. $\zeta = \sum \lambda_k \zeta_k$ gehört aber zu $\mathscr{R}$, denn, da alle $\lambda_k \geqslant 0$ sind, liegt sein Imaginärteil in V_+. Man überzeugt sich jedoch leicht, dass die *reellen* Quadrate von Vektoren aus $\mathscr{R}$ negativ sind.

Die Bedingung ist *hinreichend*. Falls sie erfüllt ist, besteht der kleinste konvexe Kegel $\mathfrak{k}$, der alle ρ_e enthält, der also aus den Punkten $\xi = \sum \lambda_e \rho_e$ mit $\lambda_e \geqslant 0$ besteht, aus lauter raumartigen Vektoren. Er hat also mit dem Vorkegel V_+ und dem Nachkegel V_- nur die Spitze $\xi = 0$ gemein. Daher gibt es eine Tangentialebene $\alpha_\nu \xi^\nu = 0$ an V_+ die V_+ von $\mathfrak{k}$ separiert. Man hat etwa $\alpha_\nu \xi^\nu \geqslant 0$ für $\xi \in V_+$ und $\alpha_\nu \xi^\nu \leqslant 0$ für $\xi \in \mathfrak{k}$ und schliesslich $\alpha_\nu \xi^\nu \leqslant 0$ für $\xi \in V_-$. Ebenso erhält man eine Tangentialebene $\beta_\nu \xi^\nu = 0$ an V_-, die V^+ von $\mathfrak{k}$ separiert, derart dass $\beta_\nu \xi^\nu \geqslant 0$ für $\xi \in V_-$, $\beta_\nu \xi^\nu \leqslant 0$ für $\xi \in \mathfrak{k}$ und $\beta_\nu \xi_\nu \leqslant 0$ für $\xi \in V_+$. α und β sind Nullvektoren, die durch $(\alpha\beta) = -2$ normiert werden können. Es existiert dann eine Transformation $\Lambda \in L_+^\uparrow$, die α auf $(1, 1, 0, 0)$ und β auf $(-1, 1, 0, 0)$ abbildet. Nun ist für $\xi \in \mathfrak{k}$ erstens $\alpha_\nu \xi^\nu \leqslant 0$ und zweitens $\beta_\nu \xi^\nu \leqslant 0$, also $\xi^1 \geqslant \xi^0$ und $\xi^1 \geqslant -\xi^0$. Insbesondere gilt in diesem Koordinatensystem $\rho_e^1 > |\rho_e^0|$ für $l = 1, 2 \cdots N$.

Jetzt lässt sich leicht zeigen, dass die ρ_e in der Form $\rho_e = \Lambda^{-1} \zeta_e$ geschrieben werden können, wobei $(\zeta_1 \cdots, \zeta_N) \in \mathscr{R}_N$ und $\Lambda \in L_+(C)$. Man setze etwa

$$\zeta_e^0 = i\rho_e^1, \quad \zeta_e^1 = i\rho_e^0, \quad \zeta_e^2 = \rho_e^2, \quad \zeta_e^3 = \rho_e^3$$

oder $\zeta_e = \Lambda \rho_e$ mit

$$\Lambda = \begin{pmatrix} 0 & i & 0 & 0 \\ i & 0 & 0 & 0 \\ 0 & 0 & 1 & 0 \\ 0 & 0 & 0 & 1 \end{pmatrix} \in L_+(C).$$

Damit ist der Satz bewiesen.

Es scheint leider unbekannt zu sein, ob sich *ohne zusätzliche Annahmen* das im vorigen Abschnitt hergeleitete Regularitätsgebiet noch weiter vergrössern lässt. Sicher aber ist, dass durch eine solche Erweiterung die reellen Regularitätspunkte nicht betroffen werden. Dies, weil man leicht Funktionen angeben kann, die zwar in $\mathscr{R}_N'$ regulär sind aber in einem beliebig vorgegebenen reellen Punkt ausserhalb $\mathscr{R}_N'$ singulär werden. Es sei etwa $(\xi_1 \cdots, \xi_N)$ ein reeller Punkt ausserhalb $\mathscr{R}_N'$. Dann gibt es nach unserem *Satz* $\lambda_k \geqslant 0$ mit $\sum \lambda_k = 1$ so, dass $(\sum \lambda_k \xi_k)^2 = 0$ oder $(\sum \lambda_k \xi_k)^2 - 1 = 0$ wird. Die beiden Funktionen verschwinden in

$\mathscr{R}_N{}'$ nicht, wohl aber verschwindet eine davon im vorgegebenen Punkt. Die Reziproke von dieser ist die gesuchte Funktion.

5. Starke und schwache Lokalität, CPT Invarianz [30]

Unter der Lokalität versteht man die Forderung, dass physikalische Grössen, die durch lokale Operationen aus den Feldoperatoren aufgebaut sind, für raumartige Separation kommutieren. Eine etwas andere Forderung, aus der in vernünftigen Theorien die erste folgt, verlangt, dass zwei beliebige Feldoperatoren in Punkten, die durch eine raumartige Distanz getrennt sind, entweder kommutieren oder antikommutieren. Diese *starke Lokalität* führt zu einer Vergrösserung des Regularitätsgebietes der W-Funktionen. Zur Diskussion dieser Frage ist eine neue Bezeichnungsweise angebracht. Es sei

$$\mathscr{W}_\nu(x_0, x_1 \cdots, x_N) = \langle \overset{(0)}{\psi_{\nu_0}}(x_0) \overset{[(1)}{\psi_{\nu_1}}(x_1) \cdots \overset{(N)}{\psi_{\nu_N}}(x_N) \rangle_0 \quad \ldots (5.1)$$

und für komplexe Vektoren $(z_0, z_1 \cdots, z_N)$

$$\mathscr{W}_\nu(z_0, z_1 \cdots, z_N) = W_\nu(z_1 - z_0, z_2 - z_1 \cdots, z_N - z_{N-1}) \quad \ldots (5.2)$$

$\mathscr{W}$ ist regulär, falls $(z_1 - z_0, z_2 - z_1 \cdots, z_N - z_{N-1})$ in $\mathscr{R}_N{}'$ liegt. Das so für die Vektoren $(z_0, z_1 \cdots, z_N)$ definierte Gebiet bezeichnen wir mit $\mathfrak{S}_N{}'$, die darin enthaltenen reellen Punkte mit $(r_0, r_1 \cdots, r_N)$. Aus dem Satz des vorigen Abschnittes folgt, dass für $i \neq k$ $(r_i - r_k)^2 < 0$ ist. Doch ist dieses System von Ungleichungen im allgemeinen nicht charakterisierend. Die Lokalität hat daher zur Folge, dass

$$\langle \overset{(0)}{\psi_{\nu_0}}(r_0) \overset{(1)}{\psi_{\nu_1}}(r_1) \cdots \overset{(N)}{\psi_{\nu_N}}(r_N) \rangle_0 = \sigma \langle \overset{(k_0)}{\psi_{\nu_{k_0}}}(r_{k_0}) \overset{(k_1)}{\psi_{\nu_{k_1}}}(r_{k_1}) \cdots \overset{(k_N)}{\psi_{\nu_{k_N}}}(r_{k_N}) \rangle_0$$
$$\ldots (5.3)$$

ist, wobei σ die Signatur der Permutation der antikommutierenden Felder ist. In $\mathscr{W}$ Funktionen ausgedrückt lautet (5.3)

$$\mathscr{W}_\nu(r_0, r_1 \cdots, r_N) = \sigma \widetilde{\mathscr{W}}_{\bar\nu}(r_{k_0}, r_{k_1} \cdots, r_{k_N}) \quad \ldots (5.4)$$

$\widetilde{\mathscr{W}}_\nu$ gehört zu den permutierten Feldoperatoren. (5.4) lässt sich offenbar analytisch fortsetzen. So ergibt sich schliesslich mindestens Regularität der Funktionen im kleinsten, bezüglich den Permutationen von $z_0, z_1 \cdots, z_N$ invarianten Gebiet, das $\mathfrak{S}_N{}'$ enthält. Die Frage, ob dadurch die starke Lokalität ausgeschöpft sei, wollen wir nicht diskutieren. [37]

Nun gibt es aber unter den $(N+1)!$ Permutationen der z_k genau eine nicht triviale, die nicht zu einer Vergrösserung des Regulatitätsgebietes $\mathfrak{S}_N'$ Anlass gibt. Diese lautet

$$\langle \overset{(0)}{\psi_{\nu_0}}(r_0)\overset{(1)}{\psi_{\nu_1}}(r_1)\cdots \overset{(N)}{\psi_{\nu_N}}(r_N)\rangle_0 = \sigma\langle \overset{(N)}{\psi_{\nu_N}}(r_N)\cdots \overset{(1)}{\psi_{\nu_1}}(r_1)\overset{(0)}{\psi_{\nu_0}}(r_0)\rangle_0$$
$$\dots(5.5)$$

oder (in wohl klarer Bezeichnungsweise)

$$\overset{\rightarrow}{\mathscr{W}_\nu}(z_0, z_1\cdots, z_N) = \sigma\overset{\leftarrow}{\mathscr{W}_\nu}(z_N\cdots, z_1, z_0) \quad\dots(5.5')$$

Mit $(\zeta_1\cdots, \zeta_N) \in \mathscr{R}_N'$, $\zeta_k = z_k - z_{k-1}$ ist nämlich auch $(-\zeta_N, -\zeta_{N-1}, \cdots, -\zeta_1) \in \mathscr{R}_N'$, denn dieser Punkt geht durch PT in den Punkt $(\zeta_N, \zeta_{N-1}\cdots, \zeta_1)$ über und die Definition von $\mathscr{R}_N'$ ist symmetrisch in den Vektoren ζ_k. Falls in einer Theorie nur die Vertauschungsrelationen (5.5) bestehen (diese beziehen sich ausdrücklich auf die reellen Punkte von $\mathfrak{S}_N'$), dann soll sie *schwach lokal* heissen.

Es ist nun bemerkenswert, dass (5.5) zu einer Beziehung zwischen Vakuumerwartungswerten in *beliebigen Punkten* $x_0, x_1\cdots, x_N$ führt. Zunächst folgt nämlich aus (3.1) und unsern Definitionen mit $\Lambda = PT$ für die reellen Punkte aus $\mathfrak{S}_N'$

$$\langle \overset{(0)}{\psi_{\nu_0}}(r_0)\overset{(1)}{\psi_{\nu_1}}(r_1)\cdots \overset{(N)}{\psi_{\nu_N}}(r_N)\rangle_0 = (-1)^n\langle \overset{(0)}{\psi_{\nu_0}}(-r_0)\overset{(1)}{\psi_{\nu_1}}(-r_1)\cdots \overset{(N)}{\psi_{\nu_N}}(-r_N)\rangle_0$$

und mit (5.5)

$$= (-1)^n\sigma\langle \overset{(N)}{\psi_{\nu_N}}(-r_N)\cdots \overset{(1)}{\psi_1}(-r_1)\overset{(0)}{\psi_{\nu_0}}(-r_0)\rangle_0$$

schliesslich also

$$\langle \overset{(0)}{\psi_{\nu_0}}(r_0)\overset{(1)}{\psi_{\nu_1}}(r_1)\cdots \overset{(N)}{\psi_{\nu_N}}(r_N)\rangle_0 =$$
$$(-1)^n\sigma\langle \overset{(0)}{\psi_{\nu_0}}{}^\star(-r_0)\overset{(1)}{\psi_{\nu_1}}{}^\star(-r_1)\cdots \overset{(N)}{\psi_{\nu_N}}{}^\star(-r_N)\rangle_0{}^\star \quad\dots(5.6)$$

n bedeutet dabei die Zahl der unpunktierten Indizes, die in $(\nu_0, \nu_1\cdots, \nu_N)$ auftreten. (5.6) lässt sich aber analytisch fortsetzen. Man definiert dazu

$$\langle \overset{(0)}{\psi_{\nu_0}}{}^\star(x_0)\overset{(1)}{\psi_{\nu_1}}{}^\star(x_1)\cdots \psi_{\nu_N}{}^\star(x_N)\rangle_0 = \tilde{W}_\nu(\xi_1\cdots, \xi_N) \quad\dots(5.7)$$

worauf (5.6) von der folgenden Form

$$W_\nu(\zeta_1\cdots, \zeta_N) = (-1)^n\sigma\tilde{W}_\nu{}^\star(-\zeta_1{}^\star\cdots, -\zeta_N{}^\star) \quad\dots(5.8)$$

für $\zeta_k = \rho_k$ wird. Dadurch ist die analytische Fortsetzung evident. Das Wesentliche an der Abbildung $\zeta_k \to -\zeta_k{}^\star$ ist die Tatsache, dass sie $\mathscr{R}_N$ auf sich selbst abbildet. Daher kann man in (5.8) auf beiden Seiten zum reellen Rand von $\mathscr{R}$ gehen und findet mit (5.7) und (5.1) die gesuchte Beziehung

$$\langle \overset{(0)}{\psi_{\nu_0}}(x_0)\overset{(1)}{\psi_{\nu_1}}(x_1)\cdots \overset{(N)}{\psi_{\nu_N}}(x_N)\rangle_0 =$$

$$(-1)^n\sigma\langle \overset{(N)}{\psi_{\nu_N}}(-x_N)\cdots \overset{(1)}{\psi_{\nu_1}}(-x_1)\overset{(0)}{\psi_{\nu_0}}(-x_0)\rangle_0 \quad \ldots(5.9)$$

Zu der Ableitung, die von (5.5) zu (5.9) führte, muss das folgende bemerkt werden

(1) Es genügt (5.5) in einer reellen Umgebung eines beliebigen Punktes $(r_0, r_1\cdots, r_N)$ als gültig anzunehmen, dann folgt (5.5) für beliebige $(r_0, r_1\cdots, r_N)$ durch analytische Fortsetzung.

(2) Aus (5.9) kann umgekehrt (5.5) abgeleitet werden. Dazu setze man in (5.9) für $(x_0, x_1\cdots, x_N)$ den Punkt $(r_0, r_1\cdots, r_N)$ und verwende eine zur ersten Gleichung nach (5.5) analoge Gleichung. Die Gleichungen (5.5) und (5.9) sind also äquivalent.

(3) Falls es gelingt, eine Transformation $\theta\psi = \psi'$ so zu finden, dass sich die rechte Seite von (5.9) als $\langle \overset{(N)}{\psi_{\nu_N}}'(x_N)\cdots \overset{(1)}{\psi_{\nu_1}}'(x_1)\overset{(0)}{\psi_{\nu_0}}'(x_0)\rangle_0$ schreiben lässt, dann ist θ ein Anti-Automorphismus (Automorphismus abgesehen von der Umkehrung der Faktorenreihenfolge) der Theorie.* Bei weitem die wichtigste Wahl von θ ist die von Pauli zuerst allgemein gefundene Transformation

$$\psi_{\nu}'(x) = \theta\psi_{\nu}(x) = (-1)^n\psi_{\nu}(-x) \quad \text{für eindeutige Darstellung}$$

$$\psi_{\nu}'(x) = \theta\psi_{\nu}(x) = i(-1)^n\psi_{\nu}(-x) \quad \text{für zweideutige Darstellung.}$$

$$\ldots(5.10)$$

Dieses θ hat die wesentliche Eigenschaft, dass $\theta\psi^\star = (\theta\psi)^\star$ wird, dass also möglicherweise vorhandene Realitätseigenschaften auch nach der Transformation erhalten bleiben.† Natürlich gehört die Forderung, dass θ ein Anti-Automorphismus der Theorie sei, zu einer bestimmten Wahl von σ in (5.5). Aus den Gleichungen

---

* In andern Worten: Die Theorie ist bezüglich der *antiunitären* Transformation $\overset{\circ}{\theta}\psi = \psi'^\star = \psi^0$ invariant, denn die rechte Seite von (5.9) schreibt sich dann:

$$\langle \overset{(0)}{\psi_{\nu_0}}{}^0(x_0)\overset{(1)}{\psi_{\nu_1}}{}^0(x_1)\cdots \overset{(N)}{\psi_{\nu_N}}{}^0(x_N)\rangle^\star$$

† Die scheinbar natürlichste Festlegung $\psi_{\nu}'(x) = \overset{\circ}{\theta}\psi_{\nu}(x) = (-1)^n\psi_{\nu}(-x)$ für alle Felder und $\sigma = 1$ in (5.5) widerspricht dieser Forderung, wie wir im 1. Abschnitt gesehen haben. Ausserdem werden wir im nächsten Abschnitt sehen, dass der Wert von σ in (5.5) nicht willkürlich ist, sondern Einschränkungen unterliegt, die wesentlich von der positiv definiten Metrik im Raum der Zustände herrühren. Diese Einschränkungen verbieten in normalen Theorien das obige $\overset{\circ}{\theta}$.

$$\langle \overset{(0)}{\psi_{\nu_0}}(x_0)\overset{(1)}{\psi_{\nu_1}}(x_1) \cdots \overset{(N)}{\psi_{\nu_N}}(x_N)\rangle_0 = \langle \overset{(N)}{\psi_{\nu_N}}'(x_N) \cdots \overset{(1)}{\psi_{\nu_1}}'(x_1)\overset{(0)}{\psi_{\nu_0}}'(x_0)\rangle_0$$

$$\dots(5.11)$$

folgt mit (5.10) und (5.9) $\sigma = -1$, falls die Zahl der zweideutigen Felder in (5.5) das doppelte einer ungeraden Zahl ist, und $\sigma = +1$, falls die Zahl der zweideutigen Felder in (5.5) durch 4 teilbar ist. Andere Fälle treten nicht auf, weil die Vakuumerwartungswerte mit ungerader Zahl von zweideutigen Feldern verschwinden. Dieser Wert von σ stimmt mit der Signatur der Permutation überein, welche die zweideutigen Felder in der Gleichung (5.5) erfahren. Wir haben also das

CTP Theorem: Die Vertauschungsrelationen (5.5), wobei σ die Signatur der Permutation der Felder zu zweideutigen Darstellungen ist, sind äquivalent zu den Gleichungen (5.11), wo die gestrichenen Felder durch (5.10) definiert sind.

(4) Wir bleiben nun bei dieser Wahl von σ und diskutieren kurz die schwache Lokalität. Es ist wohlbekannt, dass das Hauptproblem mathematischer Natur der Feldtheorie darin besteht, zu entscheiden, ob die allgemeinen Postulate der Quantentheorie zusammen mit der (starken) Lokalität überhaupt eine nicht triviale Lösung zulassen. Dabei bedeutet 'nicht trivial', dass etwa die Streumatrix von der Einheitsmatrix verschieden ist. Es ist überflüssig, auf den deprimierenden Stand unserer Kenntnisse in dieser Frage hinzuweisen.

Für die schwache Lokalität *stellt sich dieses Problem nicht*. Diese ist nach dem oben abgeleiteten Theorem vollständig äquivalent zur Symmetrie θ. Von dieser aber kann man leicht zeigen, dass sie mit den übrigen Postulaten der Quantentheorie verträglich ist. So lässt sich jede CTP invariante Streumatrix durch Felder extrapolieren, die (5.11) erfüllen, also schwach lokal sind.[28]

Die starke Lokalität führt im Gegensatz dazu nicht zu Symmetrieeigenschaften der Streumatrix, sondern zu Analyzitätseigenschaften der Matrixelemente die man in etwas erweitertem Sinn als Dispersionsrelationen bezeichnen kann.[28,34]

6. Der Zusammenhang zwischen Spin und Statistik[31]

Währenddem der Wert von σ in (5.5) bisher unbestimmt blieb, gibt der Satz von Spin und Statistik in seiner engsten Fassung darüber Auskunft, welchen Wert σ für den Vakuumerwartungswert des Produktes von einem Feld mit seinem konjugiert komplexen haben kann. Daraus folgt dann, welche Felder $\psi_\nu(x)$

sicher nicht mit $\psi_\mu{}^\star(y)$ für raumartige Separationen kommutieren können.

In diesem Abschnitt wird zum ersten Male die Positivität des Skalarproduktes wesentlich ausgenützt. Zwar wurde schon im 5. Abschnitt das konjugiert komplexe $\psi^\star$ eines Feldes ψ benutzt. Was aber eigentlich gebraucht wurde, war lediglich die Existenz eines *hermiteschen* Skalarprodukts.

Es gilt der folgende

Satz: ν stehe für $\alpha_1 \cdots \alpha_n, \dot\beta_1 \cdots \dot\beta_m$. Aus der schwachen Vertauschungsrelation

$$\langle \psi_\nu{}^\star(x)\psi_\mu(y)\rangle_0 = (-1)^{n+m+1}\langle \psi_\mu(y)\psi_\nu{}^\star(x)\rangle_0 \qquad \ldots (6.1)$$

für $(x-y)^2 < 0$ folgt

$$\psi_\nu(x)\Omega = \psi_\mu{}^\star(x)\Omega = 0 \qquad \ldots (6.2)$$

Dabei bedeutet Ω den Zustand des Vakuums.

Bemerkungen: (1) (6.1) ist tatsächlich eine schwache Vertauschungrelation, denn nach dem *Satz* im 4. Abschnitt sind die reellen Vektoren in $\mathscr{R}'$ identisch mit den raumartigen Vektoren.

(2) (6.2) steht als Abkürzung für die Gleichung

$$\psi(f)\Omega = \psi^\star(f)\Omega = 0 \qquad \ldots (6.2')$$

wobei

$$\psi(f) = \int f^\mu(x)\psi_\mu(x)\,\mathrm{d}^4x \qquad \ldots (6.3)$$

und

$$\psi^\star(f) = \int f^{\mu\star}(x)\psi_\mu{}^\star(x)\,\mathrm{d}^4x \qquad \ldots (6.3')$$

mit zulässigen Testfunktionen gemittelte Operatoren sind.

Beweis: Aus (6.1) und (5.9) folgt

$$\langle \psi_\nu{}^\star(x)\psi_\mu(y)\rangle_0 = -\langle \psi_\mu(-y)\psi_\nu{}^\star(-x)\rangle_0 \qquad \ldots (6.4)$$

für beliebige x und y. Multipliziert man beide Seiten mit $f^{\nu\star}(x)f^\mu(y)$ und integriert über x und y, so steht

$$\|\psi(f)\Omega\|^2 = -\|\psi^\star(g)\Omega\|^2 \qquad \ldots (6.5)$$

da $g^\mu(x)$ ist für $f^{\mu\star}(-x)$ gesetzt. Aus (6.5) folgt die Behauptung.*

Unser Satz enthält ein wesentliches Element über den Zusammenhang von Spin mit Statistik, indem er aussagt, dass ein *eindeutiges* Feld, welches

$$\langle [\psi_\nu{}^\star(x), \psi_\mu(y)]_+\rangle_0 = 0 \quad \text{für} \quad (x-y)^2 < 0$$

---

* Diese Schlussweise lässt sich offenbar auf spezielle Vakuumerwartungswerte mit mehreren Faktoren verallgemeinern. Es ist mir unbekannt, wohin eine solche Verallgemeinerung führt.

erfüllt, das Vakuum annihiliert. Dasselbe ist wahr für ein *zweideutiges* Feld, bei welchem, wieder falls $(x-y)^2 < 0$,

$$\langle [\psi_\nu{}^\star(x), \psi_\mu(y)]_-\rangle_0 = 0$$

ist.

Ohne Zusatzannahmen scheint man aber nicht den erwünschten Schluss ziehen zu können, nämlich dass aus (6.4) das *Verschwinden* des Feldes $\psi_\nu(x)$ folgt.

Als solche Zusatzannahme kann man etwa das Postulat der *starken Lokalität* verwenden, nach welchem Feldoperatoren bei raumartiger Separation entweder kommutieren oder antikommutieren. Wir haben dann die

Folgerung: Aus der starken Lokalität und aus (6.1) folgt $\psi_\nu(x) = 0$.

Beweis: Zunächst folgt (6.2) und daraus für die reellen Punkte in $\mathfrak{S}_n{}'$

$$\langle \varphi_0(r_0)\varphi_1(r_1)\cdots \psi_\mu(r_k)\cdots \varphi_N(r_N)\rangle_0 =$$
$$\sigma\langle \varphi_0(r_0)\varphi_1(r_1)\cdots \varphi_N(r_N)\psi_\mu(r_k)\rangle_0 = 0 \quad \ldots (6.6)$$

Dabei ist σ ein Vorzeichen und φ_e sind beliebige andere Felder der Theorie. Da $(r_0, r_1 \cdots, r_N)$ ein Regularitätspunkt der linken Seite von (6.6) ist, folgt allgemein

$$\langle \varphi_0(x_0)\varphi_1(x_1)\cdots \psi_\mu(x_k)\cdots \varphi_N(x_N)\rangle_0 = 0 \quad \ldots (6.7)$$

Es verschwinden also alle Vakuumerwartungswerte, die das Feld ψ_μ als Faktor enthalten. Damit verschwindet auch ψ_μ.

Man kann die *Folgerung* natürlich noch durch andere zusätzliche Annahmen erzwingen. Nicht sehr einleuchtend scheint es, (6.2) durch ein Postulat für unmöglich zu erklären. Falls man dagegen bereit ist, für die Felder eine Asymptotenbedingung[28] zu verlangen, so stellt (6.2) einen Widerspruch dar. Man hat weiter den Vorteil, dass man von Teilchen sprechen kann und die Folgerung wirklich etwas mit Statistik zu tun hat.

Wir möchten aber eher die Meinung vertreten, dass sich die Frage, ob die positive Metrik sich mit der (starken) Lokalität verträgt, eben doch nicht auf die Dauer zur Seite schieben lässt. Schwächt man die Lokalität ab, so hat man einen viel zu weiten Rahmen, in dem es allerdings keine Widersprüche gibt, der aber auch keine interessanten Schlüsse mehr zulässt. Vergisst man die positive Metrik, so bleibt freilich noch viel Schwieriges zu tun übrig,[35] schafft man sie aber ab, so läuft man Gefahr, dass der ganze, scheinbar gesicherte Grund in einem Meer von Willkür untergeht.

Dass aber der Satz von Spin und Statistik in merkwürdiger

Weise die starke Lokalität und die positive Metrik als Voraussetzung benützt, möchte man gerne als ein Zeichen dafür hinnehmen, dass die Beschäftigung mit ihm auch weiterhin fruchtbar bleibt—nachdem er lange Zeit der getreue Gefährte eines grossen Physikers war. Dieser Artikel wurde im November 1958 fertig geschrieben und war als Gabe zum 60. Geburtstag von W. Pauli gedacht. Der Verfasser konnte sich nach dem unerwarteten Hinscheiden von Wolfgang Pauli nicht zu einer Umarbeitung entschliessen.

LITERATUR

1. Heisenberg, W. und Pauli, W. *Z. Phys.* **56**, 1, 1929: **59**, 168, 1930
2. Dirac, P. A. M. *Proc. Roy. Soc. A* **114**, 243, 1927
3. Jordan, P. *Z. Phys.* **44**, 473, 1927
4. Jordan, P. und Wigner, E. *Z. Phys.* **47**, 631, 1928
5. Jordan, P. und Pauli, W. *Z. Phys.* **47**, 151, 1928
6. Heisenberg, W. *Z. Phys.* **43**, 172, 1927
7. Jordan, P. *Ergebn. exakt. Naturw.* **7**, 206, 1928
8. Pauli, W. *Handbuch der Physik*, 2. Auflage Bd. 24/1. p. 258
9. Bohr, N. und Rosenfeld, L. *Mat.-fys. Medd.* **12**, No. 8, 1933
10. l.c. 8) p. 256
11. Pauli, W. und Weisskopf, V. *Helv. phys. Acta* **7**, 709, 1934
12. Pauli, W. *Ann. Inst. Poincaré* **6**, 137, 1936
13. Dirac, P. A. M. *Proc. Roy. Soc. A* **155**, 447, 1936
14. Fierz, M. *Helv. phys. Acta* **12**, 3, 1939; **23**, 412, 1950
15. Wigner, E. *Ann. Math., Princeton*, **40**, 149, 1939
    Bargmann, V. und Wigner, E. *Proc. Nat. Acad. Sci., Wash.* **34**, 211, 1948
    Wigner, E. *Z. Phys.* **124**, 665, 1947
16. Pauli, W. *Phys. Rev.* **58**, 716, 1940
17. Pauli, W. und Belinfante, F. J. *Physica* **7**, 177, 1940
18. Feynman, R. P. *Phys. Rev.* **76**, 749, 1949
19. Pauli, W. *Progr. theor. Phys., Osaka* **15**, 145, 1943
20. Pauli, W. *Revs. mod. Phys.* **15**, 145, 1943
21. Källén, G. *Encyclopedia of Physics* Bd. 5/1 p. 199
22. Schwinger, J. *Phys. Rev.* **82**, 914, 1951
23. Wigner, E. *Nachr. Ges. Wiss. Göttingen* **1932**, 546
24. Lüders, G. *Mat.-fys. Medd.* **28**, No. 5, 1954
25. Pauli, W. *Niels Bohr and the Development of Physics*, p. 30. 1955. London
26. Lüders, G. *Z. Naturf.* **13a**, 254, 1958
27. Klein, O. *J. Phys. Radium* **9**, 1938 insbesondere p. 7
28. Lehmann, H., Symanzik, R. and Zimmermann, W. *Nuovo Cim.* **6**, 319, 1957 und frühere Arbeiten
29. Wightman, A. *Phys. Rev.* **101**, 860, 1956
    Hall, D. und Wightman, A. *Mat.-fys. Medd.* **31**, No. 5, 1957
30. Jost, R. *Helv. phys. Acta* **30**, 409, 1957
31. Burgoyne, N. *Nuovo Cim.* **8**, 607, 1958
32. l. c. 21) p. 196
33. v. d. Waerden, B. L. *Die gruppentheoretische Methode.* 1932. Berlin
34. Aus der sehr reichhaltigen Literatur über diesen Gegenstand
    Lehmann, H. *Nuovo Cim.* **10**, 579, 1958
35. Källén, G. und Wightman, A. *Mat. Fys. Skr.* **1**, No. 6, 1958
36. Jost, R. *Helv. phys. Acta* Pauli Heft
37. Dazu Ruelle, D. *Helv. phys. Acta* **32**, 135, 1959

PAULI AND THE THEORY OF THE SOLID STATE

H. B. G. CASIMIR

*'Ich mag diese Physik des festen Körpers
nicht ... zwar habe ich damit angefangen'
(I don't like this solid state physics ... I
initiated it though)*

The foregoing quotation summarizes Pauli's attitude towards solid state physics. As a matter of fact it was one of the few subjects in physics—gas discharges and the theory of the chemical bond were others—towards which he showed a profound dislike. Of course Pauli was mainly occupied with really fundamental problems but this might only explain his lack of interest not his antipathy. Applied science for instance he treated with humorous condescension and he could be thoroughly amused when according to his own saying he had not understood one single word of a lecture on advanced design of thermionic valves or some similar subject. What irritated him in solid state physics was the lack of mathematical rigour and logical completeness and the introduction of vaguely defined models that are tantamount to unverifiable mathematical hypotheses and are only of value when used in conjunction with an intelligent classification of a mass of experimental data. On the other hand he admired Onsager's work on order–disorder transitions: there the model, though primitive, is well defined, the mathematical problem challenging and Onsager's solution a masterpiece.

And yet he claimed—almost ruefully—to have started the subject. Now since solid state physics endeavours to explain the properties of solids from first principles it is obvious that anyone who has made important contributions to the basic ideas of quantum mechanics has also had a far-reaching influence on the development of solid state physics, and from this point of view Pauli's influence may have been even greater than he supposed. More specifically we may mention the Pauli principle which in its wave-mechanical form is at the bottom of the very notions of

137

electron bands and holes; Pauli's wave-mechanical theory of
electron spins that clarifies and extends previous work, and is
essential in all work on paramagnetic resonance; and finally the
idea of nuclear spin which after a lengthy and somewhat subdued
career in spectroscopy suddenly blossomed into a surprisingly
fruitful activity by the discovery of nuclear spin resonance. But
Pauli was not thinking of this general type of influence: he was
referring to one single paper on the paramagnetism of free
electrons.* As a matter of fact this paper has played a major
part in the development of the theory of solids. We shall try to
discuss its significance in some detail.

In 1926 when Pauli wrote his one and only solid state paper the
theoretical framework of quantum theory was rapidly nearing
completion. One by one the curious extrapolations of older
quantum theory that had been obtained by painstaking analysis
of spectroscopical data were reduced to first principles. Heisenberg had shown how Pauli's exclusion principle could be incorporated into the wave-mechanics of many-particle systems;
among the results was the explanation of the absence of paramagnetism in the ground state of helium. On the other hand
ideas concerning the quantum mechanical treatment of the
statistics of gases were unsettled. Both the Bose–Einstein
statistics and the Fermi–Dirac statistics were known but they
were more or less regarded as equivalent possibilities and it was a
moot question whether the one or the other would describe the
behaviour of a material gas. Pauli's paper is essentially a contribution to this discussion. He reasons that Heisenberg's work on
the helium spectrum is a strong argument in favour of applying
Fermi–Dirac statistics to an electron gas and then proceeds to
discuss such an ideal gas as a rough model for the electrons in a
metal; his primary object is not the discussion of the properties
of metals in the light of the new quantum mechanics but rather the
construction of a test case.

Pauli's mathematical treatment of quantum statistics shows his
usual mastership. He applies the methods of Gibbs and notably
the 'grand ensemble', a chapter at which many students of statistical mechanics had been looking askance—if at all. He explains
in some detail that just as the introduction of a canonical ensemble
serves to deal with the condition $E = \sum \epsilon_s = \text{constant}$, the introduc-
tion of a grand ensemble eliminates the condition $N = \sum n_s = \text{constant}$. Once he has established the formalism he can easily
generalize Fermi–Dirac statistics for particles with spin. There

* Z. Phys. **41**, 81, 1927.

can be no doubt that this is by far the most elegant and straight-forward method of dealing with quantum statistics and it is surprising that several subsequent authors have preferred other methods that are far more clumsy and laborious.

As late as 1938 H. A. Kramers sought to remedy this situation by a paper 'Didaktisches zur Verwendung der Grand Ensembles in der Statistik'.*

The sections on the general formalism of quantum statistics are followed by a calculation of the magnetic susceptibility. He finds a weak temperature-independent paramagnetism that is of the same order of magnitude as the expected diamagnetism of the atoms so that the total susceptibility of a non-ferromagnetic metal may be either positive or negative but always of the same order of magnitude. This is in agreement with experiments.

Pauli does not clinch the argument, however. He does not state explicitly that electrons do in fact obey Fermi–Dirac statistics whereas Bose–Einstein statistics remain possible for other gases—this he corrects in a footnote to a later publication—and although he points out that the electron gas is fully degenerate he fails to remark that this explains why the conduction electrons give no appreciable contribution to the specific heat.

It was left to Sommerfeld to fully appreciate the implications of Pauli's ideas. Starting where Lorentz had left off and introducing Pauli's idea of a Fermi gas of electrons, he could show that many of the outstanding difficulties of the older theory automatically disappeared. Soon afterwards Bloch initiated the study of electron wave functions in a periodic potential. From then on solid state physics has been a rapidly growing branch of science. Its adepts will gratefully acknowledge their indebtedness to Pauli's pioneer work. Let us try also to obviate those features that Pauli found objectionable.

In preparing this note I have been greatly assisted by Dr. H. J. G. Meyer to whom I want to express my sincere thanks.

* *Proc. Acad. Sci. Amst.* **41**, 10, 1938; collected papers p. 738.

QUANTUM THEORY OF SOLIDS

R. E. PEIERLS

This article will deal with the quantum theory of solids, and will single out for attention those parts of the subject in which Pauli's work has exerted a major influence.

In enumerating the branches of physics to which Pauli made important contributions, one is liable to overlook the theory of solids, both because his papers on the subject were not numerous, and because he was often critical of the study of solids as a serious part of theoretical physics. A field in which it is often necessary to make crude assumptions if one wants to gain an insight into the essential features of a problem, and in which it is the fashion to make much cruder assumptions than necessary, was bound to offend his high standards; but he started off important trains of thought in many of these problems and took a close interest in many more.

It is probably no exaggeration to say that the modern electron theory of metals was started by Pauli's paper on the paramagnetism of an electron gas.[1] Let us remember the situation at the time this paper was written. The evidence then already indicated clearly that the carriers of electricity in metals had to be electrons. Perhaps the most direct argument came from the acceleration experiments, which determined directly the mass-to-charge ratio of the carriers. Many authors had therefore attempted to apply the known laws of mechanics and of thermodynamics to the motion of electrons in metals.

The result of these studies was a very tantalizing situation in which for every prediction which agreed with observation, there were others which disagreed completely; for every argument which appeared to lead to a reasonable determination of one of the parameters in the theory from the experimental data, there were others yielding completely different values.

For example, the high conductivities of typical metals suggested that the electron density in a metal was high, of the order of one electron per atom. The conductivity of an electron gas is given by

$$\sigma = \tfrac{1}{3}e^2 n\tau/m$$

where e and m are the charge and mass of the carriers, n their number per unit volume, and τ the collision time, which may be expressed as l/v, where v is the velocity of the carriers, and l their mean free path. If one took n to be equal to the number of valence electrons, and v as the thermal velocity, the observed conductivities required mean free paths of the order of ten times the lattice spacing or more, even at room temperature, and it was hard to believe that l could be much larger in order of magnitude.

This was supported by the order of magnitude of the Hall coefficient, which measures the transverse potential produced in a current-carrying conductor by a transverse magnetic field. This is proportional to $1/ne$. For some metals this coefficient had the opposite sign to the one expected for negative carriers, and this was a difficulty, but the magnitude was almost invariably that corresponding to one or a few electrons per atom.

In this case one would have expected a contribution to the specific heat from the electrons. According to the equi-partition law, each electron should have contributed $\tfrac{3}{2}k$ to the specific heat of a metal, and with one electron per atom this would have given an excess of 50 per cent over the Dulong–Petit value; but the specific heats of all metals were in excellent agreement with the Dulong–Petit law at high temperatures and showed the decrease expected from the Debye theory at low temperatures.

One might have tried to put the blame on the use of kinetic theory for the electrons; perhaps the kinetic energy of the electrons for some reason did not grow with temperature as expected. This appeared to be contradicted by the value of the Wiedemann–Franz coefficient, which measures the ratio of thermal to electrical conductivity, and therefore the ratio of the thermal energy carried by the conduction electrons to their charge. The value of this coefficient was in reasonable agreement with that predicted from kinetic theory.

Another serious disagreement related to the magnetic properties of metals. The presence of free electrons with spins suggested a paramagnetic behaviour following Curie's law, with a constant depending only on the electron density. Many metals do indeed show a paramagnetic susceptibility, but it is practically independent of temperature, instead of being inversely proportional to the absolute temperature as required by Curie's law, and very much less in magnitude than predicted at room temperature for about one electron per atom.

At this time, Pauli's exclusion principle had already proved itself in the description of atomic structure, and Fermi[2] had discussed the consequences of assuming the same principle to hold for the particles of a gas. It seems that Fermi had in mind an ordinary gas of atoms or molecules, for which the quantum corrections are rather academic, except at extremely low temperatures, and it was also not realized that the exclusion principle, and hence Fermi's statistics, would apply only to some particles and not to others.

Pauli's further decisive step was to realize the importance of the modified statistics for electrons in metals. On the one hand, the exclusion principle certainly applied to the different electrons within an atom, and to be consistent it was required that it should also hold for the 'free' electrons in a metal. Secondly, the low mass and high number-density of the electrons meant that the degeneracy was, even at room temperature, a very major effect.

Pauli therefore applied the new kind of statistics to the problem of electron paramagnetism. For this purpose he re-derived Fermi's result using the method of the grand ensemble, which was then not very widely used, and whose basis he therefore set out very clearly (Fermi had used the more customary derivation employing Stirling's theorem which, when the number of particles per state is only 1 or 2, is open to serious objection). The result generalizes readily to the case in which there is a magnetic field present. The magnetic susceptibility per electron is

$$\frac{3\mu^2}{2E_0}$$

where μ is the Bohr magneton, and E_0 the limiting energy of the Fermi distribution (chemical potential). This differs from the Curie value by a factor $2kT/3E_0$, and thus accounts both for the temperature independence and for the smaller magnitude of the effect, since E_0 is for most metals of the order of a few electron volts and hence much larger than kT at room temperature.

This result is easy to understand qualitatively; the exclusion principle allows two electrons of opposite spin direction to occupy the same orbital state. If one of these electrons is to reverse its spin in response to the field, this requires it to go into a state of orbital motion not already containing an electron of the favoured spin direction. Such a transition will not take place if the energy difference between the orbital states is greater than kT, so that only those electrons within an energy kT of the highest occupied state are free to follow the field. Their number is of the order of kT/E_0 of the total, and therefore the Curie susceptibility is multiplied by a factor of this kind.

This result now fitted the orders of magnitude of the susceptibilities of many paramagnetic metals. Exact agreement was not to be expected, as Pauli stressed, because the treatment of the electrons as a perfect Fermi gas was only a crude approximation. We shall return later to some of the important corrections to paramagnetism.

Nevertheless the result demonstrated that the new statistics were capable of removing some of the old contradictions in the electron theory of metals. It encouraged Sommerfeld[3] to calculate the specific heat of metals on the same basis. Again this was found to be reduced from the equi-partition value by a factor of the order of kT/E_0, since only the electrons within a distance kT of the top of the Fermi distribution are capable of making transitions to states of an energy which is about kT higher. Thus the absence of a large electronic contribution to the specific heat was immediately explained. The electronic specific heat becomes easily observable at very low temperatures, at which the lattice contribution obeys Debye's T^3 law so that the electronic part, which is linear in the temperature, becomes ultimately dominant.

Sommerfeld and his collaborators[4] also tried to extend this new approach to the transport phenomena in metals, but here some serious difficulties remained. On the new view the current was carried mainly by electrons at the edge of the Fermi distribution, and their velocity was therefore much greater than the thermal velocity under equi-partition. The collision time estimated from the observed conductivity therefore corresponded to an even greater mean free path, which was hard to understand. Moreover, the conventional idea of collisions with the atoms suggested a mean free path independent of the temperature, and hence a temperature-independent conductivity in place of a variation with the inverse square root of the temperature, which was already too slow compared with the observed behaviour as $1/T$ at high temperatures, let alone the much faster variation found at low temperatures. The anomalous sign of the Hall effect and of some of the other galvanomagnetic and similar coefficients found in certain metals, as well as the existence of an appreciable magneto-resistance effect, remained unexplained.

The next important step was taken by Bloch,[5] who studied the motion of electrons in a periodic field. He showed that the periodicity of a perfect lattice resulted in electron wave functions which were like those of free electrons, except for a modulating factor of the same periodicity as the lattice itself. It followed that electrons could move through a perfect lattice with a non-vanishing mean velocity (though this was in general smaller than for free electrons of the same energy) in the absence of an accelerating field. In other words, the conductivity of electrons in a perfect lattice was infinitely large, the resistance therefore due only to the deviations from perfect periodicity. Hence there are two main causes of electric resistivity: lattice imperfections and impurities, and the thermal vibrations of the lattice. This was in accord with the experience that the resistance of a metal was enhanced by impurities and by mechanical distortion of the crystal lattice, and with the high resistivity of alloys. The 'ideal' resistivity, which remained after the elimination of these secondary effects, was evidently temperature dependent. Above the Debye temperature, when the lattice vibrations are effectively classical, the intensity of the vibrations is proportional to T, hence the proportionality of the resistance to T in this region was immediately understood.

At low temperatures one might at first have expected that, by analogy with the scattering of X-rays, the zero-point motion of the lattice should give a finite resistivity even at zero temperature. Bloch showed that this analogy was misleading. The resistance depends on collisions in which the electron is deflected from its path, and therefore requires a change of momentum. Since even in the periodic lattice momentum is conserved except for multiples of certain basic momentum vectors (corresponding to Bragg reflections), a change of momentum of an electron requires the creation or absorption of one quantum of vibration, or phonon, which is necessarily accompanied by a transfer of energy. This is easy in the case of X-rays, whose energy is very large compared to the phonon energies; but it cannot happen with electrons which are themselves in thermal equilibrium with the lattice. No phonons of energy greater than kT are normally present, so none can be absorbed, and none can be produced because no electron can lose more than kT in energy without making a transition to an already occupied state. Hence the only possible processes are the creation and absorption of phonons of energy below kT, and these contribute equally.

The number of such 'collisions' is proportional to T^3, like the mean phonon number. However, at very low temperatures we are concerned with long-wave phonons, of a momentum proportional to kT. In a collision process in which such a phonon is produced or absorbed, the electron is therefore deflected only by an angle of the order kT/cp_0, if c is the velocity of sound, and p_0 the momentum of an electron at the edge of the Fermi distribution. Since the deflections in successive collisions are in random directions, the resultant deflection grows only as the root of the number of collisions, and a small-angle collision is therefore contributing to the resistance an amount proportional to the square of the angle. From this consideration Bloch derived a T^5 law for the 'ideal' resistance at low temperatures.

The anomalous sign of the Hall coefficient, and of some other mixed transport phenomena, found its explanation in an idea due to Heisenberg, which started from the remark that a substance in which each atom had a closed-shell configuration, i.e. in which the highest occupied shell contained as many electrons as the Pauli principle allowed, could not be a conductor of electricity, since electrons could move in it only by transferring to a state of higher energy, which required a finite amount of excitation energy. If the number of electrons was just a little less than necessary to fill the shell completely in all atoms, the remaining vacancies or 'holes' could be exchanged and in effect the current was then carried by the holes, which were carriers of positive charge.

At Heisenberg's suggestion, Peierls [6] followed up the details of this picture and verified that a positive Hall effect would result.

At first this conclusion seemed convincing only in the case of tightly bound electrons, in which one could picture the electrons as moving for most of the time in atomic orbits, and only occasionally transferring to an equivalent orbit in an adjacent atom. In this model the energy levels for the electrons are substantially the atomic levels, but somewhat broadened into 'bands' by the motion from atom to atom. In such a model it was therefore clear that one had the possibility of saturation. If there were just enough electrons to fill a number of these bands, with the higher ones empty, no conduction could result unless one imparted to some electrons enough energy to make a transition to the next band. Such a substance would be an insulator, and if the number of electrons was somewhat less hole conductivity would result.

It was not clear, however, how this picture could be applied to a more realistic case, in which the disturbance of the atomic orbits by the neighbouring atoms was a major effect. It was shown by Peierls [7] that in the opposite extreme, namely practically free electrons with only a weak periodic potential due to the atoms in the lattice, discontinuities appeared for those electron momenta for which the Bragg conditions for diffraction by the lattice were satisfied. In a one-dimensional metal this would always give rise to bands separated by energy gaps, and indeed a one-dimensional 'metal' with a chain of equi-distant atoms would always have to be an insulator for an even number of electrons per atom.

In three dimensions the position of the gap would depend on the direction of motion of the electron, and for a very weak potential the highest energy of one band would in general exceed the lowest energy of the next band; but it was clear that the question whether or not the bands were energetically separated depended on the quantitative details of the lattice symmetry and the field of force, and the possibility of an energy gap was not confined to the extreme tight-binding limit.

Brillouin[8] explored fully how the Bragg reflections for nearly free electrons led to gaps which defined for each type of structure the characteristic 'zones' in momentum space.

Wilson[9] showed how a semiconductor, i.e. a substance in which the number of carriers varied exponentially with the temperature, could be interpreted as a case in which the energy gap between the last completely filled and the next, empty, band was small enough for electrons to be raised across it by thermal excitation (intrinsic semiconductor). He also showed that an alternative, and practically more common, possibility was a substance with a wider gap, in which impurity atoms contained electrons of an energy just below the edge of the empty band, or vacant states just above the top of the filled band ('donor' and 'acceptor' semiconductivity).

These developments, in which Pauli's paper had played a crucial part, led to an understanding of the basic features of metallic conduction with the important exception of superconductivity. All other paradoxes were resolved, and the electron theory of metals had become a field in which the quantitative and detailed study of specific phenomena was feasible.

It would take us too long to follow the further development of the modern electron theory of metals beyond this early stage.

Returning to the problem of magnetism, we note that Pauli realized very clearly the crude and qualitative nature of his theory of metallic paramagnetism, and he did not expect quantitative agreement of the observed susceptibility with his model. This model omitted, in particular, two important phenomena. One of these is the fact that the electrons are not free, but move in a periodic potential field. This affects the density of states as a function of energy, and would therefore alter the amount by which the electron energy had to be increased in order to allow the reversal of a certain number of electron spins.

As long as one takes no account of the Coulomb interaction between the electrons, this correction could easily be estimated, since the density of states affects the paramagnetic susceptibility in precisely the same way as the electronic specific heat, and one should therefore be able to express the paramagnetic susceptibility exactly in terms of the observed specific heat at low temperatures, where the linear electronic contribution can be separated from the T^3 contribution due to the lattice vibrations.

But this comparison does not (and should not) give agreement, and the chief reason for this is no doubt the electron–electron interaction. The effect of this interaction is to favour (other things being equal) electron pairs with parallel spin. The reason is that two electrons with parallel spin have an antisymmetric wave function which must vanish in configuration space when the two electrons coincide, and therefore is small when they are close together. This negative correlation reduces the effect of their electrostatic repulsion.

This 'exchange' effect, which is, for example, responsible for the levels of orthohelium lying lower than the levels of parahelium with the same principal quantum numbers, will therefore help the magnetization. It is also insensitive to temperature, and does not therefore invalidate Pauli's explanation of the approximate constancy of the paramagnetic susceptibility. It will, however, increase the susceptibility. If this effect is strong enough it may, in fact, make the normal state of the metal one in which there is a large non-zero resultant electron spin, in spite of the additional kinetic energy which, according to the exclusion principle, is required to align spins. The result is ferromagnetism.

We shall not discuss the theory of ferromagnetism here, except to remark that this is usually treated by starting from a very different model, in which the interaction of the electrons in any one atom is assumed so strong that the probability of finding more or less than the normal number of electrons in the same atom is negligible, although it does not contradict the Pauli principle. This model is similar to the classical treatment of the hydrogen molecule by Heitler and London.

This model leaves no room for conductivity, and therefore appears inconsistent with the approach outlined above. This apparent contradiction is made more plausible by the remark of Mott and Jones [10] that the only elements in which ferromagnetism is found are the transition elements which contain an incomplete

$3d$ shell in addition to the outer valence electrons. The $3d$ electrons have highly concentrated wave functions, which will not strongly overlap the adjacent atoms, so that for them the tendency to balance charge may be stronger than the transfer effect stressed above, which is responsible for the conductivity. That this picture is only an approximation is illustrated by the fact that these ferromagnetic elements show an anomalously large specific heat. The additional specific heat is appreciable not only below and near the Curie point, as the Heitler–London model predicts from the change with temperature of the spin alignment, but it remains large, and even rises, at much higher temperatures. The amount of entropy associated with it is much larger than could be accounted for by the spin distribution, and evidently must arise from the mobility of the magnetic electrons, which the Heitler–London model ignores.

A correct treatment of this effect, as well as of the simultaneous presence of inner, magnetic electrons and of conduction electrons, presents considerable difficulty.

It is an interesting speculation whether there could be ferromagnetism also in the limit in which all electrons could be regarded as conduction electrons, i.e. in which one could superimpose their interaction on one-electron states of the Bloch type. The simplest form of this problem is obtained if one goes back to the limit of free electrons, i.e. ignores the periodic field of the lattice ions (one must include the average positive charge of the ions to avoid unrealistic space charge effects) but includes the Coulomb repulsion between the electrons.

Bloch[11] treated this problem in perturbation theory, and the answer suggests that ferromagnetism may result if the electron density is low enough. The dependence on density results from the fact that the Coulomb repulsion is inversely proportional to the distance between the electrons, and therefore varies with the one-third power of the density, whereas the kinetic energy which, by the Pauli principle, opposes the alignment of spins, varies as the two-thirds power of the density. However, just in the circumstances when the interaction is strong enough to outweigh the effect of the kinetic energy, the perturbation theory used by Bloch becomes invalid, so that his answer is no more than an indication. This problem of the ferromagnetism of free electrons is one of the few problems in this field which can be stated clearly in mathematical terms, and for which no solution is yet available.

In the Heitler–London model one can also see the possibility of antiferromagnetism. This results when there is a tendency for adjacent atoms to have their spins in opposite directions, as is the case for the ground state of the hydrogen molecule, because if the electron spins of adjacent atoms are opposite the Pauli principle allows each electron to utilize the space of both atoms. In the limit of free electrons this tendency is already included in the Pauli treatment of paramagnetism, but a convincing treatment of the intermediate situation between free electrons and the strongly ordered antiferromagnetic state that may arise in the Heitler–London limit would be difficult.

None of the factors mentioned so far would account for the fact that many metals show a strong diamagnetic susceptibility. Evidently the ion cores, i.e. the electrons in the inner shells, which do not take part in the conductivity, contribute a diamagnetic susceptibility of the same order as closed-shell atoms of comparable radii; but their contribution would usually be less than the Pauli paramagnetism, and it could certainly not account for anything like the strong diamagnetism of bismuth.

The diamagnetism of atoms is due to the effect of the magnetic field on the orbital motion of the electrons, which up to now had been ignored.

It was well known that in classical statistical mechanics the orbital motion of charged particles does not lead to a susceptibility.[12] At first sight one might conclude differently, since an electron with a velocity component v in the plane at right angles to the magnetic field will follow a trajectory which, when projected on that plane, is a circle of radius $r = mcv/eH$, where e, m are charge and mass of the particle, c the velocity of light, and H the field strength (Gauss units). This suggests an average magnetic moment of $evr/c = mv^2/H$. This result, i.e. a moment which does not depend on the charge of the particle, increases with its velocity, and decreases with H, is physically unreasonable. The error in the argument is that it takes no account of what happens at the borders of the region available to the electrons. If we imagine the electrons confined to a finite volume (as in a piece of metal) those whose orbits meet the surface will be reflected, and will undergo successive such reflections, following a projected path which encircles the whole region in the opposite sense to that in which an electron in the interior describes its circle. The number of such surface electrons is small, but the area encircled by their orbits is large, and one can follow this elementary reasoning to show that the net magnetic moment is just zero.

The same argument can be applied to a small part of the available volume if we include all the electrons which, at any given moment, are found inside the given volume element and not (as the erroneous argument would imply) to those whose centres of curvature lie inside the volume element.

An even simpler and more transparent way of arriving at the same conclusion is to start from the remark that the magnetic moment is given by $-\partial F/\partial H$, where F is the free energy, and H the magnetic field. Since, in classical statistical mechanics, the free energy may be obtained by carrying out the integration contained in the definition of the partition function first over momentum space and then over the coordinates, and since the only effect of the presence of a vector potential A is to shift the momentum variable at each space point by an amount eA/c, it is at once evident that the free energy is independent of H.

The more pedestrian derivation in terms of orbits, which is sensitive to the proper use of boundary conditions, gave many people the impression that one was dealing here with a very complicated situation, and this probably discouraged many from extending the treatment of the problem by the inclusion of quantum effects. This was done by Landau[13] who showed that the new feature of the quantum problem is the discrete nature of the energy levels associated with the motion in the plane perpendicular to the magnetic field. This motion is classically a simple periodic motion with twice the Larmor frequency $\omega = eH/2mc$, and naturally corresponds in quantum mechanics to discrete energy levels with a spacing $2\hbar\omega = 2\mu H$, where μ is the Bohr magneton. If the spacing of these levels is neglected compared to kT, i.e. the distance over which the (Boltzmann or Fermi) distribution function varies appreciably, so that the sum may be replaced by an integral, one obtains the classical answer. The difference between summation and integration gives corrections of the relative order of magnitude $(\mu H/kT)^2$ in the partition function, or $(\mu H)^2/kT$ in the free energy, so that, for a non-degenerate electron gas one obtains a susceptibility following Curie's law. In the case of a degenerate Fermi gas there is again only a region of energies of width kT around the edge of the Fermi distribution which contributes, and this contains a fraction kT/E_0 of the total number of electrons. Thus one obtains a temperature-independent diamagnetic susceptibility, as in Pauli's paramagnetism.

Landau's quantitative treatment of this problem shows that, both for the degenerate and the non-degenerate case, the diamagnetism amounts to one-third of the spin paramagnetism, so that Pauli's results should, for free electrons, be reduced by a factor $\frac{2}{3}$.

Landau's simple and elegant treatment was not immediately accepted by all, because of the suspicion that it is necessary to take explicit account of surface effects, which in the quantum treatment would be inconvenient. In the ensuing controversy Pauli supported Landau's findings with enthusiasm.

As long as the electrons are treated as free, the diamagnetism of the orbital motion is exactly one-third of the spin paramagnetism, and the strongly diamagnetic behaviour of certain metals remains unexplained, even if the diamagnetic effect of the closed shells inside the ions is allowed for. It is, however, evident that the periodic potential of the lattice is liable to affect the orbital motion in a different way from the spin.

One way of allowing for this periodic potential is to start from the Bloch band picture, and to include the effect of the magnetic field in mixing the different Bloch states within the same band, but neglect inter-band effects.[14] In that case the diamagnetism depends on a certain average of the curvature of the energy as a function of wave vector, over the Fermi surface. Jones[15] was able to show that a particularly strong curvature, and hence strong diamagnetism, may be expected when the Fermi surface passes close to a narrow gap between two bands, and that this appears to happen in crystals with a structure like bismuth, and in certain alloys which also show strong diamagnetism. In these cases the structure may be thought of as a slight distortion of a more symmetric lattice. A region which would be one band in the more symmetric crystal is then divided by a narrow gap into two or more bands, and this is energetically favourable if the new gap coincides approximately with the Fermi surface, since the deformation will then lower the electron states below the gap, most of which are occupied, at the expense of raising the energy level above, which is mostly empty.

In this way one can understand both the peculiar structure of these substances and the fact that they have energy surfaces which in part pass very close to such a gap, where a large curvature, and hence a strong diamagnetism, can be expected.

This situation is elucidated in much more detail by the de Haas–van Alphen effect. These authors discovered[16] that the magnetic susceptibility of bismuth single crystals shows at low temperatures an oscillatory behaviour as a function of the magnetic field. This corresponded with the prediction from the Landau theory, which led to a similar behaviour.[17] At low temperatures the partition function depends sensitively on whether or not the Fermi energy E_0 coincides with one of the quantized Landau levels. Since their spacing varies proportionately with the magnetic field, the oscillatory features are a direct consequence.

If the Fermi surface lies near a minimum or maximum of the energy as a function of wave vector, so that this function may be regarded as quadratic, the Landau theory applies except for scale factors. In this case the period of the oscillations, which are equi-distant if $1/H$ is taken as variable, their amplitude, and their variation with temperature and with the orientation of the crystal provide a great mass of experimental information which can be used to form a picture of the details of the electron motion.

By increasing the sensitivity of the experiment Shoenberg and his collaborators were able to measure the effect in many metals.[18]

To get away from the special case of a quadratic energy function, Onsager[19] made the remark that in the magnetic field the energy of the motion in the plane at right angles to the field remains constant, but that the wave vector in that plane (perpendicular momentum) will, classically speaking, change its direction in time. The electron therefore describes an orbit in momentum space which is in many cases closed, and the system can be quantized by applying the Bohr–Sommerfeld conditions to the closed orbit. This semiclassical treatment is justified because one usually deals here with high quantum numbers, since the Fermi energy is very large compared to the 'quantum' $2\mu H$.

The semiclassical treatment was exploited by Lifshitz[20] and its basis investigated by Harper and Brailsford.[21] The study of this effect has proved most fruitful in understanding the shape of the energy surfaces in many metals; in view of the simplicity of the model, which ignores many complications, such as the interaction between the electrons, lattice vibrations, and inter-band effects, it seems surprising that it leads to consistent results in impressive detail.

Dingle[22] drew attention to the broadening of the levels by collisions, which reduces the magnitude of the de Haas–van Alphen effect, and Adams[23] stressed the importance of inter-band terms, particularly in substances like bismuth, in which one is dealing with a narrow gap between two bands. It is likely that such inter-band terms are important for the steady susceptibility at low fields or high temperatures. No clear treatment of their effect on the oscillatory de Haas–van Alphen behaviour is yet available. It has been suggested[24] that one important effect is to cause, in the case of a narrow gap, strong spin–orbit coupling, which results in a non-negligible spin contribution to the susceptibility.

Up to this point this review has followed the developments arising directly or indirectly from Pauli's paper on the paramagnetism of an electron gas. Historically this was not his first contribution to solid-state physics, but the first problem which attracted his attention was the damping of infra-red radiation in ionic crystals, and the associated problem of the thermal conductivity of insulators.

It seems there is no problem in modern physics for which there are on record as many false starts, and as many theories which overlook some essential feature, as in the problem of the thermal conductivity of non-conducting crystals. Some early attempts even treat this problem in terms of purely harmonic forces between the atoms. If, in this case, a group of atoms is heated, i.e. set into violent vibration, the vibrational energy is propagated through the crystal. This transport problem does not, however, obey the phenomenological equations of heat conductivity any more than would the motion of a selected group of fast atoms in a perfect gas without collisions.

For a correct description one has to remember that the assumption of harmonic forces, i.e. forces which depend linearly on the displacements of the atoms from their equilibrium positions, is only an approximation, and that anharmonic terms, which are of second or higher degree in the displacements, are small but essential for the conduction problem, just as collisions in a nearly perfect gas are rare but essential for the transport phenomena. It is convenient to visualize the heat conduction in terms of phonons, which would travel indefinitely in the same direction if there were no anharmonicities, and to treat the anharmonic effects as causing collisions which disturb the motion of the phonons and therefore give them a limited mean free path. This picture, which will also be employed here, gives a convenient way of visualizing the problem, even at high temperatures, where quantum effects are negligible, and the concept of phonons not really necessary.

Debye,[25] who appreciated clearly the importance of anharmonic forces, gave one of his characteristic simplified treatments, in which the scattering of phonons was attributed to density fluctuations. If the elastic properties of the solid vary with density, as they must if the anharmonic terms are taken into account, then regions of varying density will scatter phonons. Since the mean square fluctuations of the density are proportional to the temperature, this model leads to a heat resistance which varies as the temperature, which, for the classical region above the

Debye temperature, is about right. Debye's model contains some of the essential features of the process, but it is not correct in detail because it treats the density fluctuations as static, whereas they are really made up of sound waves which travel with a velocity comparable to that of the waves whose scattering is to be considered, and this has a profound effect on the dynamics of the process.

Ornstein and Zernike [26] attempted to solve the problem for an elastic continuum with some anharmonic forces, but there were also some important features missing, and, if correctly treated, the continuum model still does not give a finite resistance, as we shall see.

Pauli looked at the problem with the Born–von Kàrmàn model of a linear chain of atoms with nearest-neighbour forces, in which there is only one force constant for the harmonic and one other for the anharmonic forces. He appeared to find a non-zero result for the damping of the lattice vibrations, and reported his result to a meeting of the German Physical Society. The published summary of this talk [27] is probably the only incorrect formula published under Pauli's name.

The effect of the quadratic terms in the forces is to couple different modes if the combination frequencies are in resonance, i.e. if the frequency of one mode is the same as that of the sum or difference of two others. The transfer of energy between different modes can conveniently be described in terms of phonons, and we are here concerned with a process in which two phonons merge into one or *vice-versa*.

The translational symmetry of the lattice ensures, however, that in the coupling of such modes the wave vector must also be conserved, so that for the process to occur the sum of the wave vectors of the two initial phonons must equal the final one, apart from a basic vector in reciprocal lattice space.

In the linear chain model this means that

$$f_1 + f_2 = f_3 + \text{multiple of } 2\pi/a$$

where a is the spacing, and f the phonon lattice vector, defined conventionally to lie between $-\pi/a$ and $+\pi/a$. The resonance condition (energy conservation for phonons) requires for the corresponding frequencies

$$\omega_1 + \omega_2 = \omega_3$$

Since for the Born–von Kàrmàn model the frequency is given by

$$\omega = A \left| \sin f \frac{a}{2} \right|$$

where A is a constant, we can eliminate f_3 and find the condition

$$\left| \sin f_1 \frac{a}{2} \right| + \left| \sin f_2 \frac{a}{2} \right| = \left| \sin (f_1+f_2) \frac{a}{2} \right|,$$

which can be reduced to

$$\left| \sin (f_1+f_2) \frac{a}{4} \cos (f_1-f_2) \frac{a}{4} \right| = \left| \sin (f_1+f_2) \frac{a}{4} \cos (f_1+f_2) \frac{a}{4} \right|$$

which admits only the solutions $f_1+f_2 = 4n\pi/a$, or $f_1 = 2n\pi/a$, or $f_2 = 2n\pi/a$, with n an integer. These solutions are trivial, however, since they say that one of the phonons involved has zero frequency and corresponds to a uniform displacement of the lattice. For this case the coefficient which determines the transition probability vanishes, and in any case we are not dealing with real scattering. Pauli's result probably arose from the impression that the vibrations with wave vector f and with $f + (2\pi/a)$ belonged to different modes.

Pauli was not satisfied and suggested a further study of the problem.[28] This led to the conclusion that it was impossible to satisfy the resonance condition together with the condition for the conservation of wave vector in a one-dimensional model with a frequency curve of the general type of the Born–von Kàrmàn spectrum. In three dimensions the condition could be satisfied, mainly because of the existence of different branches of the spectrum, i.e. different modes of vibration with the same wave vector, but different directions of vibration. If the wave vector is in the direction of one of the crystal axes, these correspond to longitudinal and transverse vibrations, the longitudinal modes having in general the higher frequency. It is then possible to find solutions of the conservation laws for processes in which, for example, two transverse phonons merge to form a longitudinal one, or a transverse and a longitudinal one combine to form another longitudinal one.

This seemed to indicate that there were always sufficient collisions possible to establish equilibrium amongst the phonon modes, and to give a finite heat conductivity. A quantitative calculation of this conductivity is not easy, because it would require very detailed knowledge of the phonon spectrum, which in three dimensions is a large computational task even with simple assumptions about the forces. From a knowledge of the spectrum one would have to determine the combinations of wave vectors for which the conservation laws are satisfied, and to evaluate the magnitude of the anharmonic coupling between them, and then finally to solve an integral equation for the phonon distribution.

Without carrying out such a calculation it was evident, however, that, provided this integral equation had a solution, the heat transport caused by a given temperature gradient was inversely proportional to the temperature, as long as quantum effects were negligible, i.e. at temperatures above the Debye temperature. The reason for this result is entirely in line with the simple argument of Debye, although the mechanism of phonon interaction is more complicated than in Debye's model. A T^{-1} law for the thermal conductivity seemed to agree with observation, although data on the high-temperature conductivity were—and still are— exceedingly scanty.

This was not yet, however, the full story. Pomeranchuk [29] noticed that the collision processes considered by Peierls did not lead to changes in the number of long-wave, longitudinal phonons except through their interaction with other phonons of comparable wavelength. This can be seen from the conservation laws stated above by assuming that, say, f_1 is a small wave vector (now three-dimensional). Then, since the gradient of ω with respect to f is the group velocity, which for long waves is the same as the sound velocity, one finds

$$\omega_3 - \omega_2 = c_1 \left| f_1 \right| = c_1 \left| f_3 - f_2 \right|$$

Hence f_2 and f_3 must represent two phonons with almost the same wave vector, and almost the same frequency, the ratio between the two differences being the longitudinal sound velocity. This is not possible if both belong to the same branch (both longitudinal or both transverse) since the gradient of all frequency curves is less than the longitudinal sound velocity for long waves. It also is not possible if f_2 and f_3 belong to different branches unless they are both small, since otherwise there will be a finite separation between the frequencies of the two branches.

It then follows that long-wave longitudinal phonons have a mean free path which is proportional to λ^5, or f^{-5}, since for small f the number of modes with which collisions are possible diminishes because the number of modes is proportional to $f^2 df$, and also the coupling coefficients tend to zero, since in the limit $f = 0$ we are dealing with a uniform displacement of the lattice which clearly cannot alter the dynamics. If the mean free path increases as strongly as this with wavelength, the heat transport contributed by the very long waves diverges, and for the same reason the integral equation discussed by Peierls has no solution.

Pomeranchuk therefore concluded that a finite result can be obtained only if one includes the possibility of four-phonon processes, for example the collision of two phonons in which they are destroyed and two different ones produced. For such processes there are always many possible solutions to the conservation laws. However, such processes are possible only if one either includes cubic terms in the forces, or treats the quadratic terms to second-order of perturbation theory. Such effects depend therefore on a higher power of the phonon amplitudes. The cubic terms contribute terms in the integral equation which go as T^2, and the second-order effects of the quadratic forces go as $T^{3/2}$. We therefore have to discuss an integral equation in which there are terms of different temperature dependence, the terms in T being the leading ones, but the others being necessary to make the equation soluble. Pomeranchuk conjectured that the solution of such an equation would lead to a $T^{3/2}$ or $T^{5/4}$ law for the resistance, according to whether one included the cubic terms or the second-order terms as responsible for four-phonon processes. There is no experimental decision on whether this type of behaviour occurs in any real crystals.

There was yet another surprise to come. Herring[30] pointed out that the discussions of Pomeranchuk had failed to take into account that in many crystals one is not allowed to regard the higher-frequency (longitudinal) and lower-frequency (transverse) branches as distinct, but that the corresponding frequency curves will cross or merge in certain directions. As a result there are always certain points in the spectrum near which a transition with a small change in wave vector and with a proportionately small change in frequency is possible. In such crystal types the excessively long mean free path for long-wave, longitudinal phonons disappears, and we return to the T law for the resistance. One would therefore expect to find this law in some crystals, and a more complicated behaviour, as predicted by Pomeranchuk, in others.

As far as is known today, this is now a correct statement of the theoretical position, but a detailed classification of the crystals for which one expects the one or the other behaviour, and estimates of the magnitude of the conductivity in the various cases, and experimental tests of these conclusions are still outstanding.

The fact that this is the position today, 34 years after Pauli's study of the problem, confirms his view that this is an interesting problem, and also explains why the first approach did not at once disclose all the important features of the situation.

Different problems arise when one goes to low temperatures, which require the inclusion of quantum effects. Here it was noticed by Peierls[28] that the lattice structure was of vital importance to the problem. If the crystal were replaced by an elastic continuum the conservation law for the wave vector would apply without the possibility of adding a basic vector in the reciprocal space. It would then be quite analogous to the part played by momentum conservation in collision between molecules, and the sum of the wave vectors of all phonons would be conserved just like the total momentum of a gas. Collisions between phonons would then be unable to destroy a general drift of the phonon gas any more than collisions between molecules can stop the flow of gas in a tube with smooth walls.

This is of no importance in the thermal conductivity of a gas, since molecular collisions conserve the number of molecules, so that in a tube with closed ends a drift would result in an accumulation of gas at one end, and would set up a pressure gradient which would stop the drift. (The point has some connection, however, with the fact that the heat conductivity of a gas can be measured only in circumstances in which convection is avoided.) In the case of phonons there is no conservation law for their number, and a temperature gradient necessarily causes a gradient in phonon density, which tends to set up a drift.

It follows that the thermal conductivity of a perfect crystal is finite only by virtue of the lattice structure, which makes possible collisions in which the total wave vector changes by a basic reciprocal vector. A simple example of such a process would be the collision of two phonons travelling to the right, with wavelengths somewhat shorter than four times the basic lattice period. Since a wavelength of twice the lattice period corresponds to a standing wave in which alternative planes of atoms vibrate with opposite phase, the result is a wave travelling to the left. This reversal of the group velocity has earned such processes the unattractive name of Umklapp processes.

It is evident that a collision of this type can occur only if at least one of the phonons initially present has a wave vector which amounts to at least one-third of the smallest reciprocal-lattice vector. Since at low temperatures the population of phonons of any given frequency decreases exponentially with temperature, it follows that the rate of Umklapp processes should also get exponentially small at low temperatures, and this leads to an exponential rise of the thermal conductivity.

This exponential rise was found in experiments at Oxford by

Berman and others.[31] There are probably several reasons why it was not discovered earlier. One is that there is no quantitative theory, and therefore it is not clear how low the temperature has to be before the exponential law becomes dominant. In the early theory the temperature at which this started was over-estimated. Secondly the exponential law is pronounced only for a nearly perfect crystal, since imperfections can lead to scattering even of long waves without conservation of wave vector, since they do not possess the translational symmetry of the lattice. It was overlooked that imperfections for this purpose include the presence of different isotopes amongst the crystal atoms, since the mass difference of the isotopes makes them respond differently to the passage of waves, and this, too, is a deviation from the perfect lattice behaviour. This point was mentioned by Pomeranchuk,[32] but it was used in the interpretation of the experiments only when careful low-temperature work showed that some substances behaved according to the predicted exponential law and others did not, and that the first type were those in which there was one dominant isotope of each element present.

Finally, another factor comes in from the finite size of the specimens. At low temperatures the mean free path of the phonons becomes so long that it may be comparable with the size of the crystal used, and one approaches conditions similar to the Knudsen regime in low-pressure gases, where boundary scattering outweighs the internal collisions, and the apparent conductivity becomes size dependent. This size effect has been discussed by Casimir,[33] and the joint effect of all these factors on the low-temperature conductivity has been discussed by Klemens.[34]

The problem of disposing of the phonon and electron drift also results in complications in the theory of the electric conductivity of metals, but it would not be appropriate to discuss these here, since they are probably an outstanding example of solid-state problems which Pauli regarded as too complex to be worth his attention.

Our discussion of solid-state problems will also not include Pauli's work on spin transitions in variable fields, and on the general problem of non-equilibrium states in statistical mechanics, which are all relevant to important parts of solid-state theory, but which are discussed in other articles in this volume.

REFERENCES

1. Pauli, W. *Z. Phys.* **41**, 81, 1927
2. Fermi, E. *Z. Phys.* **36**, 902, 1926

6*

3. Sommerfeld, A. *Z. Phys.* **47**, 1, 1928
4. Sommerfeld, A. *Z. Phys.* **47**, 43, 1928
5. Bloch, F. *Z. Phys.* **52**, 555, 1928
6. Peierls, R. *Z. Phys.* **53**, 255, 1929
7. Peierls, R. *Ann. Phys. Lpz.* **4**, 121, 1930
8. Brillouin, L. *Quantenstatistik*, 1931. Berlin
9. Wilson, A. H. *Proc. Roy. Soc. A* **133**, 458, 1931; **134**, 277, 1931
10. Mott, N. F. and Jones, H. *Properties of Metals and Alloys.* 1936. Oxford
11. Bloch, F. *Z. Phys.* **57**, 545, 1929
12. Bohr, N. *Dissertation*, Copenhagen, 1911: van Leeuwen, Miss, *Dissertation*, Leiden, 1919
13. Landau, L. *Z. Phys.* **64**, 629, 1930
14. Peierls, R. *Z. Phys.* **80**, 763, 1933
15. Jones, H. *Proc. Roy. Soc. A* **144**, 225, 1934: **147**, 396, 1934
16. de Haas, W. J. and van Alphen, *Proc. Acad. Sci., Amst.* **33**, 1106, 1930
17. Peierls, R. *Z. Phys.* **81**, 186, 1933
18. Shoenberg, D. *Phil. Trans. A* **245**, 1, 1952: *Progress of Low-Temperature Physics*, vol. 2. 1957
19. Onsager, L. *Phil. Mag.* **43**, 1006, 1952
20. Lifshitz, I. M. and Kosevitch, A. M. *Zh. eksp. teor. Fiz.* **29**, 730, 1955
21. Harper, P. G. *Proc. phys. Soc., Lond. A* **68**, 874, 1955
     Brailsford, A. D. *Proc. phys. Soc., Lond. A* **70**, 275, 1957
22. Dingle, R. B. *Proc. Roy. Soc. A* **211**, 517, 1952
23. Adams, E. N. *Phys. Rev.* **89**, 633, 1953
24. Yafet, Y. *Phys. Rev.* **85**, 478, 1952: **106**, 679, 1957
25. Debye, P. *Vorträge über die kinetische Theorie der Materie und der Elektrizität.* 1914. Leipzig
26. Ornstein, L. S. and Zernike, F. *Proc. Acad. Sci., Amst.* **19**, 1295, 1925
27. Pauli, W. *Verh. dtsch. phys. Ges.* (3) **6**, 10, 1925
28. Peierls, R. *Ann. Phys. Lpz.* **3**, 1055, 1929
29. Pomeranchuk, I. *J. Phys. Moscow* **4**, 259, 1941
30. Herring, C. *Phys. Rev.* **95**, 954, 1954
31. Berman, R. *Advanc. Phys.* **2**, 103, 1953: Berman, R., Foster, E. L. and Ziman, J. M. *Proc. Roy. Soc. A* **237**, 344, 1956
32. Pomeranchuk, I. *J. Phys., Moscow* **7**, 197, 1943
33. Casimir, H. B. G. *Physica* **5**, 495, 1938
34. Klemens, P. G. *Proc. Roy. Soc. A* **208**, 108, 1951

STATISTISCHE MECHANIK

MARKUS FIERZ

EINLEITUNG

W. Pauli hat seit vielen Jahren regelmässig eine Vorlesung über statistische Mechanik gehalten, durch die er immer wieder in aufmerksamen Zuhörern Verständnis für den Reiz und die Bedeutung dieser schönen Theorie zu wecken vermag. Wenn nun auch jeder Autor für das was er vorbringt selber die Verantwortung übernehmen wird, so glaube ich doch, dass in diesem Aufsatze die Art wie die Probleme gesehen und bewertet werden deutlich auf das zurückweisen, was ich seinerzeit in jener Vorlesung gelernt habe.

Wie Boltzmann und Gibbs gegen Ende des vorigen Jahrhunderts danach trachteten, die statistische Mechanik systematisch zu begründen, war ihre Stellung in mancher Hinsicht recht schwierig. Die Atome und ihre Bewegungen, durch die die thermodynamischen Eigenschaften der Körper erklärt werden sollten, galten vielen noch als hypothetische Fiktionen. Jedenfalls war nichts sicheres über ihre physikalischen Eigenschaften bekannt und so konnte der statistischen Mechanik mit einem gewissen Recht der Vorwurf gemacht werden, sie erkläre das bekannte— d.s. die Gesetze der phänomenologischen Thermodynamik—durch unbekanntes. Abgeschreckt durch den Misserfolg aller Versuche, die Gesetze der Optik und Elektrodynamik mit Hilfe mechanischer Modelle zu beschreiben, glaubten zahlreiche Gelehrte auch in der Wärmelehre auf ein mechanisches Modell verzichten zu sollen. Es schien ihnen richtiger, die Wärme, wie die elektrische Energie, als eine besondere Energieform aufzufassen, deren Umwandlung in andere Energieformen durch die Thermodynamik beschrieben wird. Durch solche Argumente in die Verteidigung gedrängt sagt Boltzmann in der Einleitung zu seiner 'Gastheorie':[1] 'Ja, wenn die Geschichte der Wissenschaft zeigt, wie oft sich erkenntnistheoretische Generalisationen als falsch erwiesen haben, kann da nicht auch einmal die augenblickliche moderne Richtung, sowie die Unterscheidung qualitativ verschiedener Energieformen als

Rückschritt erkannt werden?—Wer sieht in die Zukunft? Darum
freie Bahn für jede Richtung, weg mit jeder Dogmatik in ato-
mistischem und antiatomistischem Sinne! Indem wir obendrein
die Vorstellungen der Gastheorie als mechanische Analogieen
bezeichnen, drücken wir schon durch die Wahl dieses Wortes aus,
wie weit wir von der Vorstellung entfernt sind, als träfen sie in
allen Stücken die wahre Beschaffenheit der kleinsten Theile der
Körper.'

Heute, nachdem die Atomphysik überall zentrales Forschungsge-
biet geworden ist, können wir uns nicht mehr leicht vorstellen,
wie schwer Boltzmann und Gibbs um Verständnis ihrer Ideen
zu kämpfen hatten. Es ist in dieser Hinsicht bezeichnend,
dass selbst Planck sich erst zur Boltzmann'schen Auffassung
der Entropie als statistische Grösse bekehrt hat, als ihm kein
anderer Weg zur Ableitung des von ihm entdeckten Strahlungs-
gesetzes mehr übrig blieb. Heute scheint es jedem Physiker
natürlich, auch die Thermodynamik atomistisch zu begründen,
denn wir empfinden stark, wie fremdartig sonst diese Theorie,
in ihrem ganzen Aufbau, anderen Gebieten der theoretischen
Physik gegenüber steht.

Insbesondere scheint uns merkwürdig, dass hier Wärme und
Arbeit überall streng unterschieden werden müssen, obwohl im 1.
Hauptsatz ihre Äquivalenz festgestellt wird. Dabei ist diese
Unterscheidung nur möglich, wenn man sich auf die Existenz
adiabatischer Wände beruft. Diese sollen zwar selber keine
thermodynamischen Eigenschaften haben, aber dennoch den
Ausgleich von Temperaturdifferenzen verhindern. In der Theorie
der chemischen Gleichgewichte müssen zudem Katalysatoren
eingeführt werden, die jede chemische Reaktion verunmöglichen.
Hier handelt es sich gewiss um Fiktionen, für deren Existenz man
sich nicht auf die Erfahrung berufen kann, und die Pauli darum
mit Recht 'Zaubermittel' genannt hat.

Die statistische Mechanik hat keine Zaubermittel nötig. Sie
erklärt das eigentümliche thermodynamische Verhalten als
makroskopische Erscheinung eines Systems, das unvorstellbar
viele mikroskopische Freiheitsgrade besitzt. Die Unterscheidung
von Wärme und Arbeit verliert dabei ihren absoluten Sinn: die
Wärme ist derjenige Anteil der Energie, der den makroskopisch
nicht beobachteten Freiheitsgraden zugeschrieben werden muss.
Was aber makroskopisch beobachtet wird, hängt wesentlich von
den Beobachtungsmöglichkeiten ab. Darum ist die Wärme, und
damit die Entropie, in der statistischen Mechanik streng genommen immer nur relativ zu einem makroskopischen Beobachter

definiert. Man kann aber hier, über die Thermoydnamik hin-
ausgehend, allen makroskopischen Zuständen, seien sie nun
Gleichgewichte oder nicht, eine Entropie zuschreiben.

Diese erweist sich, wie Boltzmann gezeigt hat, als ein Mass für
die 'Wahrscheinlichkeit' des betrachteten makroskopischen Zustandes. Sie ist durch die Menge mikroskopischer Zustände
bestimmt, die alle zum gleichen makroskopischen Zustand Anlass
geben. Zugleich gibt sie an, wie häufig ein solcher Zustand im
Verlaufe der Zeit angetroffen werden kann. Man nimmt an, eine
Menge mikroskopischer Zustände werde in der klassischen
Mechanik durch die ihr entsprechende Phasenausdehnung
gemessen, in der Quantentheorie durch die Anzahl stationärer
Zustände, die in ihr enthalten ist. Dass dadurch aber zugleich
die zeitliche Häufigkeit gemessen wird, in welcher der dieser
Menge entsprechende makroskopische Zustand in Erscheinung
tritt, ist ein mechanisches Theorem, das man den 'Ergodensatz'
nennt. Ein allgemeiner Beweis für diesen Satz ist bisher nicht
geliefert worden, doch zweifelt wohl niemand an seiner Richtigkeit.
Denn alle Erfolge der statistischen Mechanik beruhen wesentlich
auf dieser Hypothese. Insbesondere beruht auf ihr die Theorie
der thermischen Schwankungen, d.h. der spontanen Abweichungen vom Gleichgewicht.

In der folgenden Darstellung geben wir zuerst eine, wie uns
scheint physikalisch hinreichende Formulierung des Ergodensatzes.
Daraufhin besprechen wir die verschiedenen statistischen Gesamtheiten, die wir stets als Zeitgesamtheiten auffassen. Der
Zusammenhang dieser Gesamtheiten mit den verschiedenen
Möglichkeiten ein System thermodynamisch zu beschreiben wird
diskutiert, wobei besonders auf den Umstand hingewiesen wird,
dass an kritischen Punkten, am Tripelpunkt oder an Umwandlungspunkten, die verschiedenen Gesamtheiten nicht mehr
gleichwertig sind. Die ausführliche Diskussion von Schwan-
kungserscheinungen soll dies näher illustrieren. Vor allem soll
gezeigt werden, dass in diesen Fällen Oberflächeneffekte eine
entscheidende Rolle spielen.

1. DER ERGODENSATZ[2]

Wir betrachten ein abgeschlossenes, endliches, konservatives,
klassisch-mechanisches System mit sehr vielen Freiheitsgraden f,
dessen mikroskopischer Zustand durch die $2f$ kanonischen
Koordinaten $p_k(t)$, $q_k(t)$ beschrieben wird. Wir fassen diese als
kartesische Koordinaten eines Punktes $P(t)$ in einem Euklidischen

Raume, dem Phasenraum, auf. Ein makroskopischer Zustand wird durch die Angabe des Wertes makroskopischer Variablen, wie E, die Energie, V, das Volumen in welchem sich das System befindet, $\rho(\mathbf{X}, t)$ die Dichteverteilung im Inneren dieses Volumens, usw. charakterisiert. Wir bezeichenen ihn mit (E, α) wo α alle übrigen makroskopischen Variablen, neben der Energie, zusammenfasst. Wird ein Zustand (E, α) beobachtet, dann liegt der Phasenpunkt $P(t)$ in einem gewissen Gebiet $G_{E,\alpha}$ des Phasenraums. Den makroskopischen Zuständen entspricht daher eine Einteilung des Phasenraumes in Gebiete $G_{E,\alpha}$, die desto feiner sein wird, je mehr Zustände unterschieden werden können. Alle Zustände gleicher makroskopischer Energie bilden zusammen die Energieschale G_E:

$$G_E = \sum_a G_{E,\alpha} \qquad \dots (1.1)$$

Diese soll durch die Ungleichung

$$E \leqslant H(p_k, q_k) < E + \Delta E \qquad \dots (1.2)$$

gegeben sein. Der Spielraum ΔE hängt von der Genauigkeit der makroskopischen Energiemessung ab, doch hat man sich vorzustellen, dass $\Delta E/E$ einen endlichen, nicht allzukleinen Wert besitzt.

Ist $\epsilon = H(p_k, q_k)$ der Wert der mikroskopischen Energie, so ist hierdurch eine 'Energiefläche' im Phasenraum bestimmt, auf welcher sich $P(t)$ bewegt. Die Energiefläche wird entsprechend den Gebieten $G_{E,\alpha}$ ebenfalls in Gebiete $\gamma_{E,\alpha}$ eingeteilt, welche die Phasenausdehnung

$$\omega_{\epsilon,\alpha} = \int_{G_{E,\alpha}} \delta(H(p, q) - \epsilon)\, dp dq \qquad \dots (1.3)$$

besitzen. Die Phasenausdehnung der Energiefläche selber ist dann durch

$$\omega_\epsilon = \sum_a \omega_{\epsilon,\alpha} \qquad \dots (1.4)$$

gegeben; sie soll endlich sein. Wir nehmen ferner an, die Gebiete $G_{E,\alpha}$ seien so beschaffen, dass man näherungsweise ihre Phasenausdehnung $\Omega_{E,\alpha}$ gleich $\omega_{E,\alpha}\Delta E$ setzen kann:

$$\Omega_{E,\alpha} = \int_{G_{E,\alpha}} dp dq \sim \omega_{\epsilon,\alpha}\, \Delta E \qquad \dots (1.5)$$

Die Energieschale hat dann die Ausdehnung

$$\Omega_E = \omega_\epsilon\, \Delta E \qquad \dots (1.6)$$

Maxwell und Boltzmann haben sich vorgestellt, dass der Phasenpunkt $P(t)$ im Laufe der Zeit durch jeden Punkt der Energiefläche
hindurch gehe (Ergodenhypothese). Hieraus folgt dann, mit
Hilfe des Liouville'schen Satzes, dass die mittlere Verweilzeit des
Systems im Zustande (E, α) proportional zu $\Omega_{E,\alpha} \sim \omega_{\epsilon,\alpha}$ sein wird.
Die Ergodenhypothese ist jedoch sicher unrichtig. Sie kann aber
durch die folgende, schwächere Annahme ersetzt werden:

Sei $X_{E,\alpha}(t) = 1$ wenn $P(t)$ in $G_{E,\alpha}$

 $X_{E,\alpha}(t) = 0$ wenn $P(t)$ ausserhalb $G_{E,\alpha}$

so existiert das Zeitmittel $\overline{X_{E,\alpha}}$ für 'fast alle' Anfangswerte $P(0)$.
Es hat den Wert

$$\lim_{T=\infty} \frac{1}{T} \int_0^T X_{E,\alpha}(t) \, \mathrm{d}t = \frac{\Omega_{E,\alpha}}{\Omega_E} \qquad \ldots (1.7)$$

Wir nennen diese Hypothese im folgenden 'Ergodensatz'. In
dieser Formulierung bedeutet die Wendung 'fast alle', dass es in
der Menge aller Anfangszustände p_k, q_k eine Teilmenge $\mathring{p}_k, \mathring{q}_k$
geben kann, die ein verschwindendes Mass besitzt, und für die
entweder das Zeitmittel (1.7) nicht existiert, oder für welche
dieses nicht den angegebenen Wert annimmt.

Der Ergodensatz macht nicht nur eine Aussage über das
System, sondern auch eine über den Beobachter, da bei seiner
Formulierung Bezug auf die Einteilung des Phasenraumes im
Gebiete $G_{E,\alpha}$ genommen wird. Ist er gültig, so sagen wir, das
System sei relativ zu einem gewissen Beobachter ergodisch.

Dass das Zeitmittel $\overline{X_{E,\alpha}}$ für fast alle Anfangswerte p_k, q_k
existiert, ist bewiesen. Über seinen Wert ist jedoch nichts
allgemeines bekannt. Darum weiss man nicht, wie, in einer vom
Ergodensatz unabhängigen Weise, ergodische Systeme zu charakterisieren sind, bzw. was die Beobachter auszeichnet, relativ zu
denen ein System ergodisch sein wird.

Wie Birkhoff gezeigt hat, folgt der Ergodensatz aus der metri-
schen Transitivität eines Systems. Ein System ist metrisch
transitiv, wenn nur eine einzige invariante Massbestimmung im
Phasenraum existiert: die kanonische Massbestimmung. Denn
diese ist, des Liouvilleschen Satzes wegen, invariant. Metrische
Transitivität bedeutet aber viel mehr als (1.7), denn bei ihr ist von
der durch die makroskopische Beobachtung erzeugten Einteilung
des Phasenraumes im Gebiete $G_{E,\alpha}$ nicht die Rede. Ein metrisch
transitives System ist darum relativ zu jedem Beobachter
ergodisch. Man könnte es 'absolut ergodisch' nennen. Weiter

spielt hier die Tatsache, dass makroskopische Systeme ungeheuer viele Freiheitsgrade besitzen, keine Rolle. Die grosse Zahl der Freiheitsgrade, $f \sim 10^{20}$, hat jedoch zur Folge, dass (1.7) keineswegs genau gelten muss, ja es kann $\overline{X_{E,a}}$ um viele Zehnerpotenzen von $\Omega_{E,a}/\Omega_E$ abweichen, ohne dass dies physikalisch irgend etwas ausmachen würde. (Wenn $\overline{X_{E,a}} = a \cdot \Omega_{E,a}/\Omega_E$, so muss nur $\lg a$ vernachlässigbar klein gegen f sein!)

Es ist darum durchaus möglich, dass makroskopische Systeme die nicht metrisch transitiv sind, dennoch für einen jeden physikalisch möglichen, makroskopischen Beobachter die Gleichung (1.7) annähernd erfüllen.

Hopf[2] hat bewiesen, dass ein Massenpunkt, der sich auf einer Fläche konstanter negativer Krümmung bewegt, ein 'absolut ergodisches' System vorstellt. Hier ist die Zahl der Freiheitsgrade $f = 2$. Die Tatsache, dass ein derartig einfaches System 'absolut ergodisch' ist, macht es plausibel, dass die ungleich komplizierteren Systeme der statistischen Mechanik die viel schwächere Eigenschaft (1.7) besitzen. Ein Beweis dieser Vermutung wird freilich nur möglich sein, wenn dabei die enorme Grösse von f ausgenützt wird, und wenn es gelingt, makroskopische Beobachtungen physikalisch sinnvoll zu charakterisieren.

Bisher haben wir angenommen, das System werde klassisch-mechanisch beschrieben. Man kann aber unsere Formulierung des Ergodenproblems ohne wesentliche Änderungen auf die Quantenmechanik übertragen.[3] $X_{E,a}(t)$ ist dann die Wahrscheinlichkeit im Sinne der Quantenmechanik, den Zustand (E, α) anzutreffen, und variiert zwischen 0 und 1. $\Omega_{E,a}$ ist die Anzahl nichtstationärer Eigenzustände, die alle zum selben makroskopischen Zustand gehören, Ω_E die Anzahl stationärer Zustände in der Energieschale. Man sieht leicht ein, dass der Mittelwert (1.7) existiert und verlangt wieder, dass er ungefähr den Wert $\Omega_{E,a}/\Omega_E$ haben soll. Diese Forderung ist eine Aussage über den makroskopischen Beobachter, und von Neumann[4] suchte zu beweisen, dass sie fast immer erfüllt ist. Dies geschah mit Hilfe einer Annahme über die 'Wahrscheinlichkeitsverteilung' der Beobachter. Wird diese Annahme zugestanden, so folgt aber aus ihr, worauf Landsberg und Farquhar[5] hingewiesen haben, dass ein hinreichend grosses System jederzeit für fast alle Beobachter im Gleichgewicht sein sollte. Man muss daraus schliessen, dass die Annahme von Neumann's physikalisch keinen Sinn hat. Es ist auch nicht konsequent, beim Beweise des Ergodensatzes Wahrscheinlichkeitshypothesen *a priori* einzuführen. Was nämlich schon P.u.T Ehrenfest[6] in bezug auf die alte Ergodenhypothese betonten, gilt auch für den hier formulierten Ergodensatz: er ist ein mechanisches Theorem (freilich enthält er implicite eine Charakterisierung dessen, was ein makroskopischer Zustand sein soll), das dazu dient, die sog. Wahrscheinlichkeit der makroskopischen Zustände auf Häufigkeiten in der Zeit zurückzuführen. Damit wird der Begriff der *a priori* Wahrscheinlichkeit eliminiert, und er darf nicht an anderer Stelle wieder eingeführt werden.

Hopf[2] hat für ergodische Systeme noch einen Mischungssatz bewiesen, der eine Präzisierung der Betrachtungen ist, die Gibbs[7] im 12. Kapitel seines Buches anstellte. Der Mischungssatz besagt, dass jede Dichteverteilung auf der Energiefläche sich nach sehr langer Zeit fast gleichförmig auf dieser verteilt. So bemerkenswert nun dieser Satz auch ist, mit der Tatsache, dass ein System nach einer gewissen Zeit einen thermodynamischen Gleichgewichtszustand erreicht, hat er wenig zu tun. Schon P. u. T. Ehrenfest haben nämlich bei der Kritik des Gibbs'schen 'Rührkapitels' darauf hingewiesen, dass die Zeiten, die nötig sind bis eine einigermassen gleichmässige Dichteverteilung erreicht wird, von der Grössenordnung der Poincaré'schen Wiederkehrzeiten sein müssen, während sich ja das thermodynamische Gleichgewicht meist recht schnell einstellt. Man muss sich hier klar machen, wie dieses Gleichgewicht zu kennzeichnen ist. Wir nehmen mit Boltzmann an, die Entropie eines Zustandes (E, α) sei durch

$$S(E, \alpha) = k \lg \Omega(E, \alpha)$$

gegeben. Messbare Entropiedifferenzen sind immer von der Grössenordnung kf. Wenn also der Zustand (E, α) eine merklich grössere Entropie als der Zustand (E, β) haben soll, so wird

$$\lg \Omega(E, \alpha) - \lg \Omega(E, \beta) = \epsilon f$$

sein, wobei ϵ eine kleine Zahl sein mag, ϵf aber immer noch sehr gross ist, da ja $f \sim 10^{20}$. Daher ist

$$\Omega(E, \alpha)/\Omega(E, \beta) = e^{\epsilon f}$$

ganz ungeheur gross, z.B. $\sim e^{10^{12}}$, was $\epsilon = 10^{-8}$ entspricht. Im Verlauf der Zeit kommen darum praktisch nur solche Zustände vor, für die $S(E, \alpha)$ beinahe unabhängig von α, also konstant ist. Fast unmessbar kleine Schwankungen der Entropie werden zwar auftreten. Sie entsprechen den statistischen Schwankungen des Systems um den Gleichgewichtszustand, z.B. seinen Dichteschwankungen. Der Übergang in diesen Gleichgewichtszustand tritt ein, indem der Phasenpunkt aus dem, verglichen mit $G_{E,\alpha}$

ungeheuer kleinem Gebiet $G_{E,\beta}$ herauswandert, und das ist meistens schon nach kurzer Zeit geschehen.

Die bisherigen Betrachtungen haben, so instruktiv sie sind, den grossen Mangel, dass sie, ihrer allzu grossen Allgemeinheit wegen, keinen Weg zeigen, wie die Behauptung (1.7) für ein konkretes System zu beweisen wäre.

van Hove [8] ist nun ein entscheidender, Schritt in dieser Richtung gelungen, indem er die Frage zum Ausgangspunkt nahm, wie ein System das Gleichgewicht erreicht.   Im Rahmen der Quanten-theorie ist dieses Problem zum ersten Male von Pauli [9] behandelt worden, der im Rahmen der Störungstheorie die Gleichung

$$\dot{X}_\alpha = \sum_\beta (X_\beta W_{\beta\alpha} - X_\alpha W_{\alpha\beta}) \qquad \ldots(1.8)$$

abgeleitet hat.   Hier ist $W_{\alpha\beta}$ die Übergangswahrscheinlichkeit vom Zustand α in den Zustand β.   Da $W_{\alpha\beta}/W_{\beta\alpha} = \Omega_\beta/\Omega_\alpha$, so folgt hieraus, dass die X_α asymptotisch zu Ω_α proportional werden. Pauli machte bei seiner Ableitung die Annahme, dass die Phasen des ungestörten Systems dauernd inkohärent seien, was einer Unordnungs-Annahme entspricht, wie sie auch in der Gastheorie üblich ist.

Das Ziel der Untersuchung van Hove's ist vor allem (1.8) herzuleiten, ohne von statistischen Annahmen Gebrauch zu machen.   Er betrachtet Systeme mit f Freiheitsgraden, die durch eine Hamiltonfunktion $H = H_0 + \lambda V$ beschrieben werden, wobei H_0 freie Teilchen oder Wellen, λV ihre Wechselwirkung beschreibt. Sind α Parameter, die die Eigenzustände von H_0 in natürlicher Weise beschreiben, dann sollen den makroskopischen Grössen Operatoren $A = A(\alpha)\delta_{\alpha\alpha'}$ entsprechen, wobei $A(\alpha)$ in α langsam variabel ist.

Ist

$$\varphi(t) = e^{-iHt}\varphi_0 \qquad \ldots(1.9)$$

die Schrödingerfunktion des Systems, und sind $C(\alpha)$ die Ent-wicklungskoeffizienten von φ_0 nach den Eigenzuständen von $A(\alpha)$, so ist der Erwartungswert von A zur Zeit t durch

$$\sum_{\alpha,\alpha'} C^\star(\alpha)C(\alpha')\langle\alpha|e^{iHt}Ae^{-iHt}|\alpha'\rangle = A(t) \qquad \ldots(1.10)$$

gegeben.   Nun macht van Hove von einer besonderen Eigen-schaft der Matrixprodukte der Gestalt

$$\langle\alpha|VA_1V\cdots,A_nV|\alpha'\rangle \qquad \ldots(1.11)$$

Gebrauch.   Er zeigt für die von ihm betrachteten Systeme, dass die Diagonalelemente $\alpha = \alpha'$ im limes $f = \infty$ sehr gross werden—sie

entsprechen den Selbstenergie-Termen der Strahlungstheorie—
und das ergibt eine $\delta(\alpha-\alpha')$—Singularität von (1.11) im limes
$f=\infty$. Indem er diese Eigenschaft ausnützt, wird nicht nur
Gebrauch von der Struktur der Systeme gemacht, sondern auch
von der besonderen Art, wie makroskopische Grössen charakterisiert sind. Aus der Eigenschaft der Matrix (1.11) folgt, dass
die Matrix in (1.10) die Form

$$\langle\alpha|e^{iHt}Ae^{-iHt}|\alpha'\rangle = \delta(\alpha-\alpha')f_1(\alpha)+f_2(\alpha,\alpha') \quad \dots(1.12)$$

besitzt, wobei f_2 keine δ-Singularitäten enthält. f_1 und f_2 sind
Funktionale von $A(\alpha)$ und Funktionen der Zeit:

$$f_1 = \int d\alpha''\, A(\alpha'')P(t;\alpha'',\alpha)$$
$$f_2 = \int d\alpha''\, A(\alpha'')J(t;\alpha'',\alpha',\alpha) \quad \dots(1.13)$$

Damit kann (1.10) wie folgt geschrieben werden:

$$A(t) = \int d\alpha''\, A(\alpha'') \int P(t;\alpha'',\alpha)|C(\alpha))^2\, d\alpha$$
$$+\int d\alpha''\, A(\alpha'') \int J(t;\alpha'',\alpha',\alpha)C^\star(\alpha')C(\alpha)d\alpha'd\alpha \quad \dots(1.14)$$

Nimmt man an, die $C(\alpha)$ seien inkohärent, so kann der 2. Term,
der Interferenzterm, in (1.14) gegen den ersten vernachlässigt
werden. In diesem Falle ist für den Verlauf von $A(t)$ die Funktion
$P(t:\alpha'',\alpha)$ allein massgebend, die offenbar die Wahrscheinlichkeit
darstellt zur Zeit t den Zustand α'' zu finden, wenn zur Zeit $t=0$
der Zustand α vorhanden war. van Hove hat für $P(t;\alpha'',\alpha)$ eine
Integro-Differentialgleichung hergeleitet, die dann, wenn λ als
klein gelten kann, zur Pauli'schen Gleichung (1.8) führt.
Die Annahme, die $C(\alpha)$ seien inkohärent ist eine Unordnungs-
annahme für die Zeit $t=0$, und diese genügt hier, während Pauli
angenommen hatte, die Phasen der Zustände seien zu jeder Zeit
inkohärent. van Hoves Herleitung der Transportgleichung (1.8)
ist also sicherlich ein Fortschritt. Auch ist es wahr, dass für den
Erwartungswert $\bar{A}(0)$ die Phasen der $C(\alpha)$ keine Rolle spielen,
weshalb man deren Inkohärenz dadurch rechtfertigen kann, dass
man sagt: wenn ein Beobachter sehr oft einen makroskopischen
Zustand, der durch Erwartungswerte von Operatoren A charakterisiert ist, herstellt, wird im Mittel der fernere zeitliche Ablauf
durch den 1. Term von (1.14) beschrieben. Im Einzelfall kann
zwar der Interferenzterm dieselbe Grössenordnung wie der 1. Term
besitzen, doch dies wird nur bei sehr speziellem Phasenverlauf der
$C(\alpha)$ eintreten. Eine mathematische Präzisierung dieser Behauptung fehlt freilich noch. Es schein aber, dass im limes $f=\infty$ der
Interferenzterm 'fast immer' verschwindend klein sein wird.
Schliesslich wollen wir noch bemerken, dass die Annahme, die

Operatoren A seien in den Variablen α diagonal, eine sehr weitgehende Schematisierung makroskopischer Observablen vorstellt. Wenn man z.B. ein Gas als Modell zugrunde legt, dann sind die α durch die Besetzungszahlen $n(\mathbf{k})$ der freien Teilchenzustände gegeben. Daher ist die räumliche Dichte $\rho(\mathbf{x})$ des Gases in diesem Falle keine makroskopische Variable und zwar auch dann nicht, wenn man ρ über kleine, aber doch makroskopische Volumina mittelt. Wenn es freilich gelingen sollte—und das scheint mir nicht aussichtslos—den Nachweis zu führen, dass für makroskopische Observablen A, und für 'fast alle' Werte der Phasen von $C(\alpha)$, der Interferenzterm relativ klein ist, dann würde man die schematische Darstellung der makroskopischen Zustände gerne in Kauf nehmen.

Schon jetzt lässt die Untersuchung van Hoves das Ergodenproblem in neuem Lichte erscheinen, da hier der Übergang ins thermodynamische Gleichgewicht mit spezifischen Eigenschaften makroskopischer Systeme und der in ihnen beobachtbaren Grössen in Verbindung gebracht wird.

2. DIE STATISTISCHEN GESAMTHEITEN UND IHR ZUSAMMENHANG MIT DER THERMODYNAMISCHEN BESCHREIBUNG

In einem ergodischen System, das die Energie E besitzt, ist der Zeitmittelwert einer makroskopischen Zustandsfunktion $g(E, \alpha)$ durch

$$g(E) = \sum_a g(E, \alpha)\Omega_{E,a}/\Omega_E$$

gegeben. Denkt man sich eine statistische Gesamtheit sehr vieler gleicher Systeme, deren Phasenpunkte mit der konstanten Dichte $1/\Omega(E)$ über die Energieschale verteilt sind, so sind die statistischen Mittelwerte der Funktionen $g(E, \alpha)$ gleich ihren Zeitmittelwerten.

Die statistische Gesamtheit kann dann formal die Zeitgesamtheit eines einzigen ergodischen Systems ersetzen. Wir nennen sie mit W. Gibbs 'mikrokanonische Gesamtheit'. Setzt man mit Boltzmann die Entropie $S(E, \alpha)$ eines Zustandes (E, α) gleich

$$S(E, \alpha) = k \lg \Omega_{E,a} \qquad \dots\dots(2.1)$$

so ist ihr Mittelwert

$$\bar{S}(E) = k \sum_a \frac{\Omega_{E,a}}{\Omega_E} \lg \Omega_{E,a} \qquad \dots\dots(2.2)$$

In der Summe (2.2) über α spielen, nach dem im 1. Abschnitt gesagten, nur die grössten Summanden eine Rolle, die alle, in Einheiten f gemessen, als gleich gross gelten können. Man kann darum (2.2) durch

$$k[\lg \Omega(E) - \lg M]$$

ersetzen, wobei M die Anzahl der massgebenden Summanden bedeutet. M ist die Anzahl der Zustände maximaler und annähernd gleicher Entropie, die sich makroskopisch unterscheiden lassen. Wenn nun für M irgend eine physikalisch plausible Anzahl angenommen wird, so wird doch $\lg M$ immer gegen f vernachlässigbar klein sein. Darum gilt mit sehr guter Näherung:

$$\bar{S}(E) \sim S(E) = k \lg \Omega(E) \qquad \ldots (2.3)$$

Streng genommen ist $S(E) > \bar{S}(E)$, wobei dieser Unterschied der Entropie der mittleren spontanen Abweichung der Systems vom thermodynamischen Gleichgewicht entspricht. Wir nennen $S(E)$ die 'mikrokanonische' Entropie. Sie ist die Entropie des thermodynamischen Gleichgewichtes.

Dass dies wirklich zutrifft, zeigt man bekanntlich dadurch, dass man zwei Systeme 1 und 2 betrachtet, die energetisch sehr schwach gekoppelt sind. Wenn sie die Energiewerte E_1, E_2 besitzen, so ist ihre gemeinsame Phasenausdehnung durch $\Omega_1(E_1)\Omega_2(E_2)$ gegeben; ihre Gesamtentropie ist daher

$$S(E_1; E_2) = S_1(E_1) + S_2(E_2) \qquad \ldots (2.4)$$

Dem Gleichgewicht bei gegebener Gesamtenergie $E_1 + E_2$ entspricht nun derjenige Wert von E_1 bei dem (2.4) seinen Maximalwert annimmt:

$$\frac{\partial S_1}{\partial E_1} = \frac{\partial S_2(E - E_1)}{\partial E} \qquad \ldots (2.5)$$

Setzt man

$$\frac{\partial S}{\partial E} = \frac{1}{T} \qquad \ldots (2.6)$$

so muss T die absolute Temperatur bedeuten; denn im Gleichgewicht sind die Temperaturen der beiden Systeme gleich. Bei den Differentationen (2.5) und (2.6) werden äussere Parameter des Systems, wie etwa sein Volumen, konstant gehalten. Darum entspricht in (2.6) das Differential dE der dem System reversibel zugeführten Wärme. Diese Ergebnisse rechtfertigen die Interpretation von $k \lg \Omega(E)$ als thermodynamische Entropie.

Wenn mit einem grossen System mit F Freiheitsgraden ein kleines System mit f Freiheitsgraden gekoppelt ist, so kann man sich einen Beobachter denken, der die Gesamtenergie E, und überdies den mikroskopischen Zustand des kleinen Systems messen kann. Ein makroskopischer Zustand ist somit durch E und die Angabe beschrieben, dass die p_k, q_k des kleinen Systems in den Intervallen dp_k, dq_k liegen.

Nimmt man an, dass nur Zustände mit merklicher Häufigkeit auftreten, für welche die Energie H_f des kleines Systems sehr klein gegen E ist, so kann, im Sinne einer Entwicklung nach H_f, die Phasenausdehnung eines Zustandes wie folgt geschrieben werden:

$$\Omega(E, \alpha) = \mathrm{e}^{-(1/kT)H_f(p,q)}\, dp\,dq \cdot \Omega_F(E) \qquad \ldots (2.7)$$

Dabei ist $\Omega_F(E)$ die Phasenausdehnung des grossen Systems, und T seine Temperatur:

$$\frac{\partial S_F(E)}{\partial E} = \frac{1}{T}.$$

(2.7) ist die Maxwell–Boltzmann'sche Verteilung. Eine Gesamtheit, die gemäss (2.7) verteilt ist, heisst 'kanonische Gesamtheit'. Man kann das grosse System als ein Wärmebad der Temperatur T ansehen, in dem das kleine System enthalten ist. Die Phasenausdehnung der Energieschale des Gesamtsystems ist durch

$$\Omega_F(E) \int \mathrm{e}^{(1/kT)H_f}\, dp\,dq = \Omega_F(E) \cdot Z_f(T) \qquad \ldots (2.8)$$

gegeben. Das Integral Z_f heisst das Zustandsintegral. Dieses kann wie folgt geschrieben werden:

$$Z_f(T) = \int_0^\infty \omega_f(\epsilon)\mathrm{e}^{-\epsilon/kT}\, d\epsilon \qquad \ldots (2.9)$$

Nun entspricht $\omega_f(\epsilon)\Delta\epsilon = \Omega_f(\epsilon)$ der mikrokanonischen Beschreibung des kleinen Systems. Der Übergang zum Zustandsintegral $Z_f(T)$ ist eine Laplace Transformation, die von der extensiven Variablen ϵ, der Energie, auf die intensive Variable T, die Temperatur, führt. Thermodynamisch entspricht ihr die Berührungstransformation (Legendre'sche Transformation).

$$\psi(T) = S(E) - \frac{1}{T}\, E; \qquad \frac{\partial \psi}{\partial(1/T)} = -E \qquad \ldots (2.10)$$

wo ψ die Planck'sche, charakteristische Funktion bedeutet. (2.9) und (2.10) sind dann äquivalent, wenn der Integrand in (2.9) ein sehr scharfes Maximum besitzt, oder, was auf dasselbe herauskommt, wenn die Energieschwankungen in der kanonischen

Gesamtheit sehr klein bleiben. Dies trifft immer dann zu, wenn auch die thermodynamische Transformation (2.10) nicht ausgeartet ist, d.h. wenn das System thermodynamisch ebensogut durch die (intensive) Temperatur, wie durch seine (extensive) Energie beschrieben werden kann. Die Phasenregel von Gibbs lehrt, wann das der Fall ist. Z.B. ist für ein homogenes Einstoffsystem am Tripelpunkt die Beschreibung durch $\psi(T)$ unvollständig, denn hier wird durch (2.10) einem endlichen Energieintervall eine einzige Temperatur zugeordnet.

In derartigen Fällen liefert die kanonische Gesamtheit meist keine zutreffende Beschreibung des Systems und kann z.b. nicht zur Berechnung seiner Energieschwankungen verwendet werden. Man hat hier auch zu bedenken, dass bei der Herleitung der Formel (2.8) die Wechselwirkung des Systems mit dem Wärmebad vernachlässigt wird. Das ist nun zwar gewöhnlich zulässig, denn es handelt sich um Oberflächeneffekte. Diese werden aber gerade dann, wenn sich die Schwankungen anomal verhalten, entscheidend.

Wenn man aus einem grossen System ein relativ kleines Teilvolumen herausgreift, in dem auch die Teilchenzahl variabel ist, gelangt man zur 'grossen kanonischen Gesamtheit'. Ist $Z_N(T)$ das Zustandsintegral, das das Verhalten von N Teilchen im betrachteten Volumen beschreibt, so ist diese Gesamtheit durch

$$P(T, \lambda) = \sum_{N=0}^{\infty} e^{-\lambda N} Z_N(T) \qquad \ldots (2.11)$$

charakterisiert. Per definitionem wird hier $Z_0 = 1$ gesetzt. Die Laplace Transformation, die von Z_N nach $P(\lambda)$ führt, entspricht der Berührungstransformation der Thermodynamik, die anstelle der Molenzahl das chemische Potential einführt. Aus der Phasenregel kann man wieder schliessen, wann die beiden Beschreibungen gleichwertig sind.

Auch bei der Ableitung von (2.11) ist angenommen, dass die Wechselwirkung des Teilvolumens mit seiner Umgebung vernachlässigt werden könne. An Kondensationsstellen, am Kritischen Punkt, oder immer dann, wenn sich die Schwankungen der Teilchenzahlen, die man aus (2.11) gewinnt, als anomal erweisen, hat man die Wechselwirkung mit der Umgebung, die einen Oberflächeneffekt darstellt, zu berücksichtigen, was nur im Rahmen der kanonischen Gesamtheit möglich sein wird.

Alle bisherigen Überlegungen können ohne weiteres auf eine quantenmechanische Theorie übertragen werden. Anstelle der Phasenausdehnung der Energieschale tritt dabei die Anzahl der

stationären Zustände im Energieintervall ΔE, anstelle des
Zustandsintegrals die Zustandssumme

$$\sum_n e^{-E_n/kT} = Z(T)$$

wo E_n die Energieeigenwerte des Systems sind, und wo über alle
stationären Zustände n summiert wird. Macht man von hier den
Grenzübergang zur klassischen Mechanik, so kommt man nicht
genau zu den bisherigen Formeln zurück. Wenn nämlich das
System aus N gleichartigen Teilchen besteht, so erhält man
anstelle der klassischen Phasenausdehnung selber, deren durch $N!$
dividierten Wert.

Schon Gibbs hat bemerkt, dass die durch $k \lg \Omega_E$ erklärte
Entropie eines Gases sich nicht als extensive Grösse erweist, und
hat darum vorgeschlagen, anstelle der spezifischen Phase Ω_E die
'generische Phase' $(1/N!)\Omega(E)$ zu verwenden. Eine überzeugende
Begründung dieses Vorschlages lässt sich wohl im Rahmen der
klassischen Mechanik nicht geben. Denn es ist nicht einzusehen,
warum die Entropie, die sich ja prinzipiell immer auf das Gesamt-
system bezieht, proportional zu seiner Grösse sein sollte.

Wie Einstein[10] 1924 die von Bose entdeckte Statistik auf die
Theorie idealer Gase anwandte, erschien es ihm auch paradox,
dass nach dieser Theorie die Entropie eines Gases, das aus mehreren, voneinander beliebig wenig verschiedenen Teilchensorten
besteht sich anders verhält, als diejenige eines Gases, dessen
Teilchen überhaupt nicht unterschieden werden können. Denn
damit wird in die Theorie eine schwer verständliche Unstetigkeit
hereingebracht. Diese begreifen wir heute als Quanteneffekt: die
einzigen Symmetrieklassen der Wellenfunktion, die in der Natur
vorkommen, sind bei gleichen Teilchen, je nach ihrem Spin, die
symmetrische oder die antisymmetrische.

Die Quantentheorie liefert darum automatisch immer die
'generische Phase'. Wenn ferner klassisch die Phasenausdehnung
eine dimensionsbehaftete Grösse ist, weshalb in der Entropie
eine additive Konstante willkürlich bleibt, so ist quantentheoretisch Ω_E eine Anzahl. Darum bietet sich hier eine einfache und
natürliche Möglichkeit, die Entropiekonstante zu normieren.
Auch erweist sich der 3. Hauptsatz Nernst's, und damit die
'Entartung' der Zustandsgleichungen bei tiefen Temperaturen als
Folge der Quantentheorie.

Es ist sehr bemerkenswert, dass sich hier überall die allgemeinen und formalen Prinzipien, die W. Gibbs in seiner *Statistischen Mechanik* hervorgehoben hat, als gänzlich unabhängig von
dem speziellen, klassisch-mechanischen Modell, erweisen. Desto

sonderbarer muss es scheinen, dass Nernst[11] seinen Artikel zum
hundertsten Geburtstag von W. Gibbs mit dem Satze schliesst:
'Sein Versuch, eine widerspruchslose Mechanik zu schaffen,
scheiterte an der Nichtberücksichtigung der Quantentheorie,
sodass diese Arbeit schon bei ihrem Erscheinen antiquiert war'.

Die Verkehrtheit dieses Urteils lässt die Sicherheit, mit der
Gibbs die wesentlichen Begriffe herausgearbeitet hat, nur in desto
hellerem Licht erscheinen.

3. THEORIE DER DICHTESCHWANKUNGEN, INSBESONDERE IN DER NÄHE EINES KRITISCHEN PUNKTES

Wenn ein in einem grossen Volumen V enthaltenes Teilvolumen
v durch die grosse kanonische Gesamtheit beschrieben werden
kann, so ist das mittlere Schwankungsquadrat der Teilchenzahl
n in v durch

$$\overline{\Delta n^2} = kT \frac{\partial \rho}{\partial p} \cdot \bar{n} \qquad \ldots \ldots (3.1)$$

gegeben, wo ρ die Teilchendichte und p den Druck bedeutet.
Diese Formel verliert an einer kritischen Stelle, oder überhaupt
dort, wo das Schwankungsquadrat anomal wird, d.h. nicht
proportional zu $\bar{n}$ ist, ihren Sinn.   Wir haben im vorhergehenden
Abschnitt darauf hingewiesen, dass in diesen Fällen die Koppelung
der Teilchen in v mit denjenigen in der Umgebung von v nicht
mehr vernachlässigt werden kann.   Die Folge hievon ist, dass
Dichteschwankungen in benachbarten Volumenelementen—auch
wenn diese eine makroskopische Ausdehnung besitzen—korreliert
werden.

Eine Theorie der Schwankungen in der Nähe des kritischen
Punktes ist zuerst von Ornstein und Zernicke[12] entwickelt worden.
Wir wollen hier das Ergebnis dieser Autoren in etwas anderer,
und wie uns scheint übersichtlicherer Art, herleiten.   Dabei
folgen wir teilweise der Darstellung von Klein und Tisza.[13]

Entsprechend dem, was wir oben ausgeführt haben, gehen wir
von der kanonischen Gesamtheit aus und betrachten ein Gas der
Temperatur T im Volumen V.   Wir denken uns das Volumen V
in viele kleine, aber doch makroskopische Teilvolumina v_k
eingeteilt, deren Ort je durch eine Koordinate $\mathbf{X}_k$ gegeben sein soll.
Die Zahl der Teilchen im Volumen v_k sei n_k, und wir betrachten
Zustände, in welchen die n_k nur langsam mit $\mathbf{X}_k$ variieren.   In

diesem Falle kann man den n_k eine molare, makroskopische Dichte $\rho(\mathbf{X})$ zuordnen:

$$\rho(\mathbf{X}) \sim \rho(\mathbf{X}_k) = \frac{n_k}{v_k \cdot L} \qquad \ldots (3.2)$$

Hier ist L die Loschmidt'Zahl. Im Sinne der kanonischen Gesamtheit bestimmt die Wahrscheinlichkeit $W(n_k)$ eines Zustandes seine freie Energie F gemäss

$$F/kT = -\lg W(n_k) \qquad \ldots (3.3)$$

Die freie Energie ist somit ein Funktional der Dichte $\rho(\mathbf{X})$. Nun ist es freilich unmöglich, dieses Funktional für ein bestimmtes Gasmodell zu berechnen. So wie man aber in der Gleichung (3.1) die Funktion $\rho(p)$ aus der phänomenologischen Zustandsgleichung entnimmt, so werden wir auch hier einen phänomenologischen Ansatz für $F[\rho(\mathbf{X})]$ machen, worauf uns (3.3) die Wahrscheinlichkeitsverteilung von $\rho(\mathbf{X})$ liefert. Diesen Weg ist auch Einstein[13] gegangen, als er die Theorie der statistischen Schwankungen begründete. Sei ρ_0 die mittlere Dichte, so setzen wir $\rho = \rho_0 + \mu$, und nehmen an, die Abweichungen der Dichte ρ von ihrem Mittelwert ρ_0 sei en hinreichend klein. Dann können wir $F[\rho]$ nach μ entwickeln:

$$F(\rho) - F(\rho_0) = \varphi[\mu] = \tfrac{1}{2} \int dv_x \int dv_y f(\mathbf{x}-\mathbf{y})\mu(\mathbf{x})\mu(\mathbf{y}) \qquad \ldots (3.4)$$

Lineare Terme in μ treten keine auf, weil F für $\mu = 0$ sein Minimum annimmt. Für ein homogenes, isotropes System hängt f nur von $|\mathbf{x}-\mathbf{y}|$ ab. Man wird erwarten, dass $f(\mathbf{x})$ nur für Werte von $|\mathbf{x}|$, die mit der Reichweite der Molekularkräfte vergleichbar sind, von Null verschieden ist. Wir entwickeln nun $\mu(\mathbf{x})$ in V in eine Fourier-Reihe:

$$\mu(\mathbf{x}) = \sum_k e^{i\mathbf{k}\cdot\mathbf{x}}\lambda(\mathbf{k}) \, ; \, \lambda(\mathbf{k}) = \frac{1}{V} \int e^{-i\mathbf{k}\cdot\mathbf{x}}\mu(\mathbf{x}) \, dv \qquad \ldots (3.5)$$

Da $\mu(\mathbf{x})$ reell ist, gilt

$$\lambda(\mathbf{k}) = \lambda^\star(-\mathbf{k}) \qquad \ldots (3.5')$$

Setzt man das in (3.4) ein, so folgt

$$\varphi = \tfrac{1}{2}V \sum_k g(k^2)|\lambda(\mathbf{k})|^2$$
$$g(k^2) = \int f(\mathbf{x})e^{-i\mathbf{k}\cdot\mathbf{x}} \, dv \qquad \ldots (3.6)$$

Hier wurde benützt, dass die Reichweite von $f(\mathbf{x})$ sehr klein ist, weshalb bei der Integration in (3.4) diejenige über $\frac{1}{2}(\mathbf{x}+\mathbf{y})$ den Faktor V in (3.6) liefert.

Wir setzen

$$\lambda(\mathbf{k}) = \alpha(\mathbf{k})+i\beta(\mathbf{k}) \qquad \ldots (3.7)$$

dann gilt

$$\varphi = V \sum_{k}' g(k^2)(\alpha^2(\mathbf{k})+\beta^2(\mathbf{k})) \qquad \ldots (3.8)$$

wobei die $\sum_{k}'$ nur über einen Halbraum von $\mathbf{k}$ erstreckt wird. In diesem sind die $\alpha(\mathbf{k})$ und die $\beta(\mathbf{k})$ alle voneinander unabhängig. Insbesondere sind sie statistisch unabhängig, denn gemäss (3.3) bestimmt φ ihre Wahrscheinlichkeitsverteilung. Man findet darum

$$\overline{\mu(\mathbf{x})\mu(\mathbf{y})} = \sum_{k} e^{i\mathbf{k}\cdot(\mathbf{x}-\mathbf{y})}\overline{(\alpha^2(\mathbf{k})+\beta^2(\mathbf{k}))}$$

$$= \frac{kT}{V}\sum_{k}' \frac{e^{i\mathbf{k}\cdot(\mathbf{x}-\mathbf{y})}}{g(k^2)} \qquad \ldots (3.9)$$

Um das Verhalten von (3.9), für grosse Werte von $(\mathbf{x}-\mathbf{y})$ zu studieren, entwickeln wir $g(k^2)$ nach Potenzen von k^2:

$$g(k^2) = g_0+g_1 k^2+\cdots \qquad \ldots (3.10)$$

Ersetzt man nun in (3.9) die Summe durch ein Integral, so erhält man mit (3.10):

$$\overline{\mu(\mathbf{x})\mu(\mathbf{y})} \sim \frac{kT}{g_1}\frac{\exp\{-(g_0/g_1)^{\frac{1}{2}}\cdot|\mathbf{x}-\mathbf{y}|\}}{4\pi|\mathbf{x}-\mathbf{y}|} \qquad \ldots (3.11)$$

Das ist die Formel von Ornstein und Zernicke. Die Schwankungen der Molenzahl N in einem Volumen v ist durch

$$\overline{\Delta N^2} = \int dv_x \int dv_y\, \overline{\mu(\mathbf{x})\mu(\mathbf{y})} \qquad \ldots (3.12)$$

gegeben. Ist die Reichweite der Korrelationsfunktion (3.11) klein gegen die Lineardimensionen von v, so erhält man

$$\overline{\Delta N^2} = \frac{vkT}{g_0} \qquad \ldots (3.13)$$

Vergleicht man das mit (3.1), so erkennt man, dass

$$g_0 = \frac{1}{\rho}\frac{\partial p}{\partial \rho} \qquad \ldots (3.14)$$

In der Nähe des kritischen Punktes verschwindet $\partial p/\partial \rho$, also auch g_0. Dann werden die Schwankungen anomal:

$$\overline{\Delta N^2} \sim \frac{kT}{g_1}\cdot v^{5/3} \qquad \ldots (3.15)$$

Wir wollen nun zeigen, was die phänomenologische Bedeutung von g_1 ist.

Im Sinne der Entwicklung (3.10) schreiben wir

$$\varphi(\mu) = \tfrac{1}{2}g_0 \int_V \mu^2 \, dv + \tfrac{1}{2}g_1 \int_V (\text{grad } \mu)^2 \, dv \quad \dots (3.16)$$

Wir betrachten ein Volumen v, dessen Dimensionen gross gegen $(g_1/g_0)^{1/2}$ sind und fragen nach der wahrscheinlichsten Schwankung $\mu(\mathbf{x})$, die zu einem vorgegebenen ΔN führt. Das heisst, (3.16) soll unter der Nebenbedingung

$$\int_v \mu(\mathbf{x}) \, dv = \Delta N = \mu_0 v \quad \dots (3.17)$$

zum Minimum gemacht werden. Nennen wir die Lösung dieses Variationsproblems $\mu_{\Delta N}(\mathbf{x})$, so liefert $\varphi[\mu_{\Delta N}] = \varphi(\mu_0)$ die Wahrscheinlichkeit, die Schwankung ΔN in v zu finden.

$\mu_{\Delta N}(\mathbf{x})$ ist im Inneren von v praktisch gleich μ_0 und verschwindet in der Nähe seiner Oberfläche. Dort verhält sich $|\text{grad } \mu_{\Delta N}|$ wie $\tfrac{1}{2}\mu_0(g_0/g_1)^{1/2} \exp\{-(g_0/g_1)^{1/2} \cdot r\}$, wo r den Abstand von der Oberfläche von v bedeutet. Darum wird

$$\varphi(\mu_0) = \tfrac{1}{2}\mu_0^2\{g_0 v + \tfrac{1}{4}(g_0 g_1)^{1/2} O\} \quad \dots (3.18)$$

wobei O die Oberfläche des Volumens v bedeutet. Die Schwankung ΔN in v gibt somit zu einer Oberflächenspannung $\tfrac{1}{8}(g_0 g_1)^{1/2}\mu_0^2$ Anlass, die allerdings solange $v^{1/3} \gg (g_1/g_0)^{1/2}$ ist, vernachlässigt werden kann. Während sich also, im Falle normaler Schwankungen, g_1 nur in kleinen Oberflächenkorrekturen äussert, sind die Schwankungen am kritischen Punkt durch g_1 bestimmt. Y. Roccard,[15] der als erster die Terme $\sim g_1$ betrachtet hat und mit der Kapillarität in Verbindung brachte, hat mit Hilfe gaskinetischer Betrachtungen für g_1 den Wert $a\sigma^2/6$ hergeleitet, wobei a die Van der Waals'sche Konstante in

$$\left(p + \frac{a}{v^2}\right)(v - b) = RT$$

und σ den Wirkungsradius der Moleküle bedeutet. Diese Abschätzung dürfte grössenordnungsmässig richtig sein. Infolge inkonsequenten Vorgehens gelangt aber Roccard schliesslich nicht zur Formel von Ornstein und Zernicke (3.11), die aber an kritischen Gemischen gut bestätigt ist (vergl. B. H. Zimm, *J. phys. Chem.* **54**, 306, 1950).

4. DICHTESCHWANKUNGEN EINES IDEALEN QUANTENGASES

Die im vorigen Abschnitt dargestellte Theorie der Dichteschwankungen ist halb—phänomenologischer Art und stützt sich wesentlich auf den Zusammenhang der freien Energie mit der Wahrscheinlichkeit in der kanonischen Gesamtheit. Eine Theorie auf rein statistisch-mechanischer Grundlage ist für ein ideales Quantengas möglich, das im Entartungsgebiet bekanntlich anomale Schwankungen zeigt. Diese sind verschieden, je nachdem man die Einstein–Bose oder die Fermi–Dirac Statistik zugrunde legt.

Pauli[16] hat in seiner Arbeit über den Paramagnetismus der Alkalien als erster auf den in dieser Hinsicht charakteristischen Unterschied der beiden Fälle hingewiesen. Diese Arbeit, die ja für die Metalltheorie grundlegend geworden ist, enhält in der Einleitung auch die erste übersichtliche Behandlung des idealen Bose und Fermi Gases mit Hilfe der Gibbs'schen grossen Gesamtheit.

Wir betrachten zuerst ein Bosegas, das durch eine quantisierte Wellenfunktion ψ beschrieben sein soll. Das Volumen V fassen wir der Bequemlichkeit halber als Periodizitätsbereich auf. Es ist dann

$$\psi = \frac{1}{V^{1/2}} \sum_k a_k e^{ikx} \qquad \dots (4.1)$$

wobei die a_k den Vertauschungsrelationen

$$a_k a_l^\star - a_l^\star a_k = \delta_{kl}; \qquad a_k^\star a_k = N_k \qquad \dots (4.2)$$

genügen sollen. Der Dichteoperator $\rho(\mathbf{x})$ ist durch

$$\rho(\mathbf{x}) = \frac{1}{V} \sum_{k,l} a_k^\star a_l e^{i(\mathbf{k}-\mathbf{l}),\mathbf{x}} \qquad \dots (4.3)$$

gegeben, und es ist

$$\rho(x)\rho(y) = \frac{1}{V^2} \sum a_k^\star a_l a_m^\star a_n e^{i(k-l)x+i(n-m)y} \qquad \dots (4.4)$$

Man bilde nun den Erwartungswert von (4.3) und (4.4) über eine Gesamtheit, in welcher zwischen den a_k keine Phasenbeziehungen existieren. Das liefert

$$\langle \rho(x) \rangle = \frac{1}{V} \sum_k N_k = \frac{N}{V} \qquad \dots (4.5)$$

$$\langle \rho(x)\rho(y)\rangle = \left(\frac{N}{V}\right)^2 + \frac{1}{V^2}\sum_{k,l} N_k N_l e^{i(k-l)(x-y)} + \frac{N}{V}\delta(x-y)$$

$$-\frac{1}{V^2}(N + \sum_k N_k{}^2) \qquad \dots (4.6)$$

Dabei wurden die Vertauschungsrelationen der a_k benützt. Ferner ist

$$\sum_l e^{il(x-y)} = V \cdot \delta(x-y)$$

Nun machen wir, bei festem N/V, den Grenzübergang $V \to \infty$. In den Summen (4.5) und (4.6) ist dabei der Term, welcher dem Grundzustand entspricht, (N_0), explicite hinzuschreiben; die restliche Summe kann sodann durch ein Integral ersetzt werden. Mit

$$\lim_{V=\infty} \frac{N_0}{V} = \rho_0; \qquad \lim_{V=\infty} \frac{1}{V}\sum_{k\neq 0} N_k e^{ik\cdot(x-y)} = b(r); \qquad r = |\mathbf{x}-\mathbf{y}|$$

$$\dots (4.7)$$

erhält man

$$\langle \rho(x)\rho(y)\rangle - \langle \rho\rangle^2 = 2\rho_0 b(r) + b^2(r) + \langle \rho\rangle\delta(x-y) \qquad \dots (4.8)$$

ρ_0 ist dabei die Teilchendichte im Grundzustand. $b(r)$ kann ausgewertet werden, indem man in (4.7) für die N_k die Werte einsetzt, welche die grosse kanonische Gesamtheit liefert.

$$b(r, \lambda) = \frac{1}{r}\frac{1}{(2\pi)^2}\int_{-\infty}^{+\infty} \frac{k \sin kr}{e^{k^2/k_0{}^2 + \lambda} - 1}\, dk; \qquad k_0{}^2 = \frac{2mkT}{\hbar^2} \qquad \dots (4.9)$$

$$b(0, \lambda) = \rho \qquad \dots (4.10)$$

bestimmt, falls $\lambda \neq 0$, die mittlere Dichte. Dann ist $\rho_0 = 0$. $\lambda = 0$ ist die Kondensationsstelle des Bose Gases und dort hat man

$$\rho = \rho_0 + b(0, 0) \qquad \dots (4.11)$$

zu setzen. $b(0, 0)$ stellt die Dichte der Gasphase, ρ_0 diejenige der kondensierten Phase dar, wobei ρ fest vorgegeben ist. Der Gebrauch der grossen Gesamtheit, auch im Kondensationsgebiet, ist erlaubt, da wie sich zeigen lässt, [16a] die relativen Schwankungen der N_k auch hier klein bleiben.

Das asymptotische Verhalten von $b(r)$ für $k_0 r \gg 1$, $\lambda \ll 1$, wo $e^{k^2/k_0{}^2 + \lambda} - 1$ durch $k^2/k_0{}^2 + \lambda$ ersetzt werden kann, ist durch

$$b(r, \lambda) \sim \frac{k_0{}^3}{4\pi}\frac{e^{-\lambda^{1/2}\cdot k_0 r}}{k_0 r} \qquad \dots (4.12)$$

gegeben. Im Kondensationsgebiet sind somit die Schwankungen

wieder anomal. Sie sind hauptsächlich durch den Term $2\rho_0 b(r)$ bestimmt, welcher einer Interferenz zwischen dem Grundzustand, d.h. dem Kondensat, und dem Gas entspricht. Die Schwankung der Teilchenzahl in einem Volumen v ist hier durch

$$\overline{\Delta n^2} = n_0 n_1^{2/3}; \qquad n_0 = \rho_0 v; \qquad n_1 = b(0,0)v$$

gegeben.

Die analoge Rechnung lässt sich für ein Fermi Gas durchführen. Man erhält hier

$$\langle \rho(x)\rho(y)\rangle - \langle \rho\rangle^2 = \frac{N}{V}\,\delta(x-y) - f^2(r);$$

$$f(r) = \frac{1}{(2\pi)^2 r}\int_{-\infty}^{+\infty} \frac{k\sin kr\,dk}{e^{k^2/k_0^2+\lambda}+1} \qquad \ldots(4.13)$$

Kondensation tritt hier nicht ein, sodass Terme mit ρ_0 fehlen. Wir wollen den Fall sehr starker Entartung betrachten. Sei $K = |\lambda|^{1/2}\cdot k_0$ wobei $k_0 \to 0$, K endlich. Dann wird

$$f(r) = \frac{1}{2\pi^2}\frac{1}{r^3}(\sin Kr - Kr\cos Kr) \qquad \ldots(4.14)$$

$$f(0) = \frac{1}{6\pi^2}K^3 = \rho \qquad \ldots(4.15)$$

Für das Schwankungsquadrat der Teilchenzahl n in einem kugelförmigen Volumen vom Radius R findet man

$$\overline{\Delta n^2} = \frac{(KR)^2}{2\pi^2}[\lg KR - 1{,}588\cdots] \qquad \ldots(4.16)$$

oder

$$\overline{\Delta n^2} \sim n^{2/3}\lg n \qquad \ldots(4.17)$$

Auch hier sind also die Schwankungen anomal. Sie sind viel kleiner als im klassisch-idealen Gas, verschwinden aber, auch bei völliger Entartung, nicht. Sie sind aber nicht zum Volumen des betrachteten Teilraumes, sondern zu seiner Oberfläche proportional. Die grosse kanonische Gesamtheit liefert bekanntlich $\overline{\Delta n^2} = 0$, weil in ihr Oberflächeneffekte jeder Art immer vernachlässigt sind.

5. DIE THEORIE DER ZUSTANDSGLEICHUNG UND DER PHASENUMWANDLUNGEN

Wenn für ein mechanisches Modell, das z.B. N Atome im Volumen V beschreibt, $\Omega_N(E, V)$ oder $Z_N(T, V)$ berechnet werden kann, so sind seine Zustandsgleichungen bekannt.

Ist $\phi(r)$ das Potential der Wechselwirkung zweier Atome im Abstand r, so ist die wesentliche Aufgabe die Berechnung des konfigurativen Zustandsintegrals:

$$Q_N(T, V) = \frac{1}{N!} \int_V (d\mathbf{q})^N e^{-\frac{1}{kT} \sum_{i>k} \phi(\mathbf{q}_i - \mathbf{q}_k)} \qquad \ldots (5.1)$$

Im allgemeinen erweist sich diese Aufgabe als unlösbar. Im Prinzip ist aber durch (5.1) das Verhalten des Systems bei allen Temperaturen und Dichten bestimmt; also sollte auch die Verflüssigung und die Kristallisation des Gasmodells durch (5.1) beschrieben werden.

Phasenumwandlungen äussern sich thermodynamisch als Unstetigkeiten der Zustandsgleichungen oder ihrer Ableitungen. Man kann aber nicht erwarten, dass $Q_N(T, V)$ ein unstetiges Verhalten zeigen wird. Singularitäten können nur im limes $N, V \to \infty$ auftreten. Bei diesem Grenzübergang hält man N/V fest, und darum ist es zweckmässig, zur grossen kanonischen Gesamtheit überzugehen, weil für grosse Systeme N/V durch das chemische Potential λ bestimmt wird. Da es nur auf Q_N ankommt, setzen wir

$$P(z, T, V) = \sum_0^\infty z^N Q_N(V, T); \qquad Q_0 = 1 \qquad \ldots (5.2)$$

Dabei ist z die sog. Fugazität. Die Zustandsgleichung ist dann durch die Grenzwerte

$$\frac{p}{kT} = \lim_{V = \infty} \frac{1}{V} \lg P(z, T, V) \qquad \ldots (5.3)$$

$$\rho = \lim_{V = \infty} \frac{\partial}{\partial \lg z} \frac{1}{V} \lg P(z, T, V) \qquad \ldots (5.4)$$

gegeben. Dabei bedeutet p den Druck, ρ die Teilchendichte.

Lee und Yang[17] sowie van Hove[18] haben bewiesen, dass für alle positiv-reellen Werte von z der Grenzwert (5.3), unabhängig von der Gestalt von V, existiert und eine monotone, stetige Funktion von z liefert. Die Ableitung von (5.3) nach z kann unstetig sein. Die Unstetigkeitsstellen entsprechen Punkten, in denen eine Phasenumwandlung stattfindet.

Nimmt man an, $\phi(r)$ werde für $r > r_0$ sehr gross und positiv, so bedeutet das, dass die Atome ein Eigenvolumen v_0 besitzen. Also ist N immer kleiner als $N_0 = V/v_0$. $P(z, T, V)$ ist darum ein Polynom in z vom Grade N_0. Mit Yang und Lee kann man sich für dieses Modell klar machen, wie und unter welchen mathematischen Bedingungen die Reihen (5.3) und (5.4) in der Grenze $V \to \infty$ singulär werden können. Die Nullstellen von $P(z)$, die wir ζ_a nennen wollen, liegen auf der Komplexen z-Ebene, wobei die reelle Achse von ihnen frei bleibt. Man kann nun das Polynom P in Linearfaktoren zerlegen, und dann gilt

$$\frac{1}{V}\lg P(z) = \frac{1}{V}\sum_a \lg\left(1 - \frac{z}{\zeta_a}\right) \qquad \ldots\ldots(5.5)$$

In der Grenze eines sehr grossen Volumens führt man auf der ζ-Ebene eine Nullstellendichte $d\mu(\zeta, T)$ ein und schreibt

$$\frac{p}{kT} = \int d\mu(\zeta, T)\lg\left(1 - \frac{z}{\zeta}\right); \qquad \int d\mu(\zeta, T) = \frac{1}{v_0} \quad \ldots\ldots(5.6)$$

Man erkennt, dass $p(z)$ dem Potential entspricht, dass durch die Ladungsdichte $d\mu(\zeta)$ erzeugt wird. Auf der reellen z-Achse kann darum $p(z)$ nur dann singulär werden, wenn diese an einer Stelle z_0 von einer Kurve geschnitten wird, die in der Umgebung von z_0 schon eine endliche Ladung enthält. Beim Grenzübergang müssen sich also die Nullstellen auf dieser Kurve in der Nähe des Punktes z_0 häufen. Der Sprung der Teilchendichte ρ, der beim Überschreiten der Stelle z_0 auftritt, ist proportional zur linearen Ladungsdichte auf der Kurve an der Stelle z_0.

Yang und Lee[19] haben ferner diese Verhältnisse anhand des Ising Modells näher analysiert. Dies wurde zwar ursprünglich als Modell eines Ferromagneticums eingeführt. Man kann es aber in unserem Zusammenhang auch als Modell eines 'Gittergases' beschreiben:

In einem ebenen Quadratgitter ist jeder Gitterpunkt entweder leer, oder er kann von höchstens einem Atom besetzt sein. Nur Atome in benachbarten Gitterpunkten besitzen eine Wechselwirkung mit der Energie $-U$. Ein solches 'Gas' kondensiert unterhalb der kritischen Temperatur T_c, die durch

$$\exp\left(-\frac{U}{2kT_c}\right) = 2^{1/2} - 1$$

gegeben ist.[20] Die Wurzeln des Polynoms $P(z)$ liegen hier alle auf einem Kreis vom Radius $e^{-2U/kT}$ um $z = 0$. Die Dichte der Wurzeln ist freilich nur an den beiden Stellen bekannt, in welchen der Kreis die reelle Achse der z-Ebene schneidet.

Der Dampfdruck und die Dichten der gasförmigen und der kondensierten Phase, ρ_g und ρ_k sind aber bekannt und durch

$$p/kT = \lg(1+x) + \frac{1}{2\pi}\int_\alpha^\pi \lg\tfrac{1}{2}\{1 + (1 - K\sin^2\varphi)^{1/2}\}\,d\varphi \quad \ldots\ldots(5.7)$$

mit

$$x = e^{U/kT}; \qquad K = \frac{16x(1-x)^2}{(1+x)^4}$$

$$\rho_g + \rho_k = 1; \qquad \rho_g = \tfrac{1}{2}\left(1 - \left[\frac{1+x}{(1-x)^2}(1-6x+x^2)\right]^{1/4}\right) \quad \dots (5.8)$$

gegeben. Diese Formeln gelten im Kondensationsgebiet; ausserhalb desselben sind die Zustandsgleichungen nicht abgeleitet worden. Fasst man das Ising Modell als Darstellung eines Ferromagneticums auf, so entspricht (5.7) seiner freien Energie, (5.8) der spontanen Polarisation—beides ohne äusseres Magnetfeld. Die Formel (5.7) ist von Onsager abgeleitet worden, (5.8) von Yang. Derartig vollständige und schöne Ergebnisse können für andere Modelle nicht gewonnen werden; denn die sehr speziellen algebraischen Methoden, die hier zum Ziele führten, versagen schon dann, wenn man z.B. die Wirkung eines äusseren Magnetfeldes im Ising Modell untersuchen möchte, oder wenn man statt eines ebenen Gitters ein Raumgitter zugrunde legt. In solchen Fällen ist man auf Näherungen angewiesen, die in der Nähe von Umwandlungspunkten stets sehr fragwürdig sind.

Für ein klassisch-mechanisches Gasmodell kann man insbesondere die Zustandsgleichung, die aus der grossen kanonischen Gesamtheit folgt, in Potenzen von z entwickeln:

$$p/kT = \sum_{l=1}^{\infty} b_l z^l; \qquad \rho = \sum_{l-1}^{\infty} l b_l z^l \qquad \dots (5.9)$$

Diese Reihen sind brauchbar, wenn die Dichte hinreichend klein ist. Die Koeffizienten b_l sind die sog. 'Cluster-Integrale', die von den Konfigurationen von nur l Atomen abhängig sind. Für sehr tiefe Temperaturen sind alle b_l positiv und die Terme $b_l z^l$ stellen direkt den Partialdruck der 'Moleküle' dar, die aus l Atomen bestehen. Im allgemeinen haben aber die 'Cluster-Integrale' keine direkte physikalische Bedeutung. Im Grenzfall, in welchem die Gasdichte, selbst am Kondensationspunkt, sehr klein ist, sodass das Kovolumen der Atome gegen das Gesamtvolumen vernachlässigt werden kann, ist es möglich, das Verhalten der b_l für grosse l, und damit die Konvergenz der Reihen (5.9) zu überblicken.[21]

Wählt man ein Modell, für welches das Potential der Wechselwirkung der Atome durch

$$\begin{cases} \phi(r) = \infty; & r < r_0 \\ \phi(r) = -u; & r_0 < r < r_1 \qquad \dots (5.10) \\ \phi(r) = 0; & r > r_1 \end{cases}$$

gegeben ist, so wird für grosse l

$$b_l = (v_{k_0} e^{k_0(1-\epsilon_0)u/T})^{l-1} \qquad \dots (5.11)$$

Dabei ist $v_{k_0} = \alpha(r_1 - r_0)^3$, wo α von der Ordnung 1,

$$k_0 = 6\left(1 - \pi\left(\frac{3}{4\pi}\right)^{2/3} \frac{1}{l^{1/3}}\right); \qquad \epsilon_0 = e^{-u/T}$$

Das Ergebnis (5.11) gewinnt man, indem man $v_0\rho$ vernachlässigt ($v_0 \sim r_1^3$, ρ ist die Teilchendichte), ebenso Grössen der Ordnung $e^{-u/T}$. Berücksichtigt aber werden Grössen der Ordnung $v_0\rho e^{6u/T}$. Der Term $\sim l^{-1/3}$ in k_0 entspricht der Oberflächenenergie der grossen Moleküle mit l Atomen.

Die Reihen (5.9) konvergieren hier bis und mit

$$z = z_0 = \frac{1}{v_{k_0}} e^{-6u/T}$$

Für $z = z_0$ nimmt der Druck den endlichen Wert $p_0 = Tz_0$ an, die Teilchendichte aber ist z_0. Der Dampf verhält sich also, wie zu erwarten, auch an dieser kritischen Stelle noch wie ein ideales Gas. Obwohl man mathematisch nicht beweisen kann, dass an der Stelle z_0 eine Kondensation eintritt, so kann dies doch plausibel gemacht werden.

Für ein 'eindimensionales' Gasmodell, bei welchem sich die Atome nicht im Raume, sondern auf einer Geraden bewegen, hat van Hove [22] die Zustandsgleichung streng abgeleitet. Es gilt hier

$$z \int_0^\infty e^{-(\phi(x)+p \cdot x)/T} \, dx = 1 \qquad \dots (5.12)$$

Macht man für $\phi(x)$ den Ansatz (5.10), so liefert unser Näherungsverfahren

$$p/T = \frac{z}{1 - e^{u/T}(r_1 - r_0)z} \qquad \dots (5.13)$$

was mit (5.12) übereinstimmt, falls pr_1/T vernachlässigt werden darf,

$$e^{u/T} \frac{pr_1}{T}$$

aber mitgenommen wird. Hier divergiert p an der kritischen Stelle z_0: das eindimensionale Gas kondensiert nicht, weil bei ihm den grossen Molekülen die Oberflächenenergie fehlt, die im räumlichen Falle dazu führt, dass jene, neben den freien Atomen, allein eine Rolle spielen.

Auf andere Anwendungen der Reihen (5.9), auf ihre quantenmechanische Verallgemeinerung, sowie auf andere Methoden, die

Zustandsgleichungen herzuleiten—etwa der, den Virialsatz von Clausous zugrunde zu legen—gehen wir nicht ein. Statt dessen möchten wir auf den inhaltsreichen und sehr klar abgefassten Artikel von de Boer [23] verweisen, in welchem solche Fragen ausführlich behandelt sind.

LITERATUR

Dieser Aufsatz ist im Sommer 1958 geschrieben worden, und war, wie der ganze vorliegende Band, als Gabe zu W. Pauli's 60 Geburtstage gedacht. Nach W. Pauli's unerwartetem Scheiden bringen wir ihn gleichwohl unverändert zum Abdruck.

1. Boltzmann, L. *Vorlesungen über Gastheorie.* 1896. Leipzig
2. Vergleiche zu diesem ganzen Kapitel Hopf, E. *Ergodentheorie* (Berlin, 1937) ferner Ter Haar, *Rev. mod. Phys.* **27**, 289, 1955
3. Fierz, M. *Helv. phys. Acta* **28**, 705, 1955
4. Neumann, J. v. *Z. Phys.* **57**, 80, 1929
   Pauli, W. und Fierz, M. *Z. Phys.* **106**, 572, 1937
5. Farquhar, J. E. und Landsberg, P. T. *Proc. Roy. Soc. A* **239**, 184, 1957
6. Ehrenfest, P. und T. *Encykl. math. Wiss.* 4, IV
7. Gibbs, W. *Elementare Grundlagen der statistischen Mechanik.* 1905. Leipzig
8. Hove, L. v. *Physica* **21**, 517, 1955: **23**, 411, 1957
9. Pauli, W. *Festschrift für A. Sommerfeld*, S. 30. 1928. Leipzig
10. Einstein, A. *S.B. preuss. Akad. Wiss. Phys. Math. Kl.* S. 261, 1924: S. 3, 1925
11. Nernst, W. *Naturwissenschaften* **27**, 393, 1939
12. Ornstein, L. und Zernicke, F. *Proc. Acad. Sci., Amst.* **17**, 793, 1914
13. Klein, M. J. und Tisza, L. *Phys. Rev.* **76**, 1861, 1949
14. Einstein, A. *Ann. Phys. Lpz.* **33**, 1275, 1910
15. Roccard, Y. *J. Phys. Radium* **4**, 165, 1933
16. Pauli, W. *Z. Phys.* **41**, 81, 1927
16a. Fierz, M. *Helv. phys. Acta* **29**, 47, 1956
17. Yang, C. N. und Lee, T. D. *Phys. Rev.* **87**, 404, 1952
18. Hove, L. van, *Physica* **15**, 951, 1949
19. Yang, C. N. und Lee, T. D. *Phys. Rev.* **87**, 410, 1957
20. Kramers, H. A. und Wannier, G. *Phys. Rev.* **60**, 252, 263, 1941
21. Fierz, M. *Helv. phys. Acta* **24**, 357, 1951
22. Hove, L. van *Physica* **16**, 137, 1950
23. de Boer, J. *Rep. Progr. in Phys.* **12**, 305, 1949

RELATIVITY

V. BARGMANN

1

Pauli's first papers dealt with relativity, and so did his early masterwork, the article on the theory of relativity written for the *Mathematical Encyclopedia* in 1921. This astonishing work of a twenty-year-old graduate student at once established its author as a scientist of rare depth, and of an unsurpassed power of both synthesis and critical analysis.

The second edition of the encyclopedia article appeared towards the end of Pauli's life (in English translation).[1] Fortunately, the classical text of the original version was left unchanged, but it was augmented by 23 supplementary notes, which were written in 1956 and which deal with some of the later developments of the theory.

In 1921, when the article first appeared, the physical, mathematical, and conceptual basis of relativity had been firmly established. For the special theory this had been achieved by 1911, after the major fields of classical physics (mechanics and hydrodynamics, electrodynamics, thermodynamics) had been put in relativistic form. Similarly, the mathematical structure of general relativity and the most important consequences of its field equations were well understood after Einstein had given the theory its definitive form in 1915–16. By introducing and developing the concept of parallel displacement Levi-Cività and Weyl had achieved a much deeper understanding of infinitesimal geometry, the mathematical basis of general relativity. The significance of the general covariance of the field equations (notably for the conservation laws) had been clarified by Einstein himself, by the Göttingen school (F. Klein, D. Hilbert, and E. Noether), and by H. A. Lorentz. K. Schwarzschild had obtained the first rigorous solutions of the field equations, and, in addition, the theoretical prediction of the deflection of light rays had been confirmed in 1919. The initial rapid development had come to an end.

[1] Pauli, W. *Theory of Relativity.* 1958. New York and London; Pergamon Press. Hereafter quoted as TR.

187

Thus Pauli's article appeared at a very important juncture. It gave an exposition of unsurpassed beauty, precision, depth, and completeness of the theory as it then existed. Every detail had its proper place. Above all, Pauli's critical evaluations appear as incisive and as definitive now as they were 40 years ago.

Let us now consider those parts of the article which point to future developments. One omission appears particularly conspicuous today : quantum theory is hardly mentioned, for it had not then reached the stage where it could be cast in a consistently relativistic form. (In the second edition, quantum theory is omitted for a different reason. Relativistic quantum theory has grown to such proportions that an adequate discussion would have required another book of 200 pages.)

In these early years of relativity there were, however, hopes that the problem of the existence and stability of elementary particles, with which classical electrodynamics had been unable to cope, might be solved—or at least brought closer to its solution—on the basis of general relativity. The fifth (last) part of the encyclopedia article deals with the various solutions that had been suggested. After reviewing Mie's ingenious non-linear electrodynamics (developed within special relativity) Pauli discusses the then recent attempts to solve the 'problem of matter', Weyl's generalization of Riemannian geometry—the first 'unified field theory'— and an early attempt of Einstein's to modify the general relativistic field equations in order to account for the existence and stability of elementary charged particles. In 1920 it seemed reasonable to believe that, in the last analysis, all interactions could be reduced to electromagnetic and to gravitational ones, yet none of the early attempts was successful. Weyl's geometry, profound as it was in generalizing Riemannian metric by introducing an arbitrary gauge and the concept of gauge invariance, did not lead to a unique choice of the action function nor to any understanding of the existence of elementary particles. In addition, it was not clear how the metric ought to be interpreted. If ds^2 was to be measured by 'atomic clocks' the non-integrability of the length would make these standards depend on previous history, contrary to the observation of sharp spectral lines. If, on the other hand—as Weyl suggested—no such direct connection with observable quantities ought to be postulated *a priori*, then the interpretation of the theory had to await further mathematical analysis that would reveal the behaviour of atomic systems according to the new equations. Einstein's attempt also failed to produce the desired solution of the 'problem of matter'.

It is extremely interesting to contemplate the general critical remarks concerning these attempts with which Pauli concluded the article.[2] I shall single out the following points:

(1) All attempts were based on the hope that the complicated non-linear differential equations to which they led would yield— in some unforeseeable manner—just two spherically symmetric solutions, corresponding to the electron and to the proton respectively. Pauli raises the following objection: 'It should be required that atomicity, in itself so simple and basic, should also be interpreted in a simple and elementary manner by theory and should not, so to speak, appear as a trick (Kunststück) in analysis.'

(2) The difficulty of explaining the existence of elementary particles by stabilizing gravitational forces is made particularly conspicuous by the enormous magnitude ($\sim 10^{20}$) of the ratio $e/m(k)^{1/2}$ of the gravitational mass and the electric charge of the electron (k is Newton's gravitational constant).

(3) No theory had been able to account for the asymmetry (difference in mass) of positive and negative electricity. More than that this asymmetry appeared to contradict the invariance of the theories proposed with respect to time reversal. (In fact, highly artificial suggestions had been made to circumvent this difficulty, such as the introduction of a square root (in the action function) of which the two branches should correspond to the two types of electricity.)

(4) The last point concerns the most profound question. 'Finally, a conceptual doubt should be mentioned. The continuum theories make direct use of the ordinary concept of electric field strength, even for the fields in the interior of the electron. This field strength, however, is defined as the force acting on a test particle, and since there are no test particles smaller than an electron or a hydrogen nucleus the field strength at a given point in the interior of such a particle would seem to be unobservable by definition, and thus be fictitious and without physical meaning.'

A physicist will feel both pride and humility when he reads Pauli's remarks today. In the light of our present knowledge the attempts which Pauli criticizes may seem hopelessly naïve, although it was certainly sound practice to investigate what the profound new ideas of general relativity would contribute to the understanding of the thorny problem of matter. Undoubtedly the views on the behaviour and the interaction of elementary particles have changed beyond recognition, and we do know,

[2] TR pp. 205–206

among other things, that there exist more elementary particles
than just the negative electron and the positive proton; but how
deep is our understanding of the nature and the stability of these
particles beyond the mere knowledge of their existence? And
how certain are we that in our modern theories we do not likewise
over-extend the concept of 'field' or even that of the space-time
continuum?

Only the asymmetry difficulty has been clearly removed, with
the discovery of the positron and the antiproton. Moreover, the
theoretical and experimental solution of this problem constitutes
one of the truly great achievements of physics during the last 30
years. It is quite remarkable that in this regard the highly
speculative early theories—in excluding the asymmetry in positive
and negative charges—proved more trustworthy than the experimental evidence available in 1920. True enough, the apparent
difficulty was quite independent of any special features of the
theories and was exclusively based on a simple invariance argument, so that, in all fairness, we should rather say that the
invariance argument proved more trustworthy than the experimental evidence.

2

Relativity, mainly in the form of relativistic quantum theory,
plays quite a predominant part in Pauli's scientific work. Other
contributions to this volume will evaluate in greater detail his
achievements in this field, and I consider it therefore my task to
sketch in broad outline the development of specifically relativistic
ideas in Pauli's life-time and Pauli's role in this development.

Since special and general relativity have proceeded along very
different lines it will be best to deal with them separately.

A. Special Relativity

Between 1905 and 1910 it had been the main task to extend
relativity to the various parts of physics by adjusting already
existing theories to the relativistic postulates. For small velocities
the theories could be taken for granted, and although their
relativistic generalization required ingenuity and penetrating
analysis—as, for example, in Planck's treatment of thermodynamics—there was no radical change in the conceptual or the
mathematical framework beyond the pioneering work of Einstein
and Minkowski.

With the progress of atomic physics and especially of quantum
theory, however, the role of relativity became much more creative.

The problem was no longer to 'translate' a previously established theory into a relativistic form. In increasing measure the theories were relativistic from the start, and relativistic considerations were crucial for the choice of their basic postulates.

Concurrently, due to the highly perfected experimental techniques, particles of ever higher energies became readily available (in cosmic rays as well as in accelerator beams), and while in the early years of this century the greatest effort was required even to notice any deviation from Newtonian physics, phenomena in the extreme relativistic region are now an everyday occurrence in physical laboratories all over the world. On the other hand, even the tiniest effects, such as the Lamb shift, may be measured with an astounding precision and used to test theoretical predictions.

The first new theory inspired by relativity was de Broglie's wave theory of matter. Undoubtedly it might have been formulated in a non-relativistic framework, but the fact remains that de Broglie's original work was entirely relativistic in spirit, notably the transition from Planck's $E = h\nu$ to de Broglie's $p = h/\lambda$.

It was very fortunate that during the first few years (1925–27) quantum and wave mechanics—largely an outgrowth of de Broglie's theory—were developed on a non-relativistic basis even though every worker in the field was quite aware of the necessity of ultimately making the theory relativistically invariant. In fact, there were sufficiently many difficulties to overcome without the additional burden of specifically relativistic problems.

With Dirac's theory of the electron, relativity came into its own. Here was certainly a theory which was not obtained from an established non-relativistic theory, but derived from basic quantum theoretical and relativistic postulates. The crucial quantum postulate was that the wave equation described a one-particle system, with a positive definite probability density, and that it could therefore be put in the canonical form

$$\frac{\hbar}{i} \frac{\partial \psi}{\partial t} + H\psi = 0 \qquad \ldots (D)$$

Lorentz invariance then required the equation to contain only first-order derivatives also with respect to the coordinates. The relativistic energy–momentum relation uniquely determined the form of the Dirac Hamiltonian (at least for the free electron), thus leading to the four components of the wave function (together with their curious transformation properties) and to the electronic spin. Finally, the simplest assumption for the interaction with

7*

the electromagnetic field gave the correct value of the electron's magnetic moment.

There is no need to stress here the immediate magnificent success of Dirac's equation as a one-particle theory whenever it could be legitimately applied, as in the derivation of the hydrogen spectrum or of the Klein–Nishina scattering formula. What concerned the physicists most was—understandably enough—the unforeseen occurrence of the negative energy states, which at first appeared to be the most serious shortcoming of Dirac's theory, but later turned into its most impressive achievement. The experimental discovery of pair creation and annihilation demonstrated at one stroke: (1) the equivalence of mass and energy in its most extreme form, namely, the fact that mass and energy are *wholly* (not only partially) convertible into each other, (2) the complete symmetry of positive and negative charges, thereby disposing of the asymmetry difficulty that all early attempts at a unified field theory had encountered, and (3) the correctness of Dirac's theory and, in particular, of Dirac's interpretation of the negative energy states. At the same time, however, it became quite clear that Dirac's theory could not be consistently interpreted as a *one-particle* theory. In other words, the very success of the theory demonstrated that one of its basic assumptions which had led to the Hamiltonian form of equation (D) had to be abandoned. From there on there was no longer any relativistic quantum theory apart from quantum field theory, which deals from the start with an *indefinite* number of particles.

Even before this had been clearly recognized Heisenberg and Pauli had initiated a systematic relativistic quantum field theory. A large part of the immense work in this area during the following 30 years was based on the foundations laid by Heisenberg and Pauli in their celebrated papers [3] of 1929, notwithstanding the radical change in the mathematical form and the very language of the theory in recent years, and notwithstanding the important new ideas that have been introduced, such as mass and charge renormalization.

The notorious divergence difficulties, which arise from the non-linearity of the field equations, specifically from the point interactions of the fields involved, were already clearly present in the papers of Heisenberg and Pauli. They have perhaps attracted the greatest attention, but in spite of the very considerable progress in their understanding that has been achieved in the meantime they remain unresolved.

3 Heisenberg, W. and Pauli, W. *Z. Phys.* **56**, 1, 1929: **59**, 168, 1929

Much fruitful work, however, has been done in another direction which, for want of a better term, may be called 'critical' or 'axiomatic' and which aims at a *general* exploration of the possibilities offered by relativistic quantum theory rather than at the investigation of a *specific* theory such as electrodynamics, the theory of beta decay, or meson theory. Pauli was one of the originators of this approach.

I shall concentrate mainly on the classification of field equations and the study of their symmetry properties. Once it had become evident that Dirac's theory could not consistently describe a one-particle system Dirac's equation had to be re-interpreted. In particular, the ψ function changed from a state vector into a quantized field variable. Hence there existed no *a priori* reason for the canonical form of the wave equation, and Dirac's equation became one of many possible systems of relativistic field equations.

In an early paper Pauli and Weisskopf[4] were able to demonstrate that the Klein–Gordon equation (for particles of spin 0) also led to a consistent field theory. The indefinite character of the density —which previously had ruled out the Klein–Gordon equation as a proper relativistic generalization of the Schrödinger equation— no longer presented any difficulty, for it stood now for the operator 'charge density', describing both positively and negatively charged particles that could be created and annihilated in pairs. (It should be stressed that the paper was written before any particles of spin 0 were known or suspected.)

Of the many papers on the classification of relativistic equations I shall only mention those by Dirac, Wigner, and Fierz.[5] Dirac was the first to obtain equations for all values of the spin, but he had not then a method to decide whether the classification was exhaustive, nor did he have a consistent relativistic spin definition.

The most comprehensive solution of the problem was given by Wigner with group theoretical methods. He established a precise criterion for the equivalence of relativistic systems, and he found all non-equivalent elementary systems, without any *a priori* limitations on the form of the equations. That these were differential equations was a result, but not an assumption, of Wigner's investigations. While he confirmed, of course, the results of Dirac he also obtained a new type of equation (with so-called continuous spin), whose physical significance, however, remains obscure.

[4] Pauli, W. and Weisskopf, V. *Helv. phys. Acta* **7**, 709, 1934
[5] Dirac, P. A. M. *Proc. Roy. Soc. A* **155**, 447, 1936
Wigner, E. P. *Ann. Math.* **40**, 149, 1939
Fierz, M. *Helv. phys. Acta* **12**, 1, 1939

Fierz, who was Pauli's close collaborator when he wrote his paper, studied in greater detail the physical interpretation of the formalism, in particular the definition of charge density and total charge, energy density and total energy, and the question of when total charge on the one hand, total energy on the other hand, are positive. He proved for the systems he investigated that fields of integral spin must be quantized according to Bose statistics, those of half integral spin according to Fermi statistics.

A year later Pauli published a general and very beautiful proof for this important and remarkable result.[6] It is useful to recall the hypotheses on which the proof is based: (a) The system in question is described by linear differential equations (free particles). (b) The equations are invariant under the restricted Lorentz group (exluding reflections and time reversal). (c) The commutator or anticommutator—as the case may be—is a c-number. (d) The total energy is positive. (e) Observables commute for space like separated world points. (As for (d) and (e) it turns out that for half integral spin only (d), and for integral spin only (e) is needed.) Relativity intervenes, characteristically, in the invariance requirement (b) and in the relativistic causality postulate (e).

Fifteen years later Pauli returned to this problem and extended the proof to the so-called PCT theorem.[7]

In the last five years or so work in this 'axiomatic' direction of quantum field theory has been very active; and in part it has been carried out with greatly refined mathematical techniques as compared to the earlier work mentioned here. In my opinion it constitutes important progress that the newer methods depend much less on the free particle picture or the free particle approximation. The free particle intervenes not at all or only in the form of an asymptotic condition, which is fundamentally a much more realistic approach. Among other things, both the PCT theorem[8] and the connection between spin and statistics[9] have recently been established under much more general assumptions.

Pauli followed this work with great interest, as he was always deeply interested in the logical foundations of physical theories, and in an address before the American Physical Society in January, 1956, he warmly endorsed the work by Wightman and his students.

6 Pauli, W. *Phys. Rev.* **58**, 716, 1940
7 Pauli, W. in *Niels Bohr and the Development of Physics.* 1955. New York; McGraw-Hill
8 Jost, R. *Helv. phys. Acta* **30**, 409, 1957
9 Lüders, G. and Zumino, B. *Phys. Rev.* **110**, 1450, 1958
  Burgoyne, N. *Nuovo Cim.* **8**, 607, 1958

Occasionally, however, he would express grave misgivings, in conversations more often than in print. Are not the really burning questions by-passed, and is not the attention focused on problems of secondary importance? Nobody can answer these objections at present. I am inclined to believe that what these axiomatic investigations have to teach us will be worth knowing, even when a satisfactory theory based on a profound new physical idea eventually emerges.

B. General Relativity

For many reasons, the history of general relativity (from 1920 to 1960) has been much less spectacular. The one field on which it had a decisive and most stimulating influence is cosmology. Its influence on the rest of physics, however, has been slight, notwithstanding the profound changes in our fundamental concepts which it had brought about. The fruitful interaction between theory and observation which characterized the development of cosmology and astrophysics was lacking in other fields as far as general relativity was concerned.* The observable effects predicted by general relativity are notoriously small, and, specifically, the direct gravitational interaction appears negligible compared to other forces between elementary particles (which, incidentally, does not prove at all that gravitation and general relativity may therefore be simply disregarded).

There is no need to recount here the development of the theory in any detail. This has been done by Pauli himself in the beautifully concise and lucid notes which he added to the second edition of his *Theory of Relativity*. I shall confine myself to a brief discussion of Pauli's own work and of some aspects of the present state of the theory.

Two papers of Pauli's appeared in 1919, two years before his encyclopedia article was published.[10] In the first he gave explicit expressions for the energy–momentum pseudotensor of the gravitational field in the general case (Einstein had published them in a form which is valid only under the condition that the determinant of the metric tensor is normalized to -1). He emphasized that the values he obtained were different from

* Fortunately the situation has changed since these lines were written. For the first time the gravitational line shift has been measured in a terrestrial experiment, and after this brilliant success we may look forward to a closer interaction of theory and experiment in the field of general relativity.

[10] Pauli, W. *Phys. Z.* **20**, (a) 25, (b) 457, 1919

Einstein's but that the difference was of course a vanishing divergence, as it should be.

The second paper dealt with Weyl's unified field theory. Various possible choices for the action function were discussed, in particular those which allowed static, spherically symmetric solutions. With great mathematical skill the solution of the latter problem is reduced to the solution of a single—though extremely complicated—ordinary differential equation of third-order.

Fourteen years later there appeared Pauli's most comprehensive paper on general relativity 'Über die Formulierung der Naturgesetze mit fünf homogenen Koordinaten'.[11] In 1921 Kaluza had discovered that the Einstein–Maxwell equations (the combined gravitational and electromagnetic field equations for a charge free field) permit an interesting geometric interpretation.[12] In an improved form, which is due to Oskar Klein, this interpretation may be described as follows. Let $\gamma_{\mu\nu}$ be the metric tensor of a five-dimensional Riemannian space ($\mu, \nu = 1, \cdots, 5$). Assume that the $\gamma_{\mu\nu}$ are independent of the fifth-coordinate x^5 ('cylinder condition') and that

$$\gamma_{55} = 1$$

Then the 14 field variables of the Einstein–Maxwell theory, viz. the ten components g_{ik} of the metric tensor (of four-dimensional space time) and the four components ϕ_i of the electromagnetic potential may be expressed in terms of the $\gamma_{\mu\nu}$:

$$g_{ik} = \gamma_{ik} - \gamma_{i5}\gamma_{k5}$$
$$\phi_i = (2\kappa)^{-1/2}\gamma_{i5}$$

where κ is the gravitational constant. The identification of the field variables with the geometric quantities of the five-dimensional space yields striking results. (1) The Einstein–Maxwell equations may be derived from an action principle whose Lagrangian is simply the curvature scalar of the five-dimensional space. (2) The geodesics of the five-dimensional space correspond to the paths of charged particles, the direction of the geodesics being simply related to the specific charge e/m of the particle.

Time and again this unification of gravitation and electricity as well as the geometrical interpretation of the dynamics of the Einstein–Maxwell theory have proved intriguing and fascinating. To this day it is not clear whether this interpretation has a deeper significance.

From the beginning, however, it was felt that the cylinder

11 Pauli, W. *Ann. Phys. Lpz.* 18, 305, 1933
12 TR pp. 227–232

condition and the normalization $\gamma_{55} = 1$ were quite artificial from the point of view of a truly five-dimensional geometry. Several mathematicians (Veblen and Hoffman, Schouten and van Dantzig) suggested therefore the introduction of five projective coordinates $x^1, \cdots, x^5$ so that on one hand the symmetry in the five coordinates would be maintained and yet, on the other hand, these coordinates would describe a four-dimensional manifold because only the ratios $x^1 : x^5$ would have a geometrical meaning.

In the first part of his paper Pauli gave a beautiful account of this projective geometry and its tensor analysis, which were developed from first principles, and he formulated the Einstein–Maxwell equations in projective coordinates. The second part dealt with the incorporation of spinors and of Dirac's equation into this geometrical structure. In my opinion, this is by far the most satisfactory exposition of spinors in general relativity—quite independent of the problems of a unified field theory.

As to the unification of gravitation and electricity, Pauli was later dissatisfied with what had been achieved, and the criticism in the appendix to his book is very interesting and very pertinent. It is briefly this: it is not sufficient just to represent the two fields in terms of a unified geometrical structure. The field equations, too, must be singled out by this geometrical structure, specifically by its invariance group. Applying this exacting criterion to the Einstein–Maxwell theory one would argue as follows. Since the projective formulation, as can be shown, is mathematically equivalent to the original Kaluza–Klein theory, it is sufficient to remark that in virtue of the cylinder condition and the normalization $\gamma_{55} = 1$ the invariance group is considerably smaller than the group of five-dimensional Riemannian geometry and that, therefore, many more Lagrangians may be constructed than just the curvature scalar which leads to the Einstein–Maxwell equations. Hence no genuine unification is achieved.

The criticism, incidentally, does not apply to a generalization of the theory studied by O. Klein. He abandons the cylinder condition so that each $\gamma_{\mu\nu}$ is a function of five variables. It is, however, assumed to be periodic in x^5 and may be expanded in a Fourier series whose coefficients depend on the space–time variables $x^1, \cdots, x^4$, describe presumably different particles, and are to be quantized.

Of late there has been a markedly increased interest in the mathematical analysis of 'classical' general relativity (i.e. Einstein's original theory as contrasted with any of its generalizations or modifications). This is a very desirable development both for its own sake and also in view of the endeavours to quantize general relativity. The progress of general relativity has certainly been retarded by undeniable mathematical difficulties, but even a good number of questions for whose solution the mathematical methods are available have been left unanalysed.

To mention a few: (1) Convenient criteria for the equivalence of two metric fields. Here Petrov's derivation of canonical forms of a curvature tensor for which $R_{ik} = 0$ has been extremely useful.[13] Related to this is the more difficult and more comprehensive problem of characterizing a metric field by a complete and independent set of invariants.[14] (2) A re-investigation of possible expressions that might serve as energy–momentum pseudotensors of the gravitational field.[15]

In addition there remain the deeper and much harder problems of the existence of regular solutions of the vacuum field equations which would satisfy suitable asymptotic conditions, for example, approach the Minkowskian metric at large spatial distances in an appropriate coordinate system. An answer is only known for the stationary case (all components of the metric tensor are independent of the time variable x^4): the solution is necessarily Euclidean.[16] For a static field ($g_{14} = g_{24} = g_{34} = 0$) this result has been known for many years. An intermediate result was obtained in a very interesting paper by Einstein and Pauli.[17] Using directly the variational principle for the field equations they could show that asymptotically the solution must decrease faster than $1/r$. The general stationary case was settled by Lichnérowicz.

The quantization of the gravitational field is being attacked from various directions; but the work has not yet progressed to a stage where the specific quantum theoretical problems and difficulties would be confronted.

Compared with his work in other fields, the number of Pauli's technical papers on general relativity is fairly small; but his talks before the Berne Conference[18] as well as the preface and appendix to his book contain profound thoughts on general relativity. What he had to say about the foundations of relativity, about field and matter, quantum theory and relativity, will deeply concern every physicist.

[13] Petrov, A. Z. *Sci. Not. Kazan State Univ.* **114**, 55, 1954
[14] See Komar, A. *Phys. Rev.* **111**, 1182, 1958
[15] Goldberg, J. N. *Phys. Rev.* **111**, 315, 1958
   Møller, C. *Ann. Phys.* **4**, 347, 1958
[16] TR p. 219 Note 18
[17] Einstein, A and Pauli, W. *Ann. Math.* **44**, 131, 1943
[18] Jubilee of Relativity. *Helv. phys. Acta* Suppl. IV

EXCLUSION PRINCIPLE AND SPIN

B. L. VAN DER WAERDEN

INTRODUCTION

In a textbook, the exposition of physical theories is bound to be, at least to a certain extent, *dogmatic*. The exposition starts with a hypothesis, deduces its consequences and compares them with the empirical results.

Some texts follow a *mixed method*, blending the dogmatic exposition with historical remarks, showing how the hypotheses were found. This method has great merits.

On the other hand, the *historical method* follows, step by step, the development of ideas in the minds of the theorists, as far as they can be traced in their publications. In my opinion, a thorough understanding of a physical theory can be reached only by the historical method. This method enables us to judge whether a certain hypothesis is really necessary to explain the phenomena, whether it can be modified and under what conditions a theory is valid.

In the following exposition, the historical method prevails. This implies a severe restriction of the domain of investigation.

One has to consider one paper after another, to explain the problem of the paper and the situation in which it was written, to state what was known at that time and what attempts had been made before. Notations may be modernized, proofs may be left out, but the essential ideas must be explained in every case.

In the case of Pauli's fundamental papers, the application of this method is made easy by the extremely lucid way in which Pauli always explains the problem, the contributions of others, the leading ideas of his proposed solution, the arguments in favour of it and the difficulties and new problems to which it gives rise.

The history of the discovery of the exclusion principle was narrated by Pauli in his highly instructive lecture 'Exclusion principle and quantum mechanics' given in Stockholm after the award of the Nobel prize in 1945 (Neuchâtel; Griffon, 1947). In this lecture he mentions his early work on the anomalous Zeeman effect as being 'of decisive importance for the finding of the exclusion principle'. Therefore, our investigation has to start with Pauli's paper of 1923 on the anomalous Zeeman effect.

1. THE ZEEMAN EFFECT IN STRONG FIELDS

W. Pauli, Gesetzmäßigkeiten des anomalen Zeeman effektes. *Z. Phys.* **16**, 155 (received April 1923).

In a Princeton address, published in *Science* **103**, p. 213, Pauli tells us how he felt about the anomalous Zeeman effect in his early days:

> The anomalous type of splitting was especially fruitful because it exhibited beautiful and simple laws, but on the other hand it was hardly understandable, since very general assumptions concerning the electron, using classical theory as well as quantum theory, always led to the same triplet. A closer investigation of this problem left me with the feeling that it was even more unapproachable. A colleague who met me strolling rather aimlessly in the beautiful streets of Copenhagen said to me in a friendly manner, 'You look very unhappy'; whereupon I answered fiercely 'How can one look happy when he is thinking about the anomalous Zeeman effect?'

The state of knowledge at the time when Pauli wrote his 1923 paper may be summarized as follows. Of course, it was known that the energy levels of an atom determine the spectrum by Bohr's rule

$$E_1 - E_2 = h\nu$$

In spectroscopy, several kinds of levels or states were distinguished by letters $S, P, D, F \cdots$ or by a quantum number

$$L = k - 1 = 0, 1, 2, 3 \cdots$$

Every term belongs to a singlet or multiplet system, character-ized by a maximum multiplicity

$$2S+1 = 2i = 1, 2, 3 \cdots \quad \text{(hence } S = 0, \tfrac{1}{2}, 1 \cdots)$$

Pauli uses the letters k and i; we shall use the modern notation L and S. For us, L and S are the orbital and spin momentum of the atom, but Pauli's exposition does not depend on this interpretation.

Any multiplet consists of $2S+1$ terms at most, all having the same L and S. The terms are distinguished by a quantum number J (Sommerfeld's j), which takes the values

$$J = L+S, L+S-1, \cdots, L-S \quad \text{if} \quad L \geqslant S$$
$$J = S+L, S+L-1, \cdots, S-L \quad \text{if} \quad L < S$$

The combination rules, valid in most cases, are

$$L \to L+1, \quad L \quad \text{or} \quad L-1 \quad (\text{not } 0 \to 0)$$
$$S \to S$$
$$J \to J+1, \quad J \quad \text{or} \quad J-1 \quad (\text{not } 0 \to 0)$$

If the atomic number Z (or, if the atom is ionized p times, the number $Z-p$) is even, S and J are integers, and if odd, half integers.

In a magnetic field every term splits into $2J+1$ terms, dis-tinguished by a quantum number M taking the values

$$M = J, J-1, \cdots, -J$$

If the field is weak, the terms are equidistant and their deviation from the undisturbed term is

$$E = Mgoh \quad \left(o = \frac{eH}{4\pi mc}\right)$$

g being Landé's factor

$$g = 1\tfrac{1}{2} + \frac{S(S+1)-L(L+1)}{2J(J+1)}$$

The combination rules for M are

$$M \to M \pm 1 \quad (\sigma\text{-component})$$
$$M \to M \quad\quad (\pi\text{-component})$$
$$\text{Not } 0 \to 0, \quad \text{if} \quad J \to J$$

Pauli accepts these empirical rules as known, and proceeds to consider the case of a strong magnetic field. He first gives a table of the empirical deviations E, written as multiples of oh. He next observes that the quantum numbers M and the observed ratios E/oh may be written as

$$M = M_L + M_S$$
$$E/oh = M_L + 2M_S = M + M_S$$

where M_L (Pauli's m_1) takes the integer values from L to $-L$, whereas M_S (Pauli's μ) takes the values $\pm \frac{1}{2}$ for doublets, and the values $0, \pm 1$ for triplets. The latter statement is at once generalized to arbitrary multiplets: M_S takes the values

$$S, S-1, \cdots, -S$$

The combination rule for M_S is

$$M_S \to M_S$$

This rule explains the empirical fact that for strong fields the Zeeman effect is normal.

Pauli now states the following rule:

The sum of the energies of all states of a multiplet belonging to a given value of M remains a linear function of H, when we pass from weak to strong fields.

In the special case $M = J = L + S$ there is only one state, hence the energy of this state is a linear function of H. On the other hand, if the given value of M belongs to the maximum number $2S + 1$ of states, the sum of the energies of these states in strong fields, divided by $2S + 1$, is Moh, hence, according to Pauli's rule, the same value must hold for weak fields as well, i.e. the mean of all g values belonging to a given $L \geqslant S$ is 1. These two special results had been obtained already by Heisenberg from the postulate of statistical constancy of the angular momentum.

In support of his rule, Pauli shows that Landé's whole set of factors g can be derived from it. We may add that quantum mechanics enables us to prove the rule. The sum of the energies of the states of given M is equal to the trace of a perturbation matrix and hence a linear function of H. Moreover, all experimental results are in accordance with Pauli's rule.

2. THE TWO-VALUEDNESS OF THE ELECTRON

W. Pauli, Über den Einfluss der Geschwindigkeitsabhängigkeit der Elektronenmasse auf den Zeeman-effekt. *Z. Phys.* **31**, 373 (received December 1924).

In 1923, Pauli delivered his inaugural lecture as Privatdozent in Hamburg on the periodic system of elements. In his Nobel prize lecture he writes:

The contents of this lecture appeared very unsatisfactory to me, since the problem of the closing of the electronic shells had been clarified no further. The only thing that was clear to me was that there must exist a closer relation of this problem to the theory of multiplet structure. I therefore tried to examine again critically the simplest case, the doublet structure of the alkali spectra. According to the point of view then orthodox, which was also taken over by Bohr in his lectures in Göttingen, a non-vanishing angular momentum of the atomic core was supposed to be the cause of this doublet structure.

At the end of 1924 Pauli published a paper in which he motivated his rejection of this 'orthodox' point of view. He first calculated the relativistic effect of the velocity of electrons in the K-shell upon their magnetic and mechanical momentum. He found that the non-relativistic value of the ratio of these momenta ought to be multiplied by a factor γ, the mean value of $(1 - v^2/c^2)^{1/2}$, which would be 0·924 in the case of Ba and 0·817 in the case of Hg. Now the normal and anomalous Zeeman effects do not show any influence of such a slowly decreasing factor. The empirical factors g are rational numbers depending only on the quantum numbers of the terms.

In order to explain the observed factors g by means of an angular momentum of a closed shell such as the K-shell of the alkali atoms, one would have to assume a doubling of the ratio of magnetic to mechanical momentum for electrons in the shell, and also a compensation of the classically computed relativistic effect of the velocity. The electron would have to change its magnetic moment as soon as it enters or leaves the shell, which is extremely improbable.

For this and other reasons Pauli assumes, as Sommerfeld did, that closed shells have no angular momentum and no magnetic moment. This implies that in the case of alkali atoms the angular momentum of the atom and its change of energy in a magnetic field are due to the valence electron only.

Up to this point, Pauli had only discussed the merits of two opposite hypotheses which had been proposed by others; but now he makes a sudden jump and writes the prophetic words:

'According to this point of view the doublet structure of alkali spectra as well as the deviation from Larmor's theorem is due to a particular two-valuedness of the quantum theoretic properties of the electron, which cannot be described from the classical point of view.'

This classically non-describable two-valuedness of the electron is what we now call the spin. Pauli himself, when he heard of the 'spinning electron', strongly doubted the correctness of this idea because of its classical mechanical character (Nobel prize lecture, p. 15). Hence, if we want to understand Pauli's line of thought, we must leave aside the notion 'spinning electron'. Now, what exactly did Pauli mean by 'a particular two-valuedness of the properties of the electron'?

In the following discussion, I shall use $h/2\pi$ as a unit of angular momentum, and Bohr's magneton as a unit of magnetic moment. Let us start with Pauli's formulae for strong fields (see section 1):

$$M = M_L + M_S \qquad \dots(1)$$

$$E/oh = M_L + 2M_S \qquad \dots(2)$$

What is the meaning of the quantum numbers M, M_L and M_S? In a second paper in the same Vol. 31 of Z. Phys. (p. 765, received January 1925), Pauli says that M is the total angular momentum of the atom in the direction of the field. This interpretation is due to Sommerfeld,* who was the first to define the quantum numbers J and M.

In the same paper, Pauli represents M_L as a sum of terms m_l, and M_S as a sum of terms m_s, due to the single electrons:

$$M_L = \sum m_l, \qquad M_S = \sum m_s$$

Both sums may be restricted to those electrons which are not in closed shells, for closed shells do not contribute to the magnetic moment and to the angular momentum of the atom (Pauli, loc. cit., p. 385). Hence, for an alkali atom, both sums reduce to just one term, and (1) and (2) simplify to

$$M = m_l + m_s \qquad \dots(3)$$
$$E/oh = m_l + 2m_s \qquad \dots(4)$$

The integer m_l may be interpreted in terms of classical mechanics as the angular momentum of the orbital motion of the electron in the direction of the field. *Hence, m_s means the contribution of the electron itself, apart from its orbital motion, to the total angular momentum M in the direction of the field.*

Since m_l is an integer, whereas m_s takes the values $\pm \frac{1}{2}$, it follows that M takes half-integer values only, and that J, being defined quite generally as the maximum value of M for any term of a multiplet, takes the values $L + \frac{1}{2}$ and $L - \frac{1}{2}$ for the two terms of an

* Sommerfeld, A. Zeemaneffekt des Wasserstoffs. *Phys. Z.* **17**, 491, 1916; see also Debye, P., *Phys. Z.* **17**, 507.

alkali doublet. Hence, the two-valuedness of J, which is responsible for the doublet splitting, is a logical consequence of the two-valuedness of m_s. Thus, we have found a completely satisfactory and logical explanation of the first part of Pauli's statement: '... the doublet structure ... is due to a particular two-valuedness ... of the electron'. We now turn to the second statement concerning 'the deviation from Larmor's theorem', i.e. the anomalous Zeeman effect.

The starting point of Pauli's investigation (*loc. cit.*, p. 374) was the formula for the energy of an atom in a magnetic field

$$E = -(\vec{M} \cdot \vec{H}) \qquad \dots (5)$$

where $\vec{M}$ is the magnetic moment vector. If we compare this with (2), we see that an atom with quantum numbers M_L and M_S behaves, in a strong magnetic field, just like a magnet having a magnetic moment $M_L + 2M_S$ in the direction of the field. In the case of a single valence electron, the magnetic moment of the atom would be $m_l + 2m_s$ (expressed in magnetons).

The formulae (2) and (4) hold for strong fields only, but if we consider an S state of an alkali atom we have $M_L = 0$ and $M = M_S = m_s$, and now the formula (4) holds, by Pauli's rule of permanence, for weak fields too. This means: *In the absence of an orbital angular momentum the magnetic moment of the alkali atom is exactly $2m_s$.* According to Pauli's fundamental assumptions, this magnetic moment is entirely due to the valence electron.

In the preceding analysis, I have taken care not to use any notions foreign to Pauli's line of thought, and to check every statement by referring to his own words. Yet, the analysis ended up with conclusions considerably more precise than Pauli's rather vague statement concerning a particular two-valuedness of the electron.

Why did Pauli express himself so mysteriously? Why did he not say in plain words that he assumed the electron to have an intrinsic angular momentum $m_s = \pm \frac{1}{2}$ and a magnetic moment $2m_s$? In his Nobel prize lecture (p. 15) he formulates just these two assumptions, but he ascribes them to Uhlenbeck and Goudsmit. Why did not Pauli himself draw these conclusions?

I shall try to solve this historical problem in section 4.

3. THE EXCLUSION PRINCIPLE

W. Pauli: Über den Zusammenhang des Abschlusses von Elektronengruppen im Atom mit der Komplexstruktur der Felder. *Z. Phys.* **31**. 765 (received January 1925).

In the autumn of 1924, while Pauli was writing his first paper in *Z. Phys.* **31**, a paper of the English physicist Stoner appeared (*Phil. Mag.* **48**, 79) which contained, besides improvements in the classification of electrons in closed and non-closed shells in subgroups, an important remark, which Pauli quotes as follows:

'For a given value of the principal quantum number the number of energy levels of a single electron in the alkali metal spectra in an external magnetic field is the same as the number of electrons in the closed shell of the rare gases which corresponds to this principal quantum number.'

This remark was of decisive importance in the discovery of the exclusion principle. Pauli quotes it in his Nobel prize lecture and proceeds:

'On the basis of my earlier results on the classification of spectral terms in a strong magnetic field the general formulation of the exclusion principle became clear to me.'

The principle was formulated in Pauli's second paper in *Z. Phys.* **31**, 765. After having explained the meaning of the quantum numbers n, k_1, k_2, m_1 of a single electron in an atom, Pauli enunciates his principle as follows:

'There can never be two or more equivalent electrons in an atom, for which in strong fields the values of all quantum numbers n, k_1, k_2, m_1 are the same. If an electron is present in the atom, for which these quantum numbers have definite values, this state is "occupied".'

Pauli's quantum numbers are related to the modern ones n, l, j, m_j as follows:

$$n = n, \quad k_1 = l+1, \quad k_2 = j+\tfrac{1}{2}, \quad m_1 = m_j$$

Before publishing his paper, Pauli took care to verify some additional conclusions concerning the anomalous Zeeman effect of more complicated atoms during a visit to Tübingen with the help of the spectroscopic material assembled there. Next, he had to bring his ideas into such a form that others could understand them. This was not an easy task. 'Physicists found it difficult to understand the exclusion principle, since no meaning in terms of a model was given to the fourth degree of freedom of the electron' (Pauli, Nobel prize lecture p. 15).

Today, being familiar with Pauli's principle and with the 'fourth degree of freedom' now called spin, we have no difficulty in following Pauli's exposition. First, he summarizes his results for alkali metals. In this case, the quantum numbers l, j, m_j of the valence electron coincide with L, J, M of the atom, since closed shells do not contribute to the orbital and total angular momentum of the atom.

The passage to more complicated atoms is performed by Bohr's principle of permanence, which says: If, to an ionized atom, one more electron is added, the quantum numbers of the electrons already bound remain the same as in the ionized atom. Pauli shows that in simple as well as in more complicated cases the application of this principle gives just the right variety of terms for the atom. The ramification principle of Heisenberg and Landé is shown to be in accordance with the principle of permanence.

Of special importance are, in Pauli's line of thought, the formulae for the Zeeman effect in strong fields. The principle of permanence implies the existence of quantum numbers m_j for the single electrons, the sum of which is the total angular momentum of the atom in the direction of the field:

$$M = \sum m_j$$

The part of the energy due to the field is proportional to the magnetic moment

$$M_2 = M + M_S = M_L + 2M_S$$

which can be written, by the principle of permanence, as a sum of moments of single electrons

$$M_2 = \sum m_2$$

After these preparations Pauli is now able to enunciate his basic assumption as follows: *Every electron in the atom can be characterized by one principal quantum number n and three additional quantum numbers l, j, m_j.* The number j is always $l \pm \frac{1}{2}$, as in the alkali spectra. Instead of j we can also use $m_2 = m_j \pm \frac{1}{2}$.

It is clear that the definition of these quantum numbers presented great difficulties at a time when quantum mechanics did not exist and the types of motion of the electrons had to be described by inadequate classical models. Thus, in order to define the numbers m_j and m_2, Pauli had to assume a magnetic field so strong that every electron has, independent of the others, a definite mechanical momentum m_j and a magnetic moment m_2. Pauli himself saw these difficulties very well and did not consider his point of view as final. We have to admire his courage and persistance in developing the logical consequences of his hypotheses. The subsequent development of quantum mechanics led to a complete justification of every one of his assumptions.

Next, Pauli considers the case of equivalent electrons. He notes that in this case some combinations of quantum numbers do not occur in nature; e.g. if two valence electrons are in s states belonging to different values of n, we observe a singlet S term and a triplet S term, but if both electrons have the same n, only the singlet term occurs.

This reduction of terms, says Pauli, is closely connected with the phenomenon of closed shells. The K-shell, which is closed in the normal state of He, consists of two electrons. The L-shell, which is closed in the normal state of Ne, consists of eight electrons, etc. Bohr, in his theory of the periodic system of elements, had divided these eight electrons into two subgroups of four electrons, but Stoner proposed to divide the eight electrons into a subgroup of two electrons having $l=0$, and a subgroup of six electrons having $l=1$. Also in the other closed shells Stoner assumed, for every value of $l<n$, just $2(2l+1)$ electrons to form a subgroup. (Stoner, like Pauli, used a quantum number $k=l+1$ instead of our l.)

Most important is Stoner's remark that the same number $2(2l+1)$, which gives the number of electrons in a closed shell belonging to a given value of l, is also equal to the number of possible states of an alkali atom in a magnetic field belonging to the same value of l and to a given principal quantum number of the valence electron.

As we have seen, this remark of Stoner gave Pauli the clue to his exclusion principle. He explains the fact that there are exactly $2(2l+1)$ electrons in every subgroup of a closed shell by assuming that every state, characterized by quantum numbers (n, l, j, m_j), is occupied by just one electron. Thus, for a given n and $l>0$, we have just two possibilities for $j=l\pm\frac{1}{2}$, and for every j just $2j+1$ possibilities for m_j. For $l=0$ we have $j=\frac{1}{2}$ and two possibilities for m_j. Thus we obtain, in any case, $2(2l+1)$ possibilities for the set (n, l, j, m_j).

The quantum numbers j and m_j of the single electrons were defined by Pauli only in strong fields, but he notes that for thermodynamic reasons the number of states in weak fields must be the same as in strong fields. Hence, all conclusions drawn from the exclusion principle concerning the number of states and the total momentum J of these states must be generally valid. Pauli's logic is admirable!

From the exclusion principle Pauli now deduces the numbers 2, 8, 18, 32 ... of electrons in closed shells, and the fact that the triplet S term does not occur in the case of an alkaline earth metal with two equivalent s electrons. If the two electrons would have equal quantum numbers $m_j = +\frac{1}{2}$ or $m_j = -\frac{1}{2}$, the set of four quantum numbers

$$(n, l, j, m_j) = (n, 0, \tfrac{1}{2}, m_j)$$

would be the same for both, which is excluded by the exclusion principle. Hence, the case $M = +1$ or $M = -1$ cannot occur, hence J cannot be 1, which means that the triplet S term does not occur.

Next, Pauli supposes that one electron is taken away from a closed shell. In this case one set of values (l', j', m') is missing from the sub-subgroup defined by the quantum numbers l' and j'. The angular momentum of the shell is now

$$M = \sum m_j = -m'$$

If we take for m' all possible values from $-j'$ to $+j'$, we obtain for M the values from $+j'$ to $-j'$, i.e. just the same set as in the case of a single electron. Hence, the number of states obtained by taking away one electron from a closed shell is the same as the number of states of the valence electron of an alkali metal belonging to a given n, and also the values of J are the same. This is confirmed by experience.

More generally, the number of states of a closed shell from which q electrons are missing is the same as the number of states of a set of q electrons having the same n.

Pauli gives several more applications of his exclusion principle—experience always confirmed his conclusions.

At the end of his paper Pauli expresses the hope that some time a deeper understanding of quantum mechanics might enable us to derive the exclusion principle from more fundamental hypotheses. This hope was fulfilled to a certain extent. In fact, the exclusion principle can be deduced from a more general principle of antisymmetry, which, as Pauli himself was able to show, is closely connected with the fact that electrons have a half-integer spin, and with relativistic invariance (see section 15).

4. THE SPINNING ELECTRON

W. Heisenberg: Zur Quantentheorie der Multiplettstruktur und der anomalen Zeemaneffekte. *Z. Phys.* **32**, 841 (received April 1925).

G. E. Uhlenbeck and S. Goudsmit: Ersetzung der Hypothese vom unmechanischen Zwang durch eine Forderung bezüglich des inneren Verhaltens jedes einzelnen Elektrons. *Naturwissenschaften* **13**, 953 (October 1925). Spinning Electrons and the Structure of Spectra. *Nature, Lond.* **117**, 264 (written December 1925).

L. H. Thomas: The motion of the Spinning Electron. *Nature, Lond.* **117**, 514 (written February 1926). The Kinematics of an Electron with an Axis. *Phil. Mag.* **17**, 3, p. 1 (published January 1927).

R. de L. Kronig: Spinning Electrons and the Structure of Spectra. *Nature, Lond.* **117**, 550 (published April 1925).

G. E. Uhlenbeck: *Oude en nieuwe vragen der natuurkunde.* Address, delivered April 1955. Amsterdam; North-Holland Publishing Co.

In addition to these printed papers, the following letters were used, with kind permission of the senders and the owners:

Three letters of Heisenberg to Goudsmit, dated 21 November and 9 December (1925), and 19 February (1926).

Two letters of Heisenberg to Pauli, dated 24 November and 24 December (1925).

Four letters of Pauli to Bohr, dated 5 and 26 February, 5 and 12 March (1925).

Bohr to Kronig, 26 March (1926).

Kronig to van der Waerden, 22 June (1959).

Heisenberg to van der Waerden, 23 June (1959).

Uhlenbeck to van der Waerden, 7 July (1959).

Goudsmit to van der Waerden, 14 July (1959).

Bohr to van der Waerden, July 1959.

We now return to the question raised at the end of section 2: Why did not Pauli ascribe an angular momentum $m_s = \pm \frac{1}{2}$ and a magnetic moment $2m_s$ to the electron?

Pauli's printed papers did not help me to answer this question; also, Pauli's statement in his Nobel prize lecture to the effect that he was converted to the idea of the spinning electron by Thomas' calculations on the magnitude of doublet splitting, was a complete mystery to me at first. I, therefore, wrote letters to several persons who had discussed these questions with Pauli. From this correspondence I learnt that the hypothesis of the spinning electron had been presented to Pauli and Heisenberg early in 1925 by Kronig, and again in October 1925 by Uhlenbeck and Goudsmit, and that they and Niels Bohr first rejected the hypothesis, but that Bohr and Heisenberg were converted to it in December 1925, and Pauli in March 1926. Thus, my problem enlarged itself to the more general question: For what reasons did Pauli, Heisenberg and Bohr reject the spin hypothesis in 1925, and what were the reasons for their change of mind?

After long correspondence and many talks, I got nearly complete answers to these questions. I learnt that a certain formula for the doublet splitting of alkali and hydrogen terms, found by Kronig in February 1925, transmitted through Heisenberg to Uhlenbeck, Goudsmit, Einstein and Bohr, and corrected by L.

H. Thomas, played a decisive part in the discussion. To explain this, I have to tell the whole story from the very beginning. I shall first give the facts as I learnt them from the letters and papers quoted, and next give a short comment. Part of the story is also told by Kronig in his article 'The Turning Point' in this volume. We have tried to avoid repetitions as far as possible, but some essential points had to be included in both accounts.

The hypothesis of an electron spinning around its axis was first proposed in 1921 by A. Compton (*J. Franklin Inst.* **192**, 145). However, Compton did not apply this hypothesis to the anomalous Zeeman effect, and it seems that his paper did not influence the later development.

In January 1925, R. de L. Kronig, aged 20, came to Tübingen to see Landé and Back. Landé showed Kronig a letter he had just received from Pauli, in which the exclusion principle was explained, essentially along the same lines as in Pauli's paper analysed in section 3. In the letter, as in the paper, Pauli proposed to characterize every electron in the atom by four quantum numbers (n, l, j, m_j in modern notation), j being equal to $l + \frac{1}{2}$ or $l - \frac{1}{2}$, and m_j taking the values $j, j - 1, \ldots, -j$.

Kronig at once saw the implications of this hypothesis. If the total angular momentum j differs from the orbital angular momentum l by $\pm \frac{1}{2}$, this means that every electron has, in addition to the angular momentum of its orbital motion, a momentum of its own, the projection of this momentum vector in any given direction being $\pm \frac{1}{2}$ (expressed in the unit $h/2\pi$). Formerly, this additional momentum was ascribed to the atomic core, but Pauli's point of view implied that it had to be ascribed to the electron itself.

To give this momentum a dynamic interpretation, Kronig supposed the electron to spin about its own axis.

The same day, Kronig investigated what would be the energy levels of an electron carrying a magnet of just one Bohr magneton. In the coordinate system, in which the electron is at rest at a given time, the electrical field of the atomic core would give rise, by a Lorentz transformation, to a magnetic field. The action of this field upon the magnet is reflected by a term in the energy proportional to the scalar product of the spin vector and the orbital momentum vector. For an alkali atom, a calculation of this interaction yielded a doublet splitting proportional to Z^4, where Z is the effective nuclear charge (or more precisely to $Z_i^2 Z^2$ where Z_i and Z are the screened nuclear charges effective inside and outside the atomic core), in accordance with the empirical results discussed by Landé.* The old model, in which the doublet splitting was ascribed to a magnetic moment of the core, would give a proportionality to Z^3.

This satisfactory result made Kronig hope that for hydrogen-like atoms the new effect would superpose on Sommerfeld's calculated fine structure in such a way as to make the two levels $l=j-\frac{1}{2}$ and $l=j+\frac{1}{2}$ coincide for any given j, thus explaining the observed fine structure of hydrogen terms. However, it turned out that the calculated new effect was twice the amount required by the observations.

On 8 January, Kronig met Pauli at Tübingen and explained his ideas and calculations. Pauli said: 'Das ist ja ein ganz witziger Einfall', but he remained sceptical.

Next, Kronig went to Copenhagen and discussed the problem with Heisenberg, Kramers and others. They did not approve of the idea of a spinning electron. Under the impression of this negative reaction of renowned physicists, Kronig did not publish his theory; besides, he was fully aware of several difficulties, which he enumerates as follows in his letter to me:

> First, the factor 2 already mentioned. Next, the difficulty to under-stand how a rotation of the electron about its axis would yield a magnetic moment of just one magneton. Next, the necessity to assume, for the rotating charge of an electron of classical size, velocities surpassing the velocity of light. Finally, the smallness of the magnetic moments of atomic nuclei, which were supposed, at that time, to consist of protons and electrons.

Independent of Kronig, the Dutch physicists Uhlenbeck and Goudsmit (*Physica* 5, 266, 1925) also had the idea that every term of the hydrogen spectrum ought to be characterized by three quantum numbers (n, l, j) instead of the traditional two, just as every term of an alkali spectrum has three quantum numbers (n, l, j), the only difference being that for a given j the two hydrogen terms $l=j+\frac{1}{2}$ and $l=j-\frac{1}{2}$ coincide. By similar considerations of analogy, J. C. Slater (*Proc. Wash. Acad. Sci.* Dec. 1925) also arrived at the same conclusion. The analogy argument was convincing, and the conclusion is correct, as we now know. In fact, it is a direct consequence of Pauli's postulate that every electron state be characterized by four quantum numbers (n, l, j, m_j).

At this time (1923–25), the physicists of the Copenhagen school

---

* Landé, A. Z. *Phys.* **24**, 88 and **25**, 46: see also Millikan, R. A. and Bowen, I. S. *Phys. Rev.* **32**, 1 and 764, and Goudsmit, S. *Naturwissenschaften* **9**, 995.

were trying to solve the difficulties of multiplet structure and magnetic term splitting by assuming a 'non-mechanical strain' to cause a doubling of terms. This hypothesis had been proposed by Bohr in 1923 (*Ann. Phys. Lpz.* **71**, 228) and elaborated by Heisenberg (*loc. cit.*) in April 1925. Although Bohr felt 'unhappy and desperate' over the state of things, he still maintained his hypothesis until the end of 1925 (see *Nature, Lond.* **116**, 845).

The spell was broken in October 1925 by the famous letter to *Naturwissenschaften* of Uhlenbeck and Goudsmit, transmitted to the editor by Ehrenfest. The authors did not know of Kronig's ideas; they started, just as Kronig did, from Pauli's four quantum numbers, and proposed to interpret s and m_s as quantum numbers characterizing the state of rotation of the electron. To explain the anomalous Zeeman effect, they assumed the ratio of the electron's magnetic moment to its angular momentum to be twice as large as it is for the orbital motion. The orientation of the spin vector with respect to the orbital momentum vector was made responsible for the relativity doublets.

In his address, delivered at Leiden on the occasion of his Lorentz Professorship (1955), Uhlenbeck gives the story of the discovery and publication of the idea of the spinning electron as follows:

Goudsmit and myself hit upon this idea by studying a paper of Pauli, in which the famous exclusion principle was formulated and in which, for the first time, *four* quantum numbers were ascribed to the electron. This was done rather formally; no concrete picture was connected with it. To us, this was a mystery. We were so conversant with the proposition that every quantum number corresponds to a degree of freedom, and on the other hand with the idea of a point electron, which obviously had three degrees of freedom only, that we could not place the fourth quantum number. We could understand it only if the electron was assumed to be a small sphere that could rotate . . .

Somewhat later we found in a paper of Abraham (to which Ehrenfest drew our attention) that for a rotating sphere with surface charge the necessary factor two (in the magnetic moment) could be understood classically. This encouraged us, but our enthusiasm was considerably reduced when we saw that the rotational velocity at the surface of the electron had to be many times the velocity of light! I remember that most of these thoughts came to us on an afternoon at the end of September 1925. We were excited, but we had not the slightest intention of publishing anything. It seemed so speculative and bold, that something ought to be wrong with it, especially since Bohr, Heisenberg and Pauli, our great authorities, had never proposed anything of the kind. But of course we told Ehrenfest. He was impressed at once, mainly, I feel, because of the visual character of our hypothesis, which was very much in his line. He called our attention to several points (e.g. to the fact that in 1921 A. C. Compton already had suggested the idea of a spinning

electron as a possible explanation of the natural unit of magnetism) and
finally said that it was either highly important or nonsense, and that we
should write a short note for *Naturwissenschaften* and give it him.   He
ended with the words 'und dann werden wir Herrn Lorentz fragen'.
This was done.   Lorentz received us with his well known great kindness,
and he was very much interested, although, I feel, somewhat sceptical
too.   He promised to think it over.   And in fact, already next week he
gave us a manuscript, written in his beautiful handwriting, containing
long calculations on the electromagnetic properties of rotating electrons.
We could not fully understand it, but it was quite clear that the picture
of the rotating electron, if taken seriously, would give rise to serious
difficulties.   For one thing, the magnetic energy would be so large that
by the equivalence of mass and energy the electron would have a larger
mass than the proton, or, if one sticks to the known mass, the electron
would be bigger than the whole atom!   In any case, it seemed to be
nonsense.   Goudsmit and myself both felt that it might be better for
the present not to publish anything; but when we said this to Ehrenfest,
he answered: 'Ich habe Ihren Brief schon längst abgesandt; Sie sind
beide jung genug um sich eine Dummheit leisten zu können!'

Heisenberg congratulated Goudsmit on his courageous paper,
but also asked him how he envisaged getting rid of the wrong factor
2 in the doublet splitting formula.   This formula was, of course,
the same one Kronig had found and communicated to Pauli,
Heisenberg and Kramers.   In Heisenberg's letter (21 November
1925), no derivation of the formula was given.   In his letter to
me, Uhlenbeck reports:

> After we [Uhlenbeck and Goudsmit] received the result from Heisen-
> berg, we tried to derive it ourselves.   An essential hint was given by
> Einstein (who was in Leiden at that time) when he told us to consider a
> coordinate system in which the electron is at rest and see how the
> Coulomb field transforms.   After that the calculation was of course
> rather obvious.

Thus, Kronig's explanation of the doublet splitting with the
wrong factor 2 was derived anew by Einstein, Uhlenbeck and
Goudsmit, by exactly the same Lorentz transformation Kronig
had already used.   It was this explanation that converted Niels
Bohr to the idea of the spinning electron.   In his letter to Kronig,
Bohr writes:

> When I came to Leiden to the Lorentz festivals [December 1925],
> Einstein asked the very first moment I saw him what I believed about
> the spinning electron.   Upon my question about the cause of the neces-
> sary mutual coupling between spin axis and the orbital motion, he
> explained that this coupling was an immediate consequence of the
> theory of relativity.   This remark acted as a complete revelation to me,
> and I have never since faltered in my conviction that we at last were at
> the end of our sorrows.

In letters to Pauli and to Goudsmit, dated 24 November and 9 December respectively, Heisenberg raised several objections against the idea of the spinning electron, the main objection being, once more, the factor 2. Yet, under the influence of Bohr's optimistic attitude, Heisenberg gave up his resistance before 24 December.

Pauli did not. He had met Bohr on his way from Copenhagen to Leiden at the Hamburg railway station, and strongly warned him against accepting the spin hypothesis. After the Lorentz festival Pauli met Bohr in Berlin, expressed in strong words his dissatisfaction with Bohr's conversion, and deplored that a new 'Irrlehre' should be introduced into atomic physics.

From Pauli's letters to Bohr and from his Nobel prize lecture we may conclude that Pauli's main arguments against the spin hypothesis were: (1) the wrong factor 2 in the doublet splitting formula, which did not disappear when Heisenberg and Pauli made the calculations anew by means of Heisenberg's new quantum mechanics; (2) the classical mechanical character of the hypothesis of the spinning electron. Pauli's Socratic daimon, his intuition (as we call it today) told him that the 'two-valuedness' of the electron is a typical quantum effect which cannot be described in terms of classical mechanics.

The factor 2 was at last rectified by L. H. Thomas. By a rigorous application of relativistic mechanics, Thomas obtained just the right doublet separation. His first note was written in February 1926 in Bohr's institute at Copenhagen.

It was Thomas's calculation that finally induced Pauli to accept the idea of the spinning electron in March 1926. In his Nobel prize lecture he writes:

> Although at first I strongly doubted the correctness of this idea because of its classical mechanical character, I was finally converted to it by Thomas' calculations on the magnitude of doublet splitting. On the other hand, my earlier doubts as well as the cautious expression 'classically non-describable two-valuedness' experienced a certain verification during later developments, as Bohr was able to show on the basis of wave mechanics that the electron spin cannot be measured by classically describable experiments. . . .

The hypothesis of the spinning electron consists of three parts: (1) the electron rotates; (2) it has an angular momentum $m_s = \pm \frac{1}{2}$ in a given direction; and (3) it has a magnetic moment $2m_s$.

Pauli was reluctant to accept hypothesis (1) because of its classical mechanical character. We now know that he was right. The spin cannot be described by a classical kinematic model, for such a model can never lead to a two-valued representation of the rotation group.

Logically, Pauli could have accepted (2) and (3) without accepting (1). However, it is difficult to think of an angular momentum without thinking of a rotation. Kronig, as well as Uhlenbeck and Goudsmit, presented the three hypotheses in one package.

The main reason why Pauli doubted not only (1), but also (2) and (3), certainly was the factor 2 in Kronig's calculation of the doublet separation. Pauli knew that an alkali atom behaves in a magnetic field just as if the electron had a quantized magnetic moment of 1 magneton, but the same electron seemed to behave in the field of the nucleus as if it had a magnetic moment of only $\frac{1}{2}$ magneton. After Thomas' calculations it became clear that the electron behaves in all respects like a magnet of 1 magneton. Consequently, Pauli gave up his resistance against (2) and (3), and now he also accepted (1) as a provisional model, knowing that quantum mechanics had already created a completely new situation.

Pauli's attitude towards the mental picture of a spinning electron during this year of transition is well illustrated by a remark in Pauli's essay dedicated to Niels Bohr on the occasion of his seventieth birthday (*Niels Bohr and the Development of Physics*, p. 30. 1955. London).

> After a brief period of spiritual and human confusion, caused by a provisional restriction to 'Anschaulichkeit', a general agreement was reached following the substitution of abstract mathematical symbols, as for instance psi, for concrete pictures. Especially the concrete picture of rotation has been replaced by mathematical characteristics of the representations of the group of rotations in three-dimensional space.

We have seen that the doubts of Pauli, Heisenberg and Kronig were justified in many respects. Lorentz, too, had serious doubts, which were well founded at that time. In my opinion, Pauli and Heisenberg cannot be blamed for not having encouraged Kronig to publish his hypothesis.

5. FERMI STATISTICS

E. Fermi: Zur Quantelung des idealen einatomigen Gases. *Z. Phys.* **36**, 902 (received March 1926).

W. Pauli: Über Gasentartung und Paramagnetismus. *Z. Phys.* **41**, 81 (received December 1926).

Pauli's exclusion principle was applied to statistical thermodynamics by Fermi and Dirac in two highly important, independent papers in 1926. I shall first give a short summary of Fermi's paper and of Pauli's closely related paper of December 1926.

In an ideal gas, the motions of the single molecules are independent. Each molecule moves in a field which keeps the molecules together, e.g. in the repulsion field of perfectly elastic reflecting walls. Since the ultimate results do not depend on the choice of the field, Fermi assumes the molecules to be drawn towards a fixed point O by a central force proportional to the distance. Every molecule is now a harmonic oscillator. If each molecule consists of one atom in the normal state and if this normal state is simple (i.e. does not split in a magnetic field), the state of every molecule is characterized by three quantum numbers s_1, s_2, s_3 and its energy is (if the lowest possible energy is chosen as the zero level)

$$h\nu(s_1 + s_2 + s_3) = h\nu s$$

where ν is the frequency of the oscillator.

Fermi now supposes that Pauli's exclusion principle holds for molecules, i.e. that every state can be occupied by one molecule only. A state of the gas is defined as soon as we know what states are occupied. All states of the gas having a given total number of molecules and a given total energy $W = Eh\nu$ (where E is an integer) are assumed to have equal probabilities. The probabilities of the different values of E are uniquely determined by the condition that at very large distances, where the density is small, the velocity distribution tends to Maxwell's distribution.

Starting with these assumptions, Fermi is now able to calculate the energy distribution, the mean kinetic energy, the pressure and the specific heat. Although Fermi describes the motion of the molecules by classical mechanics, his results are essentially the same as those obtained by Dirac from quantum mechanics in a fundamental paper to be discussed in section 6.

Pauli simplified Fermi's calculations by considering a 'grand ensemble', in which the number N of particles is subject to the law of chance. The resulting formulae for the mean energy and the mean number N are the same as Fermi's. Pauli also calculates the variance of the number of particles having a given energy. Next he applies Fermi's principles to a gas consisting of electrons or molecules having an angular momentum, and he studies the behaviour of such a gas in a magnetic field.

6. ANTISYMMETRIC WAVE FUNCTIONS

P. A. M. Dirac: On the theory of Quantum Mechanics. *Proc. Roy. Soc.* B **112**, 661 (received August 1926).

In 1925, quantum mechanics was born. A very good historical account of this great event was given by E. Whittaker in Vol. II of *History of the Theories of Aether and Electricity,* chaps. VIII and IX. 1953. London; Nelson. Here we shall investigate how the spin and the exclusion principle were incorporated into quantum mechanics.

Independent of each other, Dirac and Heisenberg were the first to apply wave mechanics to systems of more than one particle. Although Heisenberg's paper in *Z. Phys.* **38** precedes Dirac's by 2 or 3 months, we shall discuss Dirac's paper first.

In section 3, Dirac first remarks that Heisenberg's matrix mechanics enables one to calculate just those quantities that are of physical importance, and gives no information about quantities that one can never hope to measure experimentally. 'We should expect this very satisfactory characteristic to persist in all future developments of the theory', says Dirac.

He now considers an atom with two electrons. He denotes by (mn) that state of the atom in which one electron is in an orbit labelled m, and the other in the orbit n. The two states (mn) and (nm) are physically indistinguishable. If they are to be counted as different states, the theory would enable one to calculate the intensities $(mn) \rightarrow (m'n')$ and $(mn) \rightarrow (n'm')$ separately. However, only the sum of these intensities can be determined experimentally. Hence, Dirac prefers to adopt the alternative that (m, n) and (n, m) count as only one state.

In wave mechanics a state of an atomic system is determined by a function ψ of the coordinates q_r. If $\psi_n(x, y, z)$ is the eigenfunction for a single electron in the orbit n, the eigenfunction for the atom in the state (m, n) is, as long as interaction is neglected,

$$\psi_m(x_1, y_1, z_1)\psi_n(x_2, y_2, z_2) = \psi_m(1)\psi_n(2)$$

The eigenfunction $\psi_m(2)\,\psi_n(1)$ corresponds to the same state if we count the (mn) and (nm) states as identical. If we are to have only one row and column in the matrices corresponding to both (mn) and (nm), we must find a set of eigenfunctions ψ_{mn} of the form

$$\psi_{mn} = a_{mn}\psi_m(1)\psi_n(2) + b_{mn}\psi_m(2)\psi_n(1)$$

which set must contain only one ψ_{mn} corresponding to both (mn) and (nm). There are two ways of choosing the set of ψ_{mn}'s to satisfy the conditions. We may either take $a_{mn} = b_{mn}$, which makes each ψ_{mn} a symmetrical function of the two electrons, or $a_{mn} = -b_{mn}$, which makes ψ_{mn} antisymmetrical.

For r non-interacting electrons, the symmetrical eigenfunctions are

$$\sum \psi_1(k_1)\psi_2(k_2)\cdots\psi_r(k_r)$$

the summation extending over all permutations $(k_1, \cdots, k_r)$ of the integers $1, 2, \cdots, r$, whereas the antisymmetrical eigenfunctions are sums of the same terms with alternating signs. If there is interaction between the electrons, there will still be symmetrical and antisymmetrical eigenfunctions. Dirac's conclusion is: 'In any case the symmetrical ones alone or the antisymmetrical ones alone give a complete solution of the problem'.

Next, Dirac remarks that in the solution with antisymmetrical eigenfunctions there can be no stationary states with two or more electrons in the same orbit, which is just Pauli's exclusion principle. The symmetrical solution allows any number of electrons to be in the same orbit 'so that this solution cannot be the correct one for electrons in an atom'.

In section 4, Dirac applies the same method to an assembly of non-interacting molecules between boundary walls. The eigenfunctions of the whole system are obtained by multiplying the plane wave eigenfunctions of the molecules and forming symmetrical or antisymmetrical aggregates. All states of the system (each represented by one eigenfunction) are assumed to have the same *a priori* probability. In the symmetrical case, this assumption leads to Einstein–Bose statistics. In the antisymmetrical case Dirac's basic assumptions are essentially the same as those made by Fermi, and the calculation of the mean kinetic energy and of the pressure by standard statistical methods leads to the same formulae which Fermi had already obtained.

Dirac's conclusion is: 'The solution with symmetrical eigenfunctions must be the correct one when applied to light quanta, since it is known that the Einstein–Bose statistical mechanics leads to Planck's law of black body radiation. The antisymmetrical solution is probably the correct one for gas molecules, since it is known to be the correct one for electrons in an atom, and one would expect molecules to resemble electrons more closely than light-quanta'.

7. HEISENBERG'S THEORY OF THE HELIUM ATOM

W. Heisenberg: Mehrkörperproblem und Resonanz in der Quantenmechanik. *Z. Phys.* **38**, 411 (received June 1926). Über die Spektra von Atomsystemen mit zwei Elektronen. *Z. Phys.* **39**, 499 (received July 1926).

The leading ideas in these two papers are the same as in Dirac's theory of the many-body problem. Heisenberg too forms, in the case of two equal particles, a symmetric and an antisymmetric eigenfunction

$$\psi_m(1)\psi_n(2) + \psi_m(2)\psi_n(1) \qquad \ldots(1)$$

$$\psi_m(1)\psi_n(2) - \psi_m(2)\psi_n(1) \qquad \ldots(2)$$

and in the case of n equal particles an antisymmetrical eigenfunction

$$\sum \pm \psi_1(k_1)\psi_2(k_2) \cdots \psi_r(k_r) \qquad \ldots(3)$$

He also notes that the restriction to antisymmetrical eigenfunctions implies Pauli's exclusion principle.

In the case of the helium atom, as long as the spin is neglected, both eigenfunctions (1) and (2) are possible; they correspond to parhelium and orthohelium. In the symmetric case (1), the two electrons may be in the same state, hence, in parhelium the lowest term $1S$ occurs, but not in orthohelium. Without interaction of the two electrons, the terms (1) and (2) would have the same energy, but the interaction raises one term (usually the symmetric one) and lowers the other. In Heisenberg's second paper, some numerical evaluations are carried out.

Next, the spin is taken into account. The two electrons 1 and 2 have spin vectors $\vec{s}_1$ and $\vec{s}_2$, whose components in any direction take the values $\pm \frac{1}{2}$ only. Thus, every state of the system without spin gives rise to four states, three of which are symmetric in the spin coordinates and one antisymmetric. By Pauli's principle, the combined eigenfunction of the space coordinates and spin coordinates must be antisymmetric. Hence, there are two possibilities: either we multiply the symmetric eigenfunctions of parhelium by the antisymmetric eigenfunction of the spin coordinates, thus obtaining the singlet term system of parhelium, or we multiply the antisymmetric eigenfunctions of orthohelium by the three symmetric eigenfunctions of the spin coordinates, thus obtaining the triplet term system of orthohelium. The calculations are carried out by a method due to Kronig (Z. Phys. **33**, 261) and Dirac (Proc. Roy. Soc. **111**, 281); the results are in accordance with the evidence from the spectra of He and Li+.

Heisenberg speaks of spin coordinates, but he does not say clearly what he means by this expression. He first considers a simplified model of two electrons without orbital motion in a constant magnetic field. In this simple case, the spin coordinates are just the angular momenta of the electrons in the direction of the field. In the case of an atom, Heisenberg proceeds by analogy, replacing the external field vector by the orbital momentum vector.

The first exact definition of the notion 'spin coordinates' was given by Pauli. We shall now discuss Pauli's spin theory.

8. THE SPIN VECTOR $\vec{s}$ AND THE SPIN MATRICES s_1, s_2, s_3

W. Heisenberg and P. Jordan: Anwendung der Quantenmechanik auf das Problem der anomalen Zeemaneffekte. *Z. Phys.* **37**, 263 (received March 1926).

W. Pauli: Zur Quantenmechanik des magnetischen Elektrons. *Z. Phys.* **43**, 601 (received May 1927).

Heisenberg and Jordan were the first to calculate the doublet splitting and the anomalous Zeeman effect of atoms with one valence electron by the methods of matrix mechanics. In addition to the orbital momentum vector $\vec{k}$ with components

$$k_x = (yp_z - zp_y), \text{ etc.}$$

the authors introduce a spin vector $\vec{s}$ with components s_x, s_y, s_z. Following Pauli, we shall use heavy print for matrices and operators. In analogy to the commutation relations for k_x, k_y, k_z:

$$k_x k_y - k_y k_x = i(h/2\pi)k_z, \text{ etc.}$$

the same relations for s_x, s_y, s_z are assumed:

$$s_x s_y - s_y s_x = i(h/2\pi)s_z, \text{ etc.} \quad \dots(1)$$

and also

$$\vec{s}^2 = s_x{}^2 + s_y{}^2 + s_z{}^2 = (h/2\pi)^2 s(s+1) \quad \dots(2)$$

with $s = \frac{1}{2}$ in the case of one electron. The interaction between $\vec{k}$ and $\vec{s}$ is supposed to be given by a term in the energy proportional to $\vec{k} \cdot \vec{s}$. The part of the energy due to the external field H is assumed to be

$$(e/2m_0 c)\vec{H} \cdot (\vec{k} + 2\vec{s})$$

Starting from these assumptions, Heisenberg and Jordan calculate the terms by perturbation theory. The results are in perfect accordance with the empirical data.

Pauli replaces the matrices $s_x \cdots$ by operators operating on a Schrödinger wave function ψ and satisfying the same conditions (1) and (2). If s_x, s_y, s_z are expressed in units $\frac{1}{2}h/2\pi$, the conditions are

$$s_x s_y - s_y s_x = 2is_z \cdots \quad \dots(3)$$

$$s_x{}^2 + s_y{}^2 + s_z{}^2 = 3 \quad \dots(4)$$

The main difficulty Pauli had to solve was the definition of the coordinates of which ψ is a function. In addition to the space coordinates q, Pauli takes s_z as a coordinate assuming the values ± 1 only, the direction of the z axis being quite arbitrary. This means: the function $\psi(q, s_z)$ has just two components $\psi_\alpha(q)$ and $\psi_\beta(q)$ corresponding to $s_z = +1$ and $s_z = -1$. The probability for the coordinates q to lie between x and $x+dx$, y and $y+dy$, z and $z+dz$ and for s_z to have the value $+1$ or -1 is

$$|\psi_\alpha(x, y, z)|^2 dx dy dz \quad \text{or} \quad |\psi_\beta(x, y, z)|^2 dx dy dz$$

The simplest solution of (3) and (4) is

$$s_x(\psi_\alpha, \psi_\beta) = (\psi_\beta, \psi_\alpha)$$
$$s_y(\psi_\alpha, \psi_\beta) = (-i\psi_\beta, i\psi_\alpha)$$
$$s_z(\psi_\alpha, \psi_\beta) = (\psi_\alpha, -\psi_\beta)$$

The matrices of these transformations are the famous Pauli matrices

$$s_x = \begin{pmatrix} 0 & 1 \\ 1 & 0 \end{pmatrix}, \quad s_y = \begin{pmatrix} 0 & -i \\ i & 0 \end{pmatrix}, \quad s_z = \begin{pmatrix} 1 & 0 \\ 0 & -1 \end{pmatrix} \quad \dots (5)$$

For the passage to a new coordinate system (x', y', z'), Pauli proposes the formulae

$$\begin{cases} \psi_\alpha' = t_{11}\psi_\alpha + t_{12}\psi_\beta \\ \psi_\beta' = t_{21}\psi_\alpha + t_{22}\psi_\beta \end{cases} \quad \dots (6)$$

where T, the matrix of the t_{ij}, is a unitary matrix, i.e. the product of T by its transposed conjugate matrix $T^\dagger$ is the unit matrix $\mathbf{1}$, and

$$s_{x'} = T s_x T^{-1}, \quad s_{y'} = T s_y T^{-1}, \quad s_{z'} = T s_z T^{-1} \quad \dots (7)$$

On the other hand, s_x, s_y and s_z are the components of the vector $\vec{s}$, hence, they ought to transform, like the coordinates x, y, z themselves, by an orthogonal transformation

$$s_x = a_{11}s_{x'} + a_{12}s_{y'} + a_{13}s_{z'}, \quad \text{etc.} \quad \dots (8)$$

Pauli now shows that (7) and (8) may be brought into accordance by taking for T the matrix formed by the complex conjugates $\alpha^\star, \beta^\star, \gamma^\star, \delta^\star$ of the Cayley–Klein parameters of the orthogonal transformation (8), as defined in the book of A. Sommerfeld and F. Klein, *Theorie des Kreisels*, sections 2–4. He also remarks that all solutions of (3) and (4) can be obtained from the special solution (5) by transformations (7). Hence, the special solution (5) may be used without any loss of generality.

For the interaction between $\vec{s}$ and $\vec{k}$ and for the energy of an electron in a magnetic field, Pauli assumes the same expressions as Heisenberg and Jordan. Of course, the results are also the same. The generalization to N electrons is immediate. The wave function $\psi(q_1, \cdots, q_N, s_{z1} \cdots, s_{zN})$ is equivalent to a set of 2^N functions of the space coordinates:

$$\psi_{i_1 i_2 \cdots i_N}(q_1, \cdots, q_N) \quad \text{with} \quad i_k = \alpha_k \quad \text{or} \quad \beta_k$$

In spite of these highly satisfactory results, Pauli regarded his theory as provisional and approximate only, because, as he says, his wave equation is not invariant under Lorentz transformations and does not allow the calculation of higher-order corrections to the fine structure of hydrogen terms. He felt a better model of the magnetic electron, including quadrupole and higher effects, would be necessary to solve these difficulties.

It seems that Pauli under-estimated the importance and the final character of his methods and results. His description of the state of N electrons by a ψ function having several components which transform linearly according to a two-valued representation of the rotation group, was fundamental and final. It enabled Wigner and von Neumann to deduce all empirical rules of atomic term zoology without introducing any new assumption or any approximation (see section 10). Pauli's matrices s_k were used by Dirac to form a relativistic first-order wave equation (see section 11). Dirac's wave equation contains matrices and is similar to Pauli's, but not to the old relativistic wave equation. The step from one to two ψ components is large, whereas the step from two to four components is small; also, the step from vector algebra to a two-valued representation of the rotation group is large, the extension of this representation to the Lorentz group is much easier. In all cases, it was Pauli who made the first decisive step, and in this part of his paper there is nothing provisional or approximate.

9. GROUP-THEORETICAL DEDUCTION OF THE COMMUTATION RELATIONS

J. von Neumann: Über die analytischen Eigenschaften von Gruppen linearer Transformationen und ihrer Darstellungen. *Math. Z.* **30**, 3 (received February 1927).

J. von Neumann and E. Wigner: Zur Erklärung einiger Eigenschaften der Spektren aus der Quantenmechanik des Drehelektrons. *Z. Phys.* **47** 203 (received December 1927).

B. L. van der Waerden: Stetigkeitssätze für halbeinfache Liesche Gruppen. *Math. Z.* **36**, 780 (received May 1932).

Pauli's spin theory started with the commutation relations

$$s_x s_y - s_y s_x = 2i s_z, \quad \text{etc.} \qquad \dots (1)$$

obtained by analogy from the corresponding relations for the orbital angular momentum operators k_x, k_y, k_z.

By means of the theory of representations of Lie groups it is possible to show that the relations (1) need not be assumed. They can be deduced from the more fundamental assumption of invariance of the theory with respect to space rotations.

The fundamental idea of this deduction is due to von Neumann and Wigner. In the following presentation, I shall assume a little less and prove a little more than these authors did. They tacitly assumed the continuity of the representations of the rotation group, which is not necessary. On the other hand, they did not introduce the notion of angular momentum, whereas I shall prove that the electron has an angular momentum satisfying the relations (1).

Starting with a definite orthogonal coordinate system, we consider a single electron and suppose, as Pauli did, a state of the electron to be defined by a pair of functions (ψ_1, ψ_2) of the space coordinates x, y, z. The following proof of (1) would hold just as well for an arbitrary number N of particles and an arbitrary number n of functions $\psi_1, \cdots, \psi_n$.

If the state of the electron is subjected to an arbitrary space rotation R (or, what amounts to the same thing, if the state is left unchanged and the coordinate system subjected to the rotation R^{-1}) the new state is represented by a pair of functions (ψ_1', ψ_2'). The probability for the electron to be in a small volume dV near a point P is $\int \{\psi_1^\star \psi_1(P) + \psi_2^\star \psi_2(P)\} dV$. If P is transformed into P', and dV into dV' by the rotation R, the probability of finding the transformed electron in dV' must be equal to the probability of finding the original electron in dV, and since the volume dV' is equal to dV, we must have

$$\psi_1'^\star \psi_1'(P') + \psi_2'^\star \psi_2'(P') = \psi_1^\star \psi_1(P) + \psi_2^\star \psi_2(P) \qquad \dots (2)$$

It is reasonable to assume, like Pauli did, that $\psi_1'(P')$ and $\psi_2'(P')$ are linear functions of $\psi_1(P)$ and $\psi_2(P)$ with coefficients depending only on the rotation R:

$$\left. \begin{aligned} \psi_1'(P') &= t_{11}\psi_1(P) + t_{12}\psi_2(P) \\ \psi_2'(P') &= t_{21}\psi_1(P) + t_{22}\psi_2(P) \end{aligned} \right\} \qquad \dots (3)$$

Using one-column, two-row matrices ψ' and ψ, we may write the equations (3) in matrix form

$$\psi'(P') = T\psi(P) \qquad \ldots(4)$$

where $T = T(R)$ depends only on the rotation R. Because of (2), the matrix T must be unitary.

If $\rho = e^{i\alpha}$ is a complex number of absolute value 1, the functions ψ' and $\rho\psi'$ determine the same state, hence, the matrix T may be multiplied by an arbitrary constant factor $\rho = e^{i\alpha}$. The set of all matrices ρT, where ρ varies on the unit circle in the complex plane, may be called a *projective unitary transformation* T_{proj}.

If two space rotations R and S are applied one after another (first S, next R), we obtain a new rotation RS. Obviously,

$$T(RS) = \sigma T(R)T(S) \quad (\sigma = e^{i\beta}) \qquad \ldots(5)$$

Hence, the projective unitary transformations T_{proj} form a *projective unitary representation of the group G of spatial rotations*.

In my paper just quoted I have proved that every representation of a simple Lie group by unitary matrices is continuous. The proof holds just as well for projective unitary representations. Now the group of three-dimensional rotations is simple, hence T_{proj} is a continuous function of R.

Multiplying the matrices T by suitable factors $\rho = e^{i\alpha}$, we may always assume that their determinants are 1. Now the only freedom left is, to replace T by $-T$. Hence (5) now reads

$$T(RS) = \pm T(R)T(S) \qquad \ldots(6)$$

i.e. the matrices T form a *two-valued representation* of the group G.

For $R = 1$ we may choose $T(R) = 1$. The continuity of T_{proj} now implies: if R varies in a certain neighbourhood of 1 on G the matrices $T(R)$ may be multiplied by such factors $\rho = \pm 1$ that in the resulting matrices ρT all matrix elements differ from those of the unit matrix by less than ϵ. By this property, the factor ρ is uniquely determined. Hence the matrix ρT, which may again be called T, is a uniquely determined continuous function of R in a neighbourhood of 1 on G. For $R = S = 1$, the factor ± 1 in (6) is $+1$, hence, by continuity, it is $+1$ for all R and S in a neighbourhood U of 1. In other words, we have a *continuous univalent matrix representation of U*.

Von Neumann has proved that such a continuous local representation of a Lie group is always analytic and is determined by the matrices representing the infinitesimal transformations of the group. A simpler proof of this theorem was given in footnote 2 of my paper just quoted. Hence, the required two-valued representation $T(R)$ is uniquely determined by the matrices I_x, I_y, I_z representing the infinitesimal rotations of the group G.

An infinitesimal rotation around the x axis is given by the formula

$$\delta(x, y, z) = (0, -z, y)$$

Similar formulae hold for the y and z axes. The matrices of these infinitesimal rotations satisfy the commutation relations

$$I_x I_y - I_y I_x = I_z, \quad \text{etc.} \qquad \ldots (7)$$

Hence, by Lie's theory, the matrices representing these infinitesimal transformations in the representation $T(R)$ must satisfy the same relations.

All infinitesimal representations of the group of three-dimensional rotations, or, what amounts to the same thing, all solutions of the conditions (7) in finite matrices, have been determined by E. Cartan and H. Weyl. The main theorems are:

I. An irreducible representation is completely determined (but for a transformation SIS^{-1}) by an integer or half-integer j. The degree of the representation is $2j+1$. The matrix iI_z is a diagonal matrix with elements $j, j-1, \cdots, -j$ in the diagonal. For $j=0$ the matrices I_x, I_y, I_z are zero. For $j=\frac{1}{2}$ they are

$$I_x = (2i)^{-1}s_x, \qquad I_y = (2i)^{-1}s_y, \qquad I_z = (2i)^{-1}s_x \quad \ldots (8)$$

where s_x, s_y, s_z are Pauli's matrices defined in (5), section 8.

II. A reducible representation is completely reducible, i.e. it may be decomposed into irreducible representations.

A simple proof of I by a method of Born, Heisenberg and Jordan (*Z. Phys.* **35**, 557) may be found in my *Gruppentheoretische Methode in der Quantenmechanik*, section 17 (1932). For a direct algebraic proof of II see Casimir and v.d. Waerden, *Math. Ann.* **111**, 1. For unitary representations, II is trivial, because to every invariant subspace corresponds a completely orthogonal subspace.

In our case, we need a representation of degree 2. Hence, we have to take either the repeated trivial representation $T(R)=1$, or the irreducible representation (8).

In the case of one electron, by Pauli's basic assumptions, we need a function ψ having 2 components ψ_1, ψ_2. A rotation inverting the z axis must transform an eigenfunction $(\psi_1, 0)$ corresponding to a state with $s_z = +1$ into an eigenfunction $(0, \psi_2)$

representing a state with $s_z = -1$, hence the irreducible representation of degree 2 is the only possibility.

Now let us apply a rotation R to a pair of functions (ψ_1, ψ_2). By (3), the rotation has to be applied first to the points P, transforming every single function ψ_i into a function ϕ_i defined by

$$\phi_i(P') = \psi_i(P)$$

and next a linear transformation with constant coefficients t_{ik} has to be applied to the pair (ϕ_1, ϕ_2) at the point P':

$$\psi_i'(P') = \sum t_{ik}\phi_i(P')$$

If we want to apply an infinitesimal rotation, e.g. around the x axis, we first have to calculate the increment of the pair (ψ_1, ψ_2) for an infinitesimal rotation applied to the points P, next to apply the linear transformation I_x to the pair (ψ_1, ψ_2) without changing the point P, and finally to add the two increments. The first step gives the increment

$$\delta\psi = -(y\partial_z - z\partial_y)\psi$$

hence, the total increment is

$$K_x\psi = -(y\partial_z - z\partial_y)\psi + I_x\psi$$

where ∂_z means differentiation with respect to z, while I_x is defined by (8).

Now what is the relation between infinitesimal transformations and angular momentum? In quantum mechanics without spin, the angular momentum with respect to the x axis is

$$k_x = yp_z - zp_y = -i\hbar(y\partial_z - z\partial_y)$$

Hence, if we multiply the total infinitesimal rotation operator

$$K_x = -(y\partial_z - z\partial_y) + I_x$$

by $i\hbar$, the first term gives just the right orbital momentum operator k_x. Thus, it seems reasonable to expect that the second term I_x, multiplied by the same factor $i\hbar$, would give the spin momentum.

The proof that this is correct is given by the theorem of conservation of momentum. Let us suppose the electron to move in a field with rotational symmetry about the x axis. In this case, the energy operator H commutes with the operator of a rotation R about the x axis:

$$RH = HR$$

Differentiating R with respect to the angle of rotation ϕ, and putting $\phi = 0$, we obtain the operator of an infinitesimal rotation K_x. Hence we have

$$K_x H = H K_x$$

This means that K_x obeys a conservation law: its time derivative is zero. Now K_x is a sum of two terms

$$K_x = -(y\partial_z - z\partial_y) + I_x$$

The first term, multiplied by $i\hbar$, is the orbital momentum operator. Hence $i\hbar I_x$ is just the operator we have to add to the orbital momentum operator in order to obtain a total momentum operator for which the law of conservation holds in any rotational symmetric field. This proves our point.

The last step of this proof is due to Dirac (see section 11).

10. SYMMETRY IN THE ATOM

E. Wigner: Einige Folgerungen aus der Schrödingerschen Theorie für die Termstrukturen. *Z. Phys.* **43**, 624 (received May 1927).

J. von Neumann and E. Wigner: Zur Erklärung einiger Eigenschaften der Spektren aus der Quantenmechanik des Drehelektrons II and III. *Z. Phys.* **49**, 73 (received March 1928) and **51**, 844 (received June 1928).

J. C. Slater: The theory of complex spectra. *Phys. Rev.* **34**, 1293 (received June 1929).

Schroedinger's wave equation, Pauli's spin theory and Pauli's exclusion principle form the foundation upon which the whole theory of atomic spectra (and also of molecular spectra) rests. All empirical rules of term zoology, as explained in Hund's admirable book *Linienspektren und periodisches System der Elemente* (1927, Berlin) may be deduced from these foundations. New physical ideas are not needed.

Under these circumstances the historian may simplify. Where new physical ideas are born, he has to trace the roots of these ideas as far as possible, but where only mathematical difficulties are involved, a short account of their solution is sufficient.

Wigner's 1927 paper seems to be the first in which group theory was applied to physics. In this paper, some rules of term zoology were deduced, but the spin was still left out of account. In the papers of von Neumann and Wigner, the whole apparatus of group characters and representations was put into action and the complete system of term zoology, including selection rules, intensity formulae, Stark effect and Zeeman effect was developed.

Physicists were very unhappy that they had to learn this complicated mathematical theory. The 'group pest' was at its height. Weyl's *Gruppentheorie und Quantenmechanik* (1928) was of little help, being too difficult for most of us. Wigner's book was much easier, but the final solution of the difficulties came from Slater's paper. Slater showed that all results can be derived by using the simplest mathematics only.

The Hamiltonian of the electrons of an atom is invariant under the group of permutations of the electrons, and also under the group of space rotations and reflections. Hence, the eigenfunctions belonging to a given energy value are linearly transformed by these two groups. These linear transformations form representations of the groups. The problem is to determine these representations and to find the connection between their characteristic numbers and the quantum numbers L, S, J etc. of the corresponding terms.

Wigner and von Neumann start with an approximation in which the interaction between spin and orbital motion is neglected. In this approximation, the eigenfunctions are just products of functions $\psi_0(q_1, \cdots, q_N)$ of the space coordinates and functions $\phi(s_{z1}, \cdots, s_{zN})$ of the spin coordinates $s_{z1}, \cdots, s_{zN}$. The energy depends only on the function ψ_0. In this approximation, the permutations and rotations may be applied to the space coordinates and to the spin coordinates separately. In both cases, eigenfunctions are transformed into eigenfunctions belonging to the same energy value. Thus, we obtain, for every one of our two groups, a ψ_0 representation and a spin representation. The authors investigate these representations separately, and finally ask, what relation between the characters of the two representations must be assumed in order that an antisymmetric function of all coordinates may exist, as required by the exclusion principle.

Slater's simplification is achieved by introducing the spin and the exclusion principle at the very beginning. Slater considers only antisymmetric wave functions. He starts with wave functions $u(n_i|x_i)$ of the single electrons, each moving in a central field of force, where n_i stands for the four quantum numbers $(n\ l\ m_l\ m_s)$, and x_i symbolizes the four coordinates (three of position, one of spin) of the ith electron. From the products of these functions, antisymmetric linear combinations are formed:

$$\psi(x_1, \cdots, x_N) = \sum \pm u(n_1|x_1)\cdots u(n_N|x_N) \quad \cdots.(1)$$

In this approximation the energy depends only on the n's and l's of the single electrons, but not on the m_l and m_s. So we have, for every energy value of the undisturbed problem, as many eigenfunctions ψ as there are sets of N pairs (m_l, m_s). If two such pairs belong to the same values of n and l, the pairs must be different, and their order does not count. For example, in the case of two equivalent p electrons, we have three possibilities for m_l and two for m_s:

$$m_l = 1 \quad \text{or} \quad 0 \quad \text{or} \quad -1; \quad m_s = +\tfrac{1}{2} \quad \text{or} \quad -\tfrac{1}{2}$$

Hence, we have six possible pairs (m_l, m_s), and $(6 \times 5)/2 = 15$ possible ψ functions (1). Putting

$$M_L = \sum m_l; \qquad M_S = \sum m_s$$

we obtain the following pairs (M_L, M_S):

$$
\begin{array}{ccccc}
 & (1, 1), & (0, 1), & (-1, 1), & \\
(2, 0), & (1, 0)^2, & (0, 0)^3, & (-1, 0)^2, & (-2, 0), \\
 & (1, -1), & (0, -1), & (-1, -1), &
\end{array}
$$

the exponents 2 and 3 indicating the number of ways in which the sums M_L and M_S can be formed.

Next, the interaction between the electrons (without spin effects) is introduced as a perturbation. The perturbation commutes with M_L and M_S, hence the perturbation matrix consists of smaller matrices of 1, 2 or 3 rows along the main diagonal. Every small matrix gives rise to an equation of degree 1, 2, or 3 for the energy values; the trace of the matrix gives us the sum of the (1, 2, or 3) energy values.

Moreover, it is known that to every value of L there are $2L+1$ values of M_L (from $+L$ to $-L$), and to every value of S there are $2S+1$ values of M_S (from S to $-S$), all having the same energy, as long as the spin effect is neglected. Thus, the five pairs

$$(2, 0), \quad (1, 0), \quad (0, 0), \quad (-1, 0), \quad (-2, 0)$$

in the middle line of our list all belong to $L = 2$ and $S = 0$, i.e. to a ^1D-term. Similarly, the nine pairs

$$
\begin{array}{ccc}
(1, 1), & (0, 1), & (-1, 1) \\
(1, 0), & (0, 0), & (-1, 0) \\
(1, -1), & (0, -1), & (-1, -1)
\end{array}
$$

all belong to $L = 1$ and $S = 1$, i.e. to a multiplet ^3P. The remaining pair $(0, 0)$ can only belong to a ^1S term. Hence, the multiplets are

$$^1D, \quad ^3P, \quad ^1S$$

If the spin effect is taken into account, the two singlet terms ^1D and ^1S remain single, but ^3P splits into three terms. This is seen as follows. Starting with our nine states (M_L, M_S) belonging to the ^3P multiplet and putting

$$M = M_L + M_S$$

we find for M the following values:

$$(2), \quad (1)^2, \quad (0)^3, \quad (-1)^2, \quad (-2)$$

Now, every term of a multiplet belongs to a certain value of the quantum number J, and M takes in every case the $2J+1$ values from J to $-J$. In order to obtain the values of M with the multiplicities just mentioned, we have to take for J the values 2, 1, and 0. The corresponding values of M are

$$
\begin{aligned}
J &= 2: & 2, &\; 1, &\; 0, &\; -1, &\; -2 \\
J &= 1: & & 1, &\; 0, &\; -1 \\
J &= 0: & & & 0
\end{aligned}
$$

Hence, the ^3P multiplet consist of the three terms $^3P_2$, $^3P_1$ and $^3P_0$.

The same method can be applied in all cases; it always gives just the right variety of terms.

11. DIRAC'S THEORY OF THE ELECTRON

P. A. M. Dirac: The quantum theory of the electron. *Proc. Roy. Soc.* A **117**, 610 (received January 1928), and A **118**, 351 (received February 1928).

The statistical interpretation of quantum mechanics enables one to answer the question: What is the probability of any dynamical variable at any time having a value lying between specified limits, when the state of the system is given by a wave function ψ?

Dirac now remarks that this interpretation is made possible by the wave equation being of the form

$$(H-W)\psi = 0, \qquad W = i\hbar\partial/\partial t \qquad \dots\,(1)$$

i.e. being linear in W or in $\partial/\partial t$, so that the wave function at any time determines the wave function at any later time. However, Gordon's relativistic wave equation is of second order in $\partial/\partial t$. Our problem, says Dirac, is to obtain a wave equation of the form (1) which shall be invariant under a Lorentz transformation and equivalent to Gordon's in the limit of large quantum numbers.

In the case of no field, Gordon's equation reduces to

$$(-p_0^2 + p_1^2 + p_2^2 + p_3^2 + \mu^2 c^2)\psi = 0$$
$$(p_k = -i\hbar\partial/\partial x_k, \quad x_0 = ct) \qquad \dots\,(2)$$

Putting $p_0 = -ip_4$, Dirac replaces (2) by a first-order wave equation

$$(i \sum_1^4 \gamma_\mu p_\mu + mc)\psi = 0 \qquad \ldots (3)$$

and he shows that (2) can be derived from (3), provided the γ_μ are constant matrices satisfying

$$\gamma_\mu \gamma_\nu + \gamma_\nu \gamma_\mu = 2\delta_{\mu\nu} \qquad \ldots (4)$$

Starting with Pauli's two-row matrices s_x, s_y, s_z, Dirac succeeds in constructing a set of 4 four-row matrices γ_μ satisfying (4). Next, he proves the invariance of the wave equation (3) by showing that every solution of (4) in four-row matrices may be obtained from the original solution by a transformation

$$\gamma_\mu{}' = \tau\gamma_\mu\tau^{-1} \qquad \ldots (5)$$

To obtain the Hamiltonian for an electron in an electromagnetic field with scalar potential A_0 and vector potential $\vec{A}$, Dirac adopts the usual procedure of substituting

$$p_0 + (e/c)\cdot A_0 \quad \text{for} \quad p_0$$

and

$$p + (e/c)\vec{A} \quad \text{for} \quad \vec{p}$$

in the Hamiltonian for no field. From the resulting wave equation, a second-order wave equation is derived, which differs from Gordon's equation by two extra terms

$$(e\hbar/c)(\vec{S}\cdot\vec{B}) + (ie\hbar/c)\rho_1(\vec{S}\cdot\vec{E}) \qquad \ldots (6)$$

where $\vec{E}$ and $\vec{B}$ are the electric and magnetic vectors of the field. The components of the vector $\vec{s}$ are Pauli's two-row matrices s_x, s_y, s_z, repeated along the diagonal so as to obtain four-row matrices. The electron will therefore behave as if it had a magnetic moment

$$(e\hbar/2mc)\vec{s}$$

which is just that assumed in the spinning electron model. In Dirac's theory, this magnetic moment is not assumed, but derived from the theory, which is very satisfactory.

Dirac now proves that in a central field of force the sum of the orbital momentum vector and of the spin vector, i.e.

$$\vec{M} = \vec{m} + \tfrac{1}{2}\hbar\vec{s} \qquad \ldots (7)$$

is a constant of the motion. For a Coulomb field Dirac's theory leads, in first approximation, to the same energy levels as those obtained by Pauli and Darwin.

In his second paper Dirac derives the selection rules, the relative intensities of the lines of a multiplet, and the Zeeman effect, all in accordance with previous theories based upon the hypothesis of the spinning electron, and with experiment.

12. THE SPINNING ELECTRON IN GENERAL RELATIVITY

H. Tetrode: Allgemein-relativistische Quantentheorie des Elektrons. *Z. Phys.* **50**, 336 (received June 1928).

H. Weyl: Elektron und Gravitation. *Z. Phys.* **56**, 330 (received May 1929).

V. Fock: Geometrisierung der Diracschen Theorie des Elektrons. *Z. Phys.* **57**, 261 (received July 1929).

E. Schrödinger: Diracsches Elektron im Schwerefeld I. *S.B. preuss. Akad. Wiss.* 1932, 105 (presented Febr. 1932).

V. Bargmann: Bemerkungen zur allgemein-relativistischen Fassung der Quantentheorie. *S.B. preuss. Akad. Wiss.* 1932, 346 (presented July 1932).

L. Infeld and B. L. van der Waerden: Die Wellengleichung des Elektrons in der allgemeinen Relativitätstheorie. *S.B. preuss. Akad. Wiss.* 1933, 380 and 474 (presented Jan. 1933).

The wave equation of the spinning electron can be incorporated into general relativity by three methods; they are different in the mathematical apparatus, but equivalent from the physical point of view. 1. The method of Weyl and Fock makes use of an arbitrary orthogonal frame (Vierbein) in every point of the four-dimensional world. 2. The method of Tetrode, Schrödinger and Bargmann starts with four matrices γ^μ at every point, satisfying the generalized Dirac relations

$$\gamma^\mu\gamma^\nu + \gamma^\nu\gamma^\mu = 2g^{\mu\nu} \qquad \ldots.(1)$$

3. The method of Infeld and van der Waerden is based upon spinor analysis.

In the following simplified and unified treatment, which mainly follows the ideas of Weyl and Fock, the equivalence of the methods will be made clear.

The first method starts with four normed orthogonal vectors, whose components $h_0{}^\mu$, $h_1{}^\mu$, $h_2{}^\mu$, $h_3{}^\mu$ are functions of the co-ordinates x^μ. The orthogonality is expressed by

$$\sum g_{\mu\nu} h_0{}^\mu h_0{}^\nu = -1$$
$$\sum g_{\mu\nu} h_k{}^\mu h_k{}^\nu = +1 \quad (k = 1, 2, 3)$$
$$\sum g_{\mu\nu} h_k{}^\mu h_l{}^\nu = 0 \quad (k \neq l)$$

A wave function ψ may have two or four components ψ_α. In any case the components are defined with respect to the given orthogonal frame. We first investigate how the ψ components are to be transformed in passing from one orthogonal frame to another.

Let us start with a flat Minkowski world, in which all frames are parallel. The coordinates x^μ may be skew or even curved. Dirac's wave equation may be written as

$$\left(i \sum_0^3 \gamma^k p_k + mc\right)\psi = 0 \qquad \ldots\ldots(2)$$

The p_k are the momentum components in the directions of the vectors $\vec{h}_k$, and the γ^k are numerically fixed four-row matrices satisfying the commutation relations

$$\left.\begin{aligned} \gamma^0\gamma^0 &= -1 \\ \gamma^k\gamma^k &= +1 \quad (k = 1, 2, 3) \\ \gamma^k\gamma^l + \gamma^l\gamma^k &= 0 \quad (k \neq l) \end{aligned}\right\} \qquad \ldots\ldots(3)$$

Now let the vectors $\vec{h}_k$ be replaced by another set of orthogonal vectors $\vec{h}_j{}'$, related to the $\vec{h}_k$ by a Lorentz transformation:

$$h'_j{}^\mu = \sum o_j{}^k h_k{}^\mu \qquad \ldots\ldots(4)$$

According to Dirac, the wave equation is invariant with respect to the transformation (4), if ψ is transformed by a linear transformation T depending on the $o_j{}^k$:

$$\psi' = T\psi \qquad \ldots\ldots(5)$$

The four-row matrices T form a two-valued representation of the Lorentz group (without reflections and without time-reversal). Hence, for any orthogonal frame $\vec{h}_j{}'$, the components $\psi_\alpha{}'$ with respect to the frame are uniquely determined but for a factor ± 1.

As von Neumann has shown (Z. Phys. **48**, 876), the representation (5) is reducible, i.e. the coordinates in four-dimensional ψ space may be chosen in such a way that ψ_1, ψ_2 and also ψ_3, ψ_4 are transformed among themselves.

If the world is not flat, the transformation (5) may still be applied to the ψ components at any point, hence the components $\psi_\alpha{}'$ with respect to any orthogonal frame at any point are determined by the original functions ψ_α but for a factor ± 1. If only two ψ components ψ_1, ψ_2 or ψ_3, ψ_4 are given, the transformation T may be applied to these two components.

Now, suppose the ψ_a, $h_k{}^\mu$ and $g_{\mu\nu}$ to be differentiable functions of the coordinates x^μ. To the four given vectors $\vec{h}_k$ at a given point P we may apply a Levi Città parallel displacement along a path in any given direction, thus obtaining an orthogonal frame at any point P' in a neighbourhood of P. Let ψ_a' be the coordinates of the given wave function with respect to this frame at P'. By continuity, the arbitrary factor ± 1 in ψ' may be fixed. Now ψ' is a differentiable function on the path PP'. Comparing ψ' with ψ at P, a covariant differential $\delta\psi$ may be formed. If the path is defined by keeping all coordinates except x^μ constant, we may define a covariant derivative $\nabla_\mu\psi_a$. If the path goes into the direction of the vector $\vec{h}_k$, we may also form the component $\nabla_k\psi_a$ in the direction of this vector, and insert it into Dirac's equation instead of the ordinary derivative $\partial_k\psi_a$. Thus, an invariant wave equation is obtained:

$$(\hbar \sum \gamma^k\nabla_k + mc)\psi = 0 \qquad \ldots\ldots(6)$$

which reduces to Dirac's in the case of a flat space.

Now defining the matrices γ^μ by

$$\gamma^\mu = \sum \gamma^k h_k{}^\mu \qquad \ldots\ldots(7)$$

we have

$$\sum \gamma^k\nabla_k = \sum \gamma^k h_k{}^\mu\nabla_\mu = \sum \gamma^\mu\nabla_\mu \qquad \ldots\ldots(8)$$

and

$$\gamma^\mu\gamma^\nu + \gamma^\nu\gamma^\mu = 2g^{\mu\nu} \qquad \ldots\ldots(9)$$

Tetrode and Schrödinger start with arbitrary matrices γ^μ satisfying (9). The most general solution of (9) is, as Dirac has shown,

$$\Gamma^\mu = S\gamma^\mu S^{-1} \qquad \ldots\ldots(10)$$

the special solution γ^μ being defined by (7). However, the wave equation of Schrödinger does not depend on the choice of the matrix S, so we may just as well use the special solution (7). Also, Schrödinger's covariant derivation is equivalent to that defined by Weyl and Fock, hence the wave equations of Schrödinger and Fock are just the same:

$$(\hbar \sum \gamma^\mu\nabla_\mu + mc)\psi = 0 \qquad \ldots\ldots(11)$$

In an electromagnetic field, defined by a potential Φ_μ, we have to replace $\hbar\nabla_\mu$ by

$$\hbar\nabla_\mu - \frac{ie}{c}\Phi_\mu$$

The equation thus obtained has the property of *gauge invariance*. If ψ is replaced by $e^{i\lambda}\psi$, and Φ_μ by $\Phi_\mu - \nabla_\mu\lambda$, where λ is an arbitrary differentiable function, the wave equation will still hold.

The formalism of Infeld and myself is somewhat simpler than that of Weyl and Fock, and much simpler than that of Schrödinger and Bargmann, but the physical conclusions are just the same. The main conclusion is, that Dirac's wave equation or, in fact, any one-particle wave equation which is invariant in the sense of special relativity, can also be incorporated into general relativity.

13. SPINOR ANALYSIS

E. Weiss: Ein räumliches Analogon zum Hesseschen Übertragungsprinzip. *Dissertation* Bonn 1924.

B. L. van der Waerden: Spinoranalyse. *Nach. Ges. Wiss. Göttingen, math.-phys.* 1929, 100 (presented July 1929).

The new quantities like ψ with two or four components, which do not transform like vectors or tensors, caused great trouble to the physicists. Ehrenfest called these quantities *Spinors* and asked me on his visit to Göttingen (Summer, 1929): 'Does a Spinor Analysis exist, which every physicist can learn like Tensor Analysis, and by which all possible kinds of spinors and all invariant equations between spinors can be written down?'

In fact, such a formalism existed already. It was furnished by the theory of invariants of binary forms*, which had been extended, by E. Study and his school in Bonn, to forms in several binary variables.

Let us start with the equation of the light cone in four-space

$$x^2 + y^2 + z^2 - c^2t^2 = 0 \qquad \dots(1)$$

It may be written as

$$(x+iy)(x-iy) - (ct+z)(ct-z) = 0$$

or as

$$x^1x^2 - x^3x^4 = 0 \qquad \dots(2)$$

In covariant coordinates $x_i = \sum g_{ik}x^k$, the equation (2) reads

$$x_1x_2 - x_3x_4 = 0 \qquad \dots(3)$$

If x_1, x_2, x_3, x_4 are interpreted as homogeneous coordinates in a projective three-space, (3) is the equation of a quadric. (No restriction of reality will be imposed at this stage: the x_k are just

---

* Probably the best textbook on the subject is J. H. Grace, and A. Young, *The Algebra of Invariants*, 1903, Cambridge.

complex variables.) It is well known that there are two sets of straight lines on the surface (3), and that the surface has a parametric representation

$$x_1 = \lambda^2\mu^1 \ \Big\} \qquad x_3 = \lambda^1\mu^1 \ \Big\}$$
$$x_2 = \lambda^1\mu^2 \ \Big\} \qquad x_4 = \lambda^2\mu^2 \ \Big\} \qquad \dots(4)$$

If λ^1, λ^2 are assumed to be the complex conjugates of μ^1, μ^2, the first two coordinates x_1 and x_2 will be complex conjugates and the last two real, hence x, y, z and t will be real numbers.

Now consider a linear transformation of the λ's and an independent linear transformation of the μ's, both of determinant 1. If this pair of transformations is applied to the λ's and μ's in (4), the x_k will also undergo a linear transformation, which transforms the surface (3) into itself. If we want to have a real transformation of x, y, z, t, we must take care that real points on the surface are transformed into real points, hence we have to make the transformation of the λ's conjugate to that of the μ's. To indicate this, the indices of the λ's will be dotted. Thus, the transformations are

$$\lambda'^{\alpha} = \sum e^{\alpha}{}_{\beta}\lambda^{\beta}, \quad e^{\alpha}{}_{\beta} = (e^{\alpha}{}_{\beta})^{\star}, \ \Big\}$$
$$\mu'^{\alpha} = \sum e^{\alpha}{}_{\beta}\mu^{\beta}, \quad e^1{}_1 e^2{}_2 - e^1{}_2 e^2{}_1 = 1 \ \Big\} \qquad \dots(5)$$

The resulting real transformation of x, y, z, t not only transforms the light cone (1) itself, but it even transforms the quadratic form

$$x^2 + y^2 + z^2 - c^2 t^2$$

into itself, it has determinant 1, and it does not interchange past and future, i.e. it is a Lorentz transformation. To prove this, let us intersect the surface (4) by a plane.

$$\sum b^k x_k = 0 \qquad \dots(6)$$

The intersection is given by

$$b^1\lambda^2\mu^1 + b^2\lambda^1\mu^2 + b^3\lambda^1\mu^1 + b^4\lambda^2\mu^2 = 0$$

or by

$$\sum b_{\alpha\beta}\lambda^{\alpha}\mu^{\beta} = 0 \qquad \dots(7)$$

with

$$b^1 = X + iY = b_{\dot{2}1} \ \Big\}$$
$$b^2 = X - iY = b_{12} \ \Big\}$$
$$b^3 = cT + Z = b_{11} \ \Big\} \qquad \dots(8)$$
$$b^4 = cT - Z = b_{\dot{2}2} \ \Big\}$$

If the plane (6) is real, i.e. if the coordinates X, Y, Z, T of the vector b^k in the original coordinate system are real, it follows from (8) that b_{11} and $b_{\dot{2}2}$ are real and $b_{\dot{2}1}$ and b_{12} complex conjugates, i.e. the bi-linear form (7) is Hermitian. Hence, the real vector b^k and the Hermitian bi-linear forms are in one-to-one correspondence, and this correspondence is invariant with respect to the transformations (5). The determinant of the bi-linear form

$$D = b_{11}b_{\dot{2}2} - b_{\dot{2}1}b_{12} = -X^2 - Y^2 - Z^2 + c^2T^2 \qquad \dots (9)$$

is an invariant with respect to transformations (5), hence the corresponding transformation of X, Y, Z, T leaves the metrical form invariant. Positive Hermitian forms correspond to vectors pointing towards the future inside the light cone, so our transformations do not interchange past and future. A simple calculation shows that their determinant is 1, hence they are proper Lorentz transformations.

To a product of transformations (5) corresponds, of course, the product of the corresponding Lorentz transformations. If both matrices $(e^\alpha{}_\beta)$ and $(e^\alpha{}_\beta)$ are multiplied by -1, the Lorentz transformations do not change. The matrices $(e^\alpha{}_\beta)$ form a two-valued representation of the Lorentz group, and so do the conjugate matrices $(e^\alpha{}_\beta)$.

In my paper 'Spinoranalyse' I started with the formulae (8) without explaining how they were found. My original starting point was the geometry of the straight lines on a quadric.

From now on, b_k and b^k will denote the covariant and contravariant components of any vector in the original coordinate system (x, y, z, ct). The index 0 corresponds to the coordinate ct, the indices 1, 2, 3 to x, y, z. We have, by definition,

$$b_0 = -b^0, \qquad b_k = b^k \quad (k = 1, 2, 3)$$

and by (8), putting $X = b^1$, $Y = b^2$, $Z = b^3$ and $cT = b^0$,

$$\left. \begin{aligned} b^1 + ib^2 &= b_{\dot{2}1} \\ b^1 - ib^2 &= b_{12} \end{aligned} \right\} \qquad \left. \begin{aligned} b^0 + b^3 &= b_{11} \\ b^0 - b^3 &= b_{\dot{2}2} \end{aligned} \right\} \qquad \dots (10)$$

A *spinor* may now be defined as the set of coefficients of any form in any number of binary variables which transform like λ^α or μ^β. For example, if the form is linear in λ^α and quadratic in μ^β:

$$f = \sum b_{\alpha\beta\gamma} \lambda^\alpha \mu^\beta \mu^\gamma$$

we have a spinor $b_{\alpha\beta\gamma}$, symmetric in β and γ. The coefficients of a linear form

$$\sum b_\alpha \lambda^\alpha \quad \text{or} \quad \sum b_\alpha \mu^\alpha$$

form a *spinvector* $b_{\dot\alpha}$ or b_α. The index α or $\dot\alpha$ always takes the values 1 and 2 or $\dot{1}$ and $\dot{2}$.

To every world vector b_k or b^k corresponds, by (10), a spinor $b_{\alpha\beta}$. Just so, to a tensor t_{hk} corresponds a spinor $b_{\alpha\beta,\gamma\delta}$, etc.

To form invariants of spinors, define $\epsilon^{\alpha\beta} = \epsilon^{\alpha\beta}$ by

$$\epsilon^{12} = 1, \qquad \epsilon^{21} = -1, \qquad \epsilon^{11} = \epsilon^{22} = 0$$

From the theory of invariants it is known that every invariant of a set of spinors is obtained by multiplying a product of ϵ symbols into a product of spinors and summing over every index that occurs once as an upper and once as a lower index, e.g.:

$$2D = \sum \epsilon^{\alpha\gamma}\epsilon^{\beta\delta} b_{\alpha\beta} b_{\gamma\delta} = 2(b_{11}b_{22} - b_{12}b_{21}) \qquad \ldots(11)$$

The formulae may be shortened by defining:

$$b^\alpha = \sum \epsilon^{\alpha\beta} b_\beta \qquad \ldots(12)$$

Thus, the invariant (11) may be written as

$$2D = \sum b_{\alpha\beta} b^{\alpha\beta} \qquad \ldots(13)$$

By (9) and (13) we have

$$\sum b_k b^k = \sum g_{hk} b^h b^k = -\tfrac{1}{2} \sum b_{\alpha\beta} b^{\alpha\beta} \qquad \ldots(14)$$

Dirac's wave equation may be written as

$$\left(p_0 + \sum_1^3 s_r p_r\right)\psi + mc\chi = 0 \qquad \ldots(15)$$

$$\left(p_0 - \sum_1^3 s_r p_r\right)\chi + mc\psi = 0 \qquad \ldots(16)$$

Here s_1, s_2, s_3 are Pauli's matrices; ψ and χ are wave functions having two components each, which transform like spinor components b^α and b_β. Introducing the spinor $p_{\alpha\beta}$ by the formulae

$$p_1 + ip_2 = p_{21}, \quad \text{etc.} \qquad \ldots(17)$$

we may write (15) and (16) as

$$\sum p_{\alpha\beta}\psi^\alpha + mc\chi_\beta = 0 \qquad \ldots(18)$$

$$-\sum p_{\alpha\beta}\chi^\beta + mc\psi_\alpha = 0 \qquad \ldots(19)$$

In the presence of an electromagnetic field, $p_{\alpha\beta}$ has to be replaced by $p_{\alpha\beta} + (e/c)A_{\alpha\beta}$.

The introduction of the two pairs ψ_α, χ_β instead of Dirac's four components ψ_α is equivalent to a particular choice of Dirac's matrices γ_k, such that

$$\gamma_1\gamma_2\gamma_3\gamma_4 = \gamma_5$$

is a diagonal matrix with diagonal elements $+1, +1, -1, -1$.

For the application of my spinor calculus, this particular choice of γ_5 is necessary. In Geiger–Scheel's *Handbuch der Physik*, Vol. 24, Part I, p. 225, Pauli writes: 'Wir möchten hier bemerken, dass dieser Kalkül trotz seiner formalen Geschlossenheit nicht immer vorteilhaft ist, da die durch die Spezialisierung von γ^5 auf Diagonalform bewirkte Zerspaltung aller vierkomponentigen Größen in zwei zweikomponentige manchmal eine unnötige Komplikation der Formeln mit sich bringt.'

In the preceding exposition, the transformation from vector coordinates b^k to spinor coordinates $b_{\alpha\beta}$ was defined by the very special formulae (10), valid only for orthogonal space coordinates and for a special choice of spin coordinates. The formulae may be generalized to arbitrary skew coordinates as follows. We may put

$$b_{\alpha\beta} = \sum b^k \sigma_{k\alpha\beta} \qquad \ldots (20)$$

the $\sigma_{k\alpha\beta}$ being arbitrary complex coefficients subject to the following conditions:

$$(\sigma_{k\alpha\beta})^\star = \sigma_{k\beta\alpha} \qquad \ldots (21)$$

$$2g_{hk} = \sum \epsilon^{\alpha\gamma} \epsilon^{\beta\delta} \sigma_{h\alpha\beta} \sigma_{k\gamma\delta} \qquad \ldots (22)$$

These formulae may be taken over into general relativity. They form the starting point of the formalism of Infeld and van der Waerden mentioned in section 12.

14. WEYL'S EQUATION AND THE NON-CONSERVATION OF PARITY

H. Weyl: Elektron und Gravitation. *Z. Phys.* **56**, 330 (received May 1929).

T. D. Lee and C. N. Yang: Parity Nonconservation and a Two-Component Theory of the Neutrino. *Phys. Rev.* **105**, 1671 (received January 1957).

R. P. Feynman and M. Gell-Mann: Theory of Fermi Interaction. *Phys. Rev.* **109**, 193 (received September 1957).

The spinor calculus enables us to find all possible invariant wave equations. For example, if one wants to have a first-order wave equation with only one two-component spinor ψ^α, the only possibility, in the absence of a field, is equation (18) of section 13 without the mass term:

$$\sum p_{\alpha\beta} \psi^\alpha = 0 \qquad \ldots (1)$$

It may also be written in the form (15) of section 13

$$\left(p_0 + \sum_1^3 s_r p_r \right) \psi = 0 \qquad \ldots (2)$$

Likewise, a wave equation for a two-component spinor χ^β must have the form

$$(p_0 - \sum s_r p_r)\chi = 0 \qquad \dots (3)$$

In the presence of a field, in order to obtain a gauge invariant wave equation, we have to replace p_k by $p_k + (e/c)A_k$. These two-component wave equations were proposed by H. Weyl. They are not invariant with respect to space reflections. For this reason, Pauli rejected Weyl's equation as being 'auf die physikalische Wirklichkeit nicht anwendbar'. As far as electrons are concerned, this rejection was fully justified, but recently (1957) the use of the two-component theory for neutrino processes, in which parity is not preserved, was proposed by Lee and Yang (see also A. Salam, *Nuovo Cim.* **5**, 299, and L. Landau, *Nuclear Phys.* **3**, 127). The non-conservation of parity in β decay was experimentally proved by C. S. Wu and her collaborators (*Phys. Rev.* **105**, 1413), and confirmed by many others.

In (2) and (3), p_0 is the operator

$$p_0 = -i(\hbar/c)\partial/\partial t$$

To obtain simple formulae, Lee and Yang choose the units in such a way that $\hbar = 1$ and $c = 1$. Solutions of (2) may be obtained as plane waves

$$\psi = ae^{i(\sum p_r x_r - Wt)}$$

the factor a being a constant two-component spinor. Equation (2) requires

$$(W - \sum s_r p_r)a = 0$$

If p is the length of the momentum vector $\vec{p}$, the operator $\sum s_r p_r$ has the eigenvalues $\pm p$. Hence W must be equal to $+p$ or $-p$. If the energy is positive, we have $W = +p$ and the spin vector has the same direction as the momentum vector $\vec{p}$.

Likewise, if a plane wave satisfies (3), and if the energy is positive, the spin must be anti-parallel to the momentum vector $\vec{p}$.

Lee and Yang assumed the neutrinos to be particles of mass zero and positive energy satisfying (2), but this conclusion does not seem justified because the neutrinos might just as well satisfy (3). In fact, Feynman and Gell-Mann showed that the experimental results are best explained by assuming that the neutrino spin is anti-parallel to the momentum vector, or, as they put it, that 'neutrinos spin to the left'.

Feynman and Gell-Mann propose to use two-component wave functions not only for neutrinos, but for all particles of spin $\frac{1}{2}$.

It is very easy to re-write Dirac's equation as a wave equation for a two-component spinor ψ. One has only to write Dirac's equation in the form (15), (16) of section 13, and to eliminate χ from it, thus obtaining a second-order wave equation for ψ. This equation is, of course, identical with Dirac's second-order wave equation.

Having thus introduced two-component wave functions for all particles of spin $\frac{1}{2}$, Feynman and Gell-Mann propose a universal formula for weak coupling of four such particles, in which only the two-component wave functions ψ occur, and not their derivatives. Applied to the problem of β decay, this formula gives rise to an A- or V-interaction ($V =$ vector, $A =$ axial vector), while the other types of interaction (S, T, and P) are excluded. This is in perfect accordance with the experimental results concerning the β decay of argon-35 and neon-19 (Hermannsfeldt, Maxson, Stähelin and Allen, *Phys. Rev.* **107**, 641).

There are other experimental results, mentioned in the paper of Feynman and Gell-Mann, which also confirm their theory. For details and recent results see the article 'The Neutrino' by C. S. Wu in this volume.

15. HOLES AND POSITRONS

P. A. M. Dirac: A Theory of Electrons and Protons. *Proc. Roy. Soc.* A **126**, 360 (received December 1929).

C. D. Anderson: The Positive Electron. *Phys. Rev.* **43**, 491 (received February 1933).

M. Fierz: Über die relativistische Theorie kräftefreier Teilchen mit beliebigem Spin. *Helv. phys. Acta* **12**, 3 (received September 1938).

W. Pauli: The Connection between Spin and Statistics. *Phys. Rev.* **58**, 716 (received August 1940).

One of the great difficulties of Dirac's wave equation was, from the very beginning, the existence of states of negative energy. The jump from a normal state to such an abnormal state is not forbidden by any selection rule. Thus, one would expect all electrons to jump into these negative states, contrary to experience.

The solution of this riddle was given by Dirac's marvellous theory of holes. Dirac supposed all states of negative energy to be occupied except perhaps a few of small velocity. 'We shall have an infinite number of electrons in negative-energy states . . . but if their distribution is exactly uniform we should expect them to be completely unobservable. Only the small departures from uniformity, brought about by some of the negative-energy states being unoccupied, can we hope to observe.'

Dirac next considers the vacant states of 'holes'. From the analogy with unoccupied X-ray levels he concludes that such a hole has a positive energy and moves in an external electromagnetic field like an electron of positive charge $+e$. Because of this positive charge, Dirac assumed the holes to be protons.

However, H. Weyl showed (*Gruppentheorie und Quantenmechanik*, 2nd ed., p. 234) that the holes necessarily have the same mass as an electron. Moreover, Oppenheimer (*Phys. Rev.* **35**, 562 and 939) showed that, if the protons were holes, the electrons in the neighbourhood would jump into these holes after a mean life-time of the order of magnitude of 10^{-10} seconds. Therefore, Oppenheimer considered the holes as something different from protons, and called them *positive electrons* or *positrons*. These particles were experimentally discovered by Anderson.

Dirac's idea of holes in an infinite sea of negative-energy electrons was an intuitive idea. To make it mathematically exact, the ψ field of the electron must be subjected to a second quantization or bi-quantization. A mathematically exact theory of bi-quantization of electron–positron fields, along the lines indicated by Fock,* was given by K. Friedrichs in Part V of his book *Mathematical Aspects of the Quantum Theory of Fields* (1953. New York; Interscience). As far as I know, the Lorentz invariance of this theory has not yet been investigated. Presumably the theory is invariant as long as the interaction between the electrons is neglected.

Following Dirac, Fierz investigated relativistic wave equations for particles with arbitrary spin. For integral spin, he was able to define an energy–momentum tensor yielding a positive total energy, but for non-integral spin it turned out that there are always states of negative energy. Hence, for particles of non-integral spin the exclusion principle must be postulated, in order to obtain, by the theory of holes, a positive total energy.

In his famous 1940 paper, Pauli proved the same result under more general assumptions. He assumed the wave function U to be an arbitrary spinor or set of spinors, all having an even number of indices in the case of integral spin, and an odd number in the other case. Of the wave equation, Pauli only assumed the invariance with respect to proper Lorentz transformations (without

* Fock, V. Konfigurationsraum und zweite Quantelung, *Z. Phys.* **75**, 622 (1932). For the extension of Fock's theory to relativistic spinor fields see Wightman and Schreber, *Phys. Rev.* **98**, 812 (1954) and the literature quoted in this paper.

time-reversal and without reflections). The wave equation need not be of first order. The energy–momentum tensor T may be any homogeneous quadratic function of U and its complex-conjugate $U^\star$.

Pauli now shows that there always exists a substitution transforming the space coordinates x_k into $-x_k$ and leaving invariant the wave equation. In the case of *non-integral spin*, this substitution transforms T into $-T$. Hence, to every state with positive energy corresponds another state of negative energy, also satisfying the wave equation. Since for physical reasons it is necessary to posulate a positive total energy of the system, we must apply the exclusion principle in connection with Dirac's hole theory, says Pauli.

On the other hand, Fierz and Pauli show that in the case of *integral spin* a quantization of the particle field according to the exclusion principle by means of the invariant D function of Jordan and Pauli (*Z. Phys.* **47**, 151) is not possible. For an explanation of what this means, we must refer the reader to Pauli's original paper.

At the end of his paper, Pauli states that in his opinion the connection between spin and statistics is one of the most important applications of the special relativity principle. In fact, it is the fulfilment of his early wish to deduce the exclusion principle from other physical principles.

FUNDAMENTAL PROBLEMS

L. D. LANDAU

It is with the deepest sorrow that I send this article written in the honour of the sixtieth birthday of Wolfgang Pauli to a volume dedicated to his memory, which will always be cherished by those who had the good luck of knowing him personally.

It will be impossible now to know his opinion about the ideas expressed in this article but I am still encouraged by the thought that his views on the subject would not be very different.

It is well known that theoretical physics is at present almost helpless in dealing with the problem of strong interactions. For this reason, any remarks on the subject must necessarily be of the nature of forecasts, and their authors are peculiarly apt to find themselves barking up the wrong tree.

It was long thought that the main difficulty of the theory lies in the occurrence of infinities which can be avoided only by the use of perturbation theory. The habit of using the device of re-normalization, which had achieved brilliant success in perturbation theory, was carried so far that the concept of re-normalization acquired a certain mystical aura. The situation, however, becomes clear if, as is usual in theoretical physics, point inter-action is regarded as the limit of some 'distributed' interaction. This treatment, although it assumes weak interaction, goes considerably beyond the scope of perturbation theory, and makes possible the derivation of asymptotic expressions for the energy dependence of the basic physical quantities.[1] These expressions show that the effective interaction always diminishes with de-creasing energy, so that the physical interaction at finite energies is always less than the interaction at energies of the order of the cut-off limit which is given by the bare coupling constant appearing in the Hamiltonian.

Since the magnitude of the re-normalization increases indefin-itely with the cut-off limit, it follows that even an extremely weak interaction implies a large bare coupling constant when the cut-off radius is sufficiently small. Thus it was supposed that the main problem is to devise a theory of very strong interactions.

Further investigation showed, however, that the matter was by no means so easily dealt with. It was demonstrated by Pomeranchuk in a series of papers [2] that, as the cut-off limit is increased, the physical interaction tends to zero, no matter how large the bare coupling constant is. At about the same time Pauli and Källén [3] obtained the same result for the so-called Lee model.

The correctness of 'nullifying' the theory has often been called in question. The Lee model is a very special one, considerably differing in several respects from physical interactions; and the validity of Pomeranchuk's proofs has been doubted. In my opinion such doubts are unfounded. For example, Källén has several times put forward the view that unusual properties of the series to be summed are involved, but he has never given reasons to support this view. By now, the 'nullification' of the theory is tacitly accepted even by theoretical physicists who profess to dispute it. This is evident from the almost complete disappearance of papers on meson theory, and particularly from Dyson's assertion [4] that the correct theory will not be found in the next hundred years—a piece of pessimism which would be impossible to understand if one supposed that the present meson theory leads to finite results which we are yet unable to derive from it. It therefore seems to me inopportune to attempt an improvement in the rigour of Pomeranchuk's proofs, especially as the brevity of life does not allow us the luxury of spending time on problems which will lead to no new results.

The vanishing of the point interaction in the present-day theory leads to the idea that it is necessary to consider 'distributed', non-local, interactions. Unfortunately, the non-local nature of the interaction renders completely useless the technique of the present existing theory. Of course the undesirability of this occurrence is a poor argument against the non-local nature of the interaction; but there are stronger arguments against it. All the conclusions derived by means of the quantum theory of fields without the use of particular Hamiltonians seem to get confirmed experimentally. They include, in the first place, dispersion relations. Moreover, the number of mesons formed in high-energy collisions is in agreement with Fermi's formula, [6] which involves the use of the ideas of statistical thermodynamics for dimensions very much less than any possible radius of interaction.

The idea of the possibility of a marked modification of the existing theory without abandoning local interaction, was first suggested by Heisenberg. [7] Besides this general idea, Heisenberg has also suggested a number of further assumptions, which to me appear dubious. I shall therefore attempt to describe the general situation in what seems to me the most convincing form.

Almost 30 years ago Peierls and myself had noticed that in the region of relativistic quantum theory no quantities concerning interacting particles can be measured. and the only observable quantities are the momenta and polarizations of freely moving particles. Therefore if we do not want to introduce unobservables we may introduce in the theory as fundamental quantities only the scattering amplitudes.

The ψ operators which contain unobservable information must disappear from the theory and, since a Hamiltonian can be built only from ψ operators, we are driven to the conclusion that the Hamiltonian method for strong interaction is dead and must be buried, although of course with deserved honour.

The foundation of the new theory must consist of a new diagrammatic technique which must deal only with diagrams with 'free' ends i.e. with scattering amplitudes and their analytic continuation. The physical basis of this technique is the unitarity conditions and the principle of locality of interaction which expresses itself in the analytic properties of the fundamental quantities of the theory, such as the different kinds of dispersion relations.

As such new diagrammatic theory is not as yet constructed, we are obliged to derive the analytical properties of the vertex parts from a Hamiltonian formalism, but it requires much naivity to try to make such derivations 'rigorous', forgetting that we derive existing equations from Hamiltonians which do not really exist.

One of the conclusions of such an approach to the theory is that the old problem of the elementarity of particles finally loses its meaning, as it cannot be formulated without considering interactions between particles.

I think that the development of a theory on such lines has progressed very much in recent times and the time is not far away when the equations of the new theory will be finally written down.

But one must remember that in this case, contrary to what has happened in all the previous stages of theoretical physics, the writing down of the equations will mark not the end but only the beginning of the construction of the theory. The equations of the theory will be an infinite system of integral equations, each of which has the form of an infinite series, and it will be a hard task to learn how to work with such equations.

It is, of course, impossible to predict now how many constants

in the theory may be chosen arbitrarily.   We cannot even exclude
the possibility that the equations will have no solutions at all, i.e.
that the theory will also be nullified.   This might be regarded as
the rigorous proof of the non-locality of nature, but it might also
mean that a theory of strong interactions alone cannot exist by
itself and that weak interactions, and especially electrodynamics,
must also be included in the picture.   The infra-red 'catastrophe'
would then make the situation infinitely more complicated.

But even in the best case we have still a great struggle before
us, a struggle which has now become much more difficult without
the brilliant unerring light of the mind of Wolfgang Pauli.

REFERENCES

1. Landau, L. D. On the Quantum Theory of Fields.   *Niels Bohr and the
   Development of Physics*, p. 52.   1955.   London; Pergamon Press:
   Landau, L. D., Abrikosov, A. A. and Khalatnikov, I. M. *Nuovo Cim.*
   (10) **3**, *Suppl.* 80, 1956
2. Pomeranchuk, I. *Dokl. Akad. Nauk SSSR* **103**, 1005, 1955: **104**, 51, 1955:
   105, 461, 1955: Abrikosov, A. A., Galanin, A. D., Gorkov, L. P., Landau,
   L. D., Pomeranchuk, I. Ya. and Ter-Martirosyan, K. A. *Phys. Rev.* **111**,
   321, 1958
3. Källén, G. and Pauli, W. *Math.-fys. Medd.* **30**, No. 7, 1955
4. Dyson, F. J. *Sci. Amer.* **199** (3), 74, 1958
5. Chew, G. F. preprint; *Second United Nations International Conference on
   the Peaceful Uses of Atomic Energy*, Geneva 1958, P/2393: Pomeranchuk,
   I. Ya and Okuń, L. B. *Zh. éksp. teor. Fiz.* in press: *Soviet Physics JETP*
   in press
6. Fermi, E. *Progr. theor. Phys., Osaka* **5**, 570, 1950: *Phys. Rev.* **81**, 683,
   1951: Belen'kij, S. Z. and Landau, L. D. *Nuovo Cim.* (10) **6**, Supple. 15,
   1956
7. Heisenberg, W. *Rev. Mod. Phys.* **29**, 269, 1957

THE NEUTRINO

C. S. WU

In a letter written the very afternoon that he first received the news of the experimental proof of non-conservation of parity in beta decay, Professor W. Pauli expressed his thoughts and reactions to this unexpected development. His thoughts seemed to focus especially on the problem of the neutrino. Ending his letter in a reflective mood, Pauli wrote that 'this particle neutrino, of the existence of which I am not innocent, still persecutes me'. Later generations, having seen the triumphant success of the neutrino hypothesis,[1] probably will never fully appreciate the courage and insight it took to put forth such an outlandish idea as the existence of an elusive particle, the neutrino. In recent years, Pauli again concerned himself with the problem of the neutrino. In the fall of 1956 he was interested in the connection between the neutrino and the anti-neutrino and the conservation of leptons. Ironically, he critically looked into the rest mass of the neutrino and protested that the estimated upper limit was set too high by the application of a relativistic term resulting from the summation over spins of the emitted particles. To Pauli, the derivation of this factor should constitute an interesting chapter in itself. Clearly, he was thinking at that time of a more logical and simple theory of the neutrino; but his firm belief in the symmetry principle severely restricted his venturesome spirit. It is well known that Pauli was thoroughly acquainted with the mathematical play of the two-component, relativistic massless particle of spin $1/2$, which he discussed in detail in his *Handbuch der Physik* article[2] as early as 1932. He was also well aware of the theoretical deduction that the two-component neutrinos are then indeed invariant under (CP) and (T) operation by applying the CPT theorem.[3] What prevented Pauli from accepting such possibilities of the two-component neutrino prior to the experimental verification was the question which had always bothered him deeply: Why should the left–right symmetry, observed so well in strong interactions, break down in weak interactions? To this deep searching question there is still no answer.

So Pauli's contribution to our understanding of the neutrino is far more than merely its postulation. His work showing the five relativistic covariants[4] under the proper Lorentz transformation, his re-arrangement theorem[5] and many other quantum mechanical treatments form an integral part of the generalized theory of beta decay. In the recent development of the new theory of the neutrino, his critical thinking and his arguments on the two-component neutrino and the CPT theorem have provided invaluable guidance all along the way.

1. PRELUDE TO NEUTRINO POSTULATION

As soon as the experimental evidence from the microcalori-metric measurements[6] of the average energy of beta particles from RaE proved beyond a doubt that the continuous distribu-tion[7] is the intrinsic characteristic of the disintegration electrons, physicists knew that they were confronted with something very puzzling. Pauli, in particular, who had closely followed these experimental polemics with great interest, was convinced that the calorimetric results were very conclusive and most significant.

At about the same time, wave mechanics had been taking a hold in physics. Our understanding of the spins and statistics of nuclei gradually became clear. However, the fundamental constituents of nuclei were still protons and electrons. Therefore, according to the Ehrenfest and Oppenheimer theorem,[8] the statistics of the ^{14}N nucleus were supposed to obey Fermi–Dirac statistics. To everyone's dismay, the determination[9] of the statistics of ^{14}N revealed Bose–Einstein statistics, contrary to expectation, and therefore provided a strong argument against the proton–electron hypothesis. The consideration of spins of the nuclei led to the same conclusion. So electrons would have to be excluded from the nucleus. No better ideas about the possible constituents of the nuclei were advanced to replace the old proton–electron hypothesis at that time.

Basing his observations purely on considerations of spin and statistics, Pauli pointed out in an open letter[10] to Geiger and Meitner at the Tübingen meeting in December of 1930 that in beta decay not only was the energy apparently not conserved, but also the spin and the statistics were not conserved. The possible changes of the nuclear angular momentum during the beta transition must be zero or an integral amount ($\Delta I = n\hbar$, $n = 0$, 1, 2···). On the other hand, the intrinsic angular momentum of the electron is $\hbar/2$. The orbital angular momentum is always an integral of $\hbar$; so the angular momentum is clearly not conserved in the β^- decay if the β^- particle is the only particle emitted. Pauli went on to propose the outlandish idea of introducing a very penetrating, new neutral particle of vanishingly small mass in beta decay to save the situation.

However, he was most modest and conciliatory in his pleading for a hearing. He admitted that his remedy might appear an unlikely one; but, he went on to say: 'Nothing venture, nothing win. And the gravity of the situation with regard to the con-tinuous beta spectrum is illuminated by a pronouncement of my

respected predecessor in office, Herr Debye, who recently said to
me in Brussels, "Oh, it is best not to think about it at all . . . like
the new taxes". One ought therefore to discuss seriously every
avenue of rescue. So, dear radioactive folks, put it to the test and
judge.' He was prevented from attending the Tübingen meeting
on account of a dance in Zürich. He was very young then indeed.

Pauli made public his proposal of this strange new particle at
the Americal Physical Society meeting in Pasadena in June, 1931.
However, this hypothesis of a new undetectable particle met with
scepticism, as it was too radical for most physicists to accept with
ease. In October of that same year, Pauli and Fermi met at a
nuclear physics meeting in Rome. Beta decay was again discussed at length, and Fermi was at once attracted by the idea of the
neutrino hypothesis.

Then came the big break-through with the discovery of neutrons
by Chadwick[11] in 1932. The proton–neutron hypothesis of
nuclear constitution fitted into the whole picture beautifully. So
at the Solvay Congress[1] in Brussels in 1933, Pauli was greatly
encouraged by this favourable development and put aside
whatever reservations he might have had previously about his
neutrino hypothesis.

2. NEUTRINO HYPOTHESIS

Here is part of what Pauli proposed at that meeting:[1] 'In June
1931, during a conference in Pasadena, I proposed the following
interpretation: the conservation laws hold, the emission of
beta particles occurring together with the emission of a very
penetrating radiation of neutral particles, which has not been
observed yet. The sum of the energies of the beta particle and
the neutral particle (or the neutral particles, since one doesn't
know whether there be one or many) emitted by the nucleus in one
process, will be equal to the energy which corresponds to the upper
limit of the beta spectrum. It is obvious that we assume not only
energy conservation but also the conservation of linear momentum,
of angular momentum and of the characteristics of the statistics
in all elementary processes.

'With regard to the properties of these neutral particles, we
first learn from atomic weights that their mass cannot be much
larger than that of the electron. In order to distinguish them
from the heavy neutrons, E. Fermi proposed the name "neutrino".
It is possible that the neutrino proper mass be equal to zero, so
that it would have to propagate with the velocity of light, like
photons. Nevertheless, their penetrating power would be far

greater than that of photons with the same energy. It seems to me admissible that neutrinos possess a spin 1/2 and that they obey Fermi statistics, in spite of the fact that experiments do not provide us with any direct proof of this hypothesis. We don't know anything about the interaction of neutrinos with other material particles and with photons: the hypothesis that they possess a magnetic moment, as I had proposed once (Dirac's theory induces us to predict the possibility of neutral magnetic particles) doesn't seem to me at all well founded.'

His argument against the breakdown of the conservation laws in beta decay was very forceful. He argued that:

'The interpretation supported by Bohr[12] admits that the laws of conservation of energy and momentum do not hold when one deals with a nuclear process where light particles play an essential part. This hypothesis does not seem to me either satisfying or even plausible. In the first place the electric charge is conserved in the process, and I don't see why conservation of charge would be more fundamental than conservation of energy and momentum. Moreover, it is precisely the energy relations which govern several characteristic properties of beta spectra (existence of an upper limit and relation with gamma spectra, Heisenberg stability criterion). If the conservation laws were not valid, one would have to conclude from these relations that a beta disintegration occurs always with a loss of energy and never a gain; this conclusion implies an irreversibility of these processes with respect to time, which doesn't seem to me at all acceptable.'

He even suggested the sensitive recoil methods as a means to investigate this particle. This is what he said:

'... the experimental study of the momentum difference in beta disintegrations constitutes an extremely important problem; one can predict that the difficulties will be quite insurmountable because of the smallness of the energy of the recoil nucleus.'

Fermi was also present at the Solvay Congress, and this meeting precipitated the famous Fermi theory[13] of beta decay soon after its close. Also present at the discussion was Perrin.[14] He concluded even at that early stage that the neutrino rest mass must be small or zero. His statement was: 'The shape of the continuous beta spectrum allows us to make a reasonable hypothesis about the neutrino mass ... in order to account more or less for the position of the maximum or rather for the mean value of the electron energy, in the best known case (RaE) one must agree that the neutrino has a zero intrinsic mass like the photon.'

So at its first debut the particle was already assumed to have an intrinsic spin of $\hbar/2$, to obey Fermi–Dirac statistics, to carry no charge, and to possess only vanishingly small mass—much less than that of the electron. With all these characteristics, the particle was more than qualified to be a full-fledged member of the family of elementary particles : yet, probably no one could have foreseen what an exciting and brilliant role this elusive particle was going to play in the field of elementary particles.

3. FERMI THEORY OF BETA DECAY[13]

Using the neutrino hypothesis, Fermi laid down the fundamental formulation of the theory of beta decay which can be logically traced to his earlier contributions to quantum electrodynamics. The subsequent generalizations[15] by others did broaden the formulation to include all possible types of beta interactions, but the central idea has remained the same as when it was originally introduced.

β^- decay may be considered as

$$N \rightarrow P + e^- + \nu \qquad \qquad ....(1)$$

and β^+ decay as

$$P \rightarrow N + e^+ + \nu \qquad \qquad ....(2)$$

All these four particles (P, N, $e^\pm$, ν) are known to have spin 1/2 and to obey Fermi statistics and therefore could be represented by a quantized Dirac field. From Dirac relativistic theory, for every type of spin 1/2 elementary particle there exists a pair consisting of a particle and its corresponding anti-particle with charge and magnetic moment of opposite sign, such as an electron and its anti-particle positron. Naturally, the neutrino and its counterpart, the anti-neutrino, would be expected to have this property. Whether there is an intrinsic difference between the neutrino and the anti-neutrino was not known at the outset. The present view on this question will be discussed in section 14.

Furthermore, the absorption of a normal particle is equivalent to the creation of an anti-particle, as the absorbed normal particle can be taken from a state of negative energy which corresponds to the creation of an anti-particle ; and *vice-versa*. For mathematical convenience, it is desirable to describe the $\beta^\mp$ decay as two particles absorbed and two particles created.

$$\text{for} \quad P \xrightarrow{\beta^+ \text{ decay}} N + e^+ + \nu \quad \text{use} \quad P + e^- \xrightarrow{\beta^+ \text{ decay}} N + \nu$$
$$....(3)$$

$$\text{for} \quad N \xrightarrow{\beta^- \text{ decay}} P + e^- + \bar{\nu} \quad \text{use} \quad N + \nu \xrightarrow{\beta^- \text{ decay}} P + e^-$$
$$....(4)$$

Let us adopt the terminology that ν in the above equation represents a normal particle neutrino, $\bar{\nu}$ an anti-neutrino. So the neutrino emitted in β^+ decay is designated as the 'particle' (neutrino) and the one accompanying β^- decay is the 'anti-particle' (anti-neutrino).

The direct field coupling between $P\bar{N}$ and $e^+\nu$ is assumed to be a point interaction with $P\bar{N}$ as source and $e^+\nu$ as lepton field such as is exemplified by electromagnetic interaction where a charge can interact with a light quantum only when they are at the same place. Beta interaction might be due to a Hamiltonian interaction term

$$H = g(\bar{\psi}_P\psi_N\bar{\psi}_e\psi_\nu + \bar{\psi}_N\psi_P\bar{\psi}_\nu\psi_e) \qquad \ldots (5)$$

where g is the coupling constant measuring the strength of beta interaction analogous to e (electric charge) in the electromagnetic case. ψ_P, ψ_N, ψ_e, ψ_ν are the field operators that destroy a proton, a neutron, an electron, a neutrino or create an anti-proton, an anti-neutron, a positron, an anti-neutrino, respectively. $\bar{\psi}_P$, $\bar{\psi}_N$, $\bar{\psi}_e$, $\bar{\psi}_\nu$ create the respective normal particles or destroy the respective anti-particles. In writing this expression the complex-conjugate quantity has been added since the Lagrangian term must be Hermitian. The first term represents β^- decay and the second term corresponds to β^+ decay.

The field operator ψ is a spinor and therefore has four components, so that there are 256 independent ways in which quadrilinear combinations can be formed. However, since the interaction term is to be a scalar, it should be independent of the Lorentz frame used. In this connection, Pauli[4] had shown earlier that five, and only five, relativistically covariant quantities could be constructed under proper Lorentz transformation. These five covariants behave like scalar (S), vector (V), tensor (T), axial vector (A) and pseudoscalar (P).

The original beta interaction introduced by Fermi was a vector interaction as suggested by electrodynamics. It permits only those transitions with spin change $\Delta I = 0$ and no parity change to be of the allowed type. When the ^{6}He β^- decay which involved $\Delta I = 1$ (n_0) was concluded to be an allowed transition from its short half-life (0.82 sec) and its maximum energy ($E_{max} = 3.52$ MeV), the assumption of the original vector interaction alone was clearly inadequate. To generalize the beta interaction, Gamow and Teller[15] pointed out that altogether five possible invariant interactions could be obtained by multiplying each of the five covariants of heavy particles with the corresponding covariant of

9*

light particles.   The most general form of beta interaction should therefore be a linear combination of all these five forms

$$(C_S S + C_V V + C_T T + C_A A + C_P P),$$

Thus the generalized interaction Hamiltonian can be written as

$$H_\beta = g \sum_i C_i (\bar{\psi}_P O_i \psi_N)(\bar{\psi}_e O_i \psi_\nu) + \text{Herm. Conj.} \qquad \ldots \ldots (6)$$

where

$$
\begin{array}{ccccccc}
i = & S & V & T & & A & P \\[4pt]
C_i = & C_S & C_V & C_T & & C_A & C_P \\[4pt]
O_i = & 1 & \gamma_\mu & \dfrac{i}{2 \times 2^{1/2}} (\gamma_\mu \gamma_\nu - \gamma_\nu \gamma_\mu) & & i\gamma_5 \gamma_\mu & \gamma_5
\end{array}
$$

where $\gamma = i\alpha\beta$, $\gamma_4 = \beta$, $\gamma_5 = \gamma_1 \gamma_2 \gamma_3 \gamma_4$

$$\alpha \equiv \begin{pmatrix} \sigma & 0 \\ 0 & -\sigma \end{pmatrix}; \quad \beta \equiv \begin{pmatrix} 0 & 1 \\ 1 & 0 \end{pmatrix} \equiv \gamma_4; \quad \gamma = \begin{pmatrix} 0 & i\sigma \\ -i\sigma & 0 \end{pmatrix};$$

$$\text{and} \quad \gamma_5 \equiv \begin{pmatrix} -1 & 0 \\ 0 & +1 \end{pmatrix}$$

The constant g is related to the strength of the interaction.   The quantities of beta decay which could be measured at the early period of its development are its transition rate (half-life) and the shape of its spectrum (maximum energy and the allowed or forbidden classification).

The theoretical expression for the energy and angular distribution of the electrons in the beta decay is

$$P_{\mp}(E_\beta, \theta_\nu) \, dE =$$

$$\frac{m_0 C^2}{\hbar} \frac{G^2}{2\pi^3} \cdot F(\pm Z, E_\beta) \cdot \{(C_S^2 + C_V^2)$$

$$\times |M_F|^2 + (C_T^2 + C_A^2)|M_{GT}|^2 \} \cdot \left\{ p_\beta E_\beta \left[E_{\max} + \frac{m_\nu}{m_0} - E_\beta \right] \right.$$

$$\times \left[\left(E_{\max} + \frac{m_\nu}{m_0} - E_\beta \right)^2 - \frac{m_\nu^2}{m_0^2} \right]^{1/2} \right\} \cdot \left\{ 1 \pm \frac{b}{E_\beta} \pm \lambda \frac{p_\beta C}{E_\beta} \right.$$

$$\left. \times \cos \theta_{(\beta\nu)} + \frac{\alpha \, m_\nu / m_0}{E_\beta (E_{\max} - E_\beta + m_\nu / m_0)} \right\} dE \qquad \ldots \ldots (7)$$

where the dimensionless constant $G = (g/m_0 c^2)(\hbar/m_0 c)^{-3}$, g has the units of erg-cm³, E_β is the total energy of beta particles, including rest mass in units of $m_0 c^2$, p_β in units of $m_0 c$. $F(\pm Z, E)$ is the

Coulomb correction factor. The term containing b is the Fierz interference term and

$$b = 2\left[1 - \left(\frac{e^2 Z}{\hbar C}\right)^2\right]^{1/2} \cdot \frac{C_S C_V |M_F|^2 + C_T C_A |M_{GT}|^2}{(C_S^2 + C_V^2)|M_F|^2 + (C_T^2 + C_A^2)|M_{GT}|^2} \quad \dots(8)$$

(See section 4-C.)

$\theta_{\beta\nu}$ is the angle subtended between β and ν particles

$$\lambda = \frac{1/3(C_T^2 - C_A^2)|M_{GT}|^2 - (C_S^2 - C_V^2)|M_F|^2}{(C_T^2 + C_A^2)|M_{GT}|^2 + (C_S^2 + C_V^2)|M_F|^2} \quad \dots(9)$$

(See section 4-F.)

$\alpha = +1$ if the electron and neutrino wave functions are of opposite parity. $\alpha = -1$ if they are of the same parity (see section 13). The coupling constants C_i are real if time reversal is invariant (see section 22).

4. EXPERIMENTAL EVIDENCE FROM CLASSICAL BETA DECAY[16]

Even prior to the direct observation of the phenomenon of neutrino capture in recent years, the success of the Fermi theory of beta decay and the results of beta recoil experiments undoubtedly gave positive support to the neutrino hypothesis. Detailed discussions on this subject can be found in several review articles.[16] Here only a brief resumé will be given.

A. Allowed Spectrum Shape

According to the Fermi theory of beta decay, if one takes into account the effect of the nuclear electrostatic field on the motion of the electron, which is expressed as the Coulomb correction factor $F(Z, E_\beta)$ or known as the Fermi function, the shape of the allowed beta spectrum is simply given by the statistical factor $pE_\beta(E_{\max} - E_\beta)^2$ which is the calculated phase space corresponding to the sharing of the distribution energy between the electron and the neutrino assuming zero neutrino mass. It is well established experimentally that the shape of the allowed beta spectrum follows closely this theoretical prediction.

B. The Unique Forbidden Transitions

The allowed beta spectrum is solely determined by the statistical factor of the phase space. There is nothing very sophisticated about the theory. On the other hand, there exist some unique forbidden spectra which are radically different from the allowed shape and uniquely predicted by the theory. The successive discovery of the unique first, second and third forbidden spectra of ^{91}Y, ^{10}Be and ^{40}K, which behaved precisely as theoretically predicted, is triumphant proof of the theory of beta decay.

C. The Fierz Interference Term $\pm b/E_\beta$

Fierz[18] was the first to point out the importance of this term. Its existence would have distorted the beta spectrum according to b/E_β, but was never observed. The upper limit is put at $b = 0 \pm 0.10$ for Fermi type and $b = 0 \pm 0.04$ for G–T type. This observation implies that both S and V in Fermi type and both A and T in G–T type cannot be present with comparable strength. If one of them is dominant, the other is very weak. However, the absence of the Fierz interference term has no such clear-cut implications for two-component neutrinos (see section 11).

D. ft-Values

The mean life of decay τ will be given by

$$\frac{1}{\tau} = \int_1^{E_{\max}} p(E)\, \mathrm{d}E = \frac{m_0 c^2}{\hbar} \frac{G^2}{2\pi^3} \left(C_F{}^2 |M_F|^2 + C_{GT}{}^2 |M_{GT}|^2\right)$$

$$\times \int_1^{E_{\max}} F(Z, E_\beta)\{(E_\beta{}^2 - 1)^{1/2} E_\beta (E_{\max} - E_\beta)^2\}\, \mathrm{d}E$$

or

$$f\tau(C_F{}^2 |M_F|^2 + C_{GT}{}^2 |M_{GT}|^2) = \frac{2\pi^3 \tau_0}{G^2}$$

where

$$\tau_0 = \frac{\hbar}{m_0 c^2} = 1.3 \times 10^{-21} \text{ sec}$$

f is a dimensionless function used to denote the integral over the energy spectrum.

The classification of beta decay according to its ft-value not only leads to the assignment of the spin and parity of the nuclear levels but also contributes greatly to the understanding of the nuclear structure and nuclear forces. The most outstanding successes are the classification of the super-allowed and allowed transitions and the establishment of the group of $0^+ \to 0^+$ beta transitions in relation to isotopic spin multiplets.

E. Ratio of $|C_{GT}|^2/|C_F|^2$

The Fermi and Gamow–Teller types of interactions are found to be almost equally present, from systematic study of some simple mirror nuclei (closed shell $\pm$ one nucleon) by plotting B *versus* X of the following relation:

$$ft = \frac{B}{(1-X)|M_F|^2 + X|M_{G-T}|^2} \qquad \dots (10)$$

where X is the relative contribution of the G–T interaction.

$$X = \frac{|C_{GT}|^2}{|C_F|^2 + |C_{GT}|^2} \qquad \dots (11)$$

The ratio of $C_{GT}{}^2/C_F{}^2$ was given by one recent determination as $1 \cdot 16 \pm 0 \cdot 05$.[17] This value depends sensitively on the evaluation of the nuclear matrix elements which are not known precisely. On the other hand, the nuclear matrix elements of the neutron and ^{14}O ($0^+ \to 0^+$ transition) can be calculated exactly; that is, $M_F{}^2 = 2$ for ^{14}O and $M_F{}^2 = 1$ and $M_{GT}{}^2 = 3$ for the neutron. Therefore,

$$\frac{(ft)_{n_0}}{(ft)^{14}O} = \frac{2|C_F|^2}{|C_F|^2 + 3|C_{GT}|^2} \qquad \dots (12)$$

With the latest determination of ft-values of n_0 and ^{14}O:

$$(ft)_{n_0} = (1,187 \pm 35) \text{ sec} \quad \text{from} \quad (t_{1/2})_{n_0} = 11 \cdot 7 \pm 0 \cdot 3 \text{ min.}$$

$$\dots (13)$$

$$(f)^{14}O = (3,103 \pm 62) \text{ sec}$$

the ratio has become

$$\frac{|C_{GT}|^2}{|C_F|^2} = 1 \cdot 42 \pm 0 \cdot 08$$

This is in agreement with the ratio $1:55$ obtained from the asymmetry parameter of β^- from polarized neutrons (see section 12). Also the Fermi coupling constant g_F is obtainable from the ft-value of ^{14}O by

$$g_F{}^2 = \frac{2\pi^3(|n^2|)}{|M_F|^2} \left(\frac{\hbar}{m_0 c}\right)^6 \cdot \frac{\hbar}{(ft)^{14}O} \cdot m_0 c^2$$

where $|M_F|^2 = 2$ for $0^+ \to 0^+$ beta transition; therefore

$$|g_F| = (1 \cdot 41 \pm 0 \cdot 01) \times 10^{-49} \text{ erg-cm}^3$$

F. Recoil Experiments

While the neutrino itself cannot be directly detected as can be charged particles, its emission in a decay process imparts recoil to the parent nucleus and the energy and angular distributions of the recoil nuclei provide sensitive ways to study the phenomena of neutrino emission.

Recoil experiments can be grouped into several categories.

(1) The first group is devoted primarily to investigation of the recoil nuclei from K capture. If only a single neutrino is emitted in each K capture process, the recoil momentum will be uniquely determined by the relation

$$p = \frac{1}{c} (E^2 - M_{\nu2}C^4)^{1/2} \quad \text{or} \quad E_r = 140 \cdot 2 \frac{(E^2 - M_{\nu}^2 C^4)}{2M} \quad \ldots (14)$$

in electron volts, where E is the disintegration energy in units of mc^2 released in the K capture process. $M_\nu C^2$ is the neutrino rest energy in units of mc^2 and M is the atomic mass of the recoiling atom in a.m.u. This sharp recoil peak was strikingly demonstrated by a series of convincing and beautiful experiments. The results are summarized in *Table I*.

TABLE I

Nuclear recoil in orbital electron capture

Initial nucleus	Disintegration energy (MeV)	(E_r) cal	(E_r) exp	Ref.
^{7}Be	$0 \cdot 864 \pm 0 \cdot 003$	$57 \cdot 3 \pm 0 \cdot 5$ eV	$56 \cdot 6 \pm 1 \cdot 0$ eV	*
^{7}Be	$0 \cdot 864 \pm 0 \cdot 003$	$57 \cdot 3 \pm 0 \cdot 5$ eV	$55 \cdot 9 \pm 1 \cdot 0$ eV	†
^{37}A	$0 \cdot 816 \pm 0 \cdot 004$	$0 \cdot 711 \pm 0 \cdot 004$ cm/μsec	$0 \cdot 71 \pm 0 \cdot 06$ cm/μsec	‡
	$0 \cdot 816 \pm 0 \cdot 004$	$9 \cdot 67 \pm 0 \cdot 08$	$9 \cdot 6 \pm 0 \cdot 2$ eV	§
		$9 \cdot 65 \pm 0 \cdot 05$	$9 \cdot 63 \pm 0 \cdot 06$ eV	‖

* Smith, P. B. and Allen, J. S., *Phys. Rev.* 81, 381, 1951
† Davis, R., *Phys. Rev.* 86, 976, 1952
‡ Rodebeck, G. W. and Allen, J. S., *Phys. Rev.* 86, 446, 1952
§ Kofoed-Hansen, O., *Phys. Rev.* 96, 1045, 1954
‖ Snell, A. H. and Pleasonton, F., *Phys. Rev.* 97, 246, 1955; 100, 1396, 1955

(2) The recoil spectrum from beta decay is more involved than that of K capture because of simultaneous emission of two light particles (β and ν). The recoil energy spectrum will be continuously distributed, and the exact shape of the energy spectrum

depends sensitively on the angular correlations between the electron and the neutrino. From equation (9), the angular correlation term for various beta interactions is given by

$$
\begin{array}{c|cccc}
& S & V & T & A \\
\hline
\lambda & -1 & +1 & +1/3 & -1/3
\end{array}
$$

In vector and tensor interaction, the electron and neutrino are emitted preferentially in the same direction; the maximum of the recoil distribution shifts to higher energy. In the case of scalar and axial vectors, the two particles tend to come out in opposite

TABLE II

Nuclear decay	Method	λ	Conclusion	Ref.
Prior to parity non-conservation				
^{6}He	Recoil Spectrum		T (not A)	*
n	Recoil Spectrum	$+0 \cdot 09 \pm 0 \cdot 11$	S and T or V and A	†
		$-0 \cdot 21 \pm 0 \cdot 08$		
^{19}Ne	Recoil Spectrum	$+0 \cdot 14 \pm 0 \cdot 2$	S and T or	‡
		$-0 \cdot 15 \pm 0 \cdot 2$	V and A	
^{6}He	Angular Correlation	$+0 \cdot 34 \pm 0 \cdot 12$	T (not A)	§
Since May, 1957				
^{35}A	Recoil Spectrum	$+0 \cdot 93 \pm 0 \cdot 14$	V	‖
^{19}Ne	Recoil Spectrum		V and A or S and T	¶
^{6}He	Recoil Spectrum	$-0 \cdot 39$	A	
^{8}Li	Recoil Spectrum and Angular Correlation		A (T admixture is less than 10 per cent)	††
			A favoured	‡‡

* Allen, J. S. and Jentschke, W. K., *Phys. Rev.* **89**, 902, 1953

† Robson, J. M., *Phys. Rev.* **100**, 933, 1955

‡ $\lambda = -0 \cdot 21$. Maxson, Allen and Jentschke, *Phys. Rev.* **97**, 109, 1955
  $\lambda = +0 \cdot 14$. Good, M. L. and Lauer, E. J., *Phys. Rev.* **105**, 213, 1957
  $\lambda = -0 \cdot 15$. Alford, W. P. and Hamilton, A. R., *Phys. Rev.* **105**, 673, 1957

§ Rustad, B. M. and Ruby, S. L., *Phys. Rev.* **89**, 880, 1953; **97**, 991, 1955

‖ Herrmannsfeldt, Stahelin, Maxson, and Allen, *Phys. Rev.* **107**, 641, 1957

¶ Herrmannsfeldt, Burman, Stahelin, Allen and Braid, *Phys. Rev. Letters* **1**, 61, 1958

†† Lauritsen, Barnes, Fowler and Lauritsen, *Phys. Rev. Letters* **1**, 326, 1958
   Barnes, Fowler, Greenstein, Lauritsen and Nordberg, *Phys. Rev. Letters* **1**, 328, 1958

‡‡ Lauterjung, Schimmer and Maier-Leibnitz, *Z. Phys.* **150**, 657, 1958

directions so the maximum of the recoil distribution moves down to lower energy. The difference is very pronounced between S and V but is much less between T and A. Prior to the discovery of parity non-conservation in beta decay, the investigation of the $(\beta-\nu)$ angular correlation, either by recoil spectrum or by (β-recoil nucleus) correlation, was the only means to provide information on the types of interaction. The experimental results are summarized in *Table II*.

The linear combination of S and T was strongly favoured before May, 1957, as concluded from *Table II*. This dominating (S, T) combination was not questioned or challenged until the results of ^{35}A were reported in May of 1957. Now, the conclusion about the beta interactions based on recoil results is predominantly (V, A) combination (see Fig. 1). The cause and the unjustified assumptions which led to the erroneous conclusion of T for ^{6}He were examined and analysed in a report by Wu and Schwarzschild.[19]

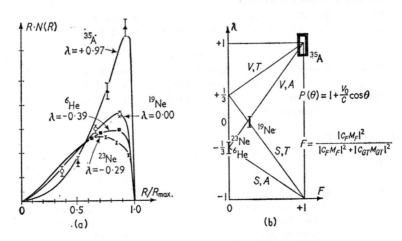

Fig. 1a. Recoil spectra of ^{6}He, ^{35}A, ^{19}Ne and ^{23}Ne.

Fig. 1b. λ *versus* $F = \dfrac{|C_F M_F|^2}{|C_F M_F|^2 + |C_{GT} M_{GT}|^2}$ relation.

(3) There have been many persistent and ingenious efforts devoted to the recoil experiments. Sherwin's recoil results[20] by using a solid source of radioactive ^{32}P and the time of flight method clearly demonstrated that the relation between the missing energy and missing momentum can be approximately expressed by $\Delta E = C \Delta p$. Kofoed-Hansen[21] proposed and carried out a series of investigations in which the current collected on the plates of a condenser is measured as a function of crossed electric

and magnetic fields. Such measurements enable both the average electron and recoil momenta to be determined, and also the charge spectrum of recoil ions. The latest development of recoil technique by Snell and Pleasanton[22] is capable of providing high precision to the most complicated charge spectrum of the recoil nuclei.

5. NON-CONSERVATION OF PARITY IN BETA DECAY

The theory of beta decay is a phenomenological one. From its investigation one hopes to gain insight concerning the nature of the neutrino and the types of beta interaction. The recent discovery of non-conservation of parity and charge conjugation in beta decay has made possible a great advance in the theory of the neutrino. The sequence of the development unfolds in the following sections.

If parity is not conserved in beta interaction, then the interaction Hamiltonian H should include a pseudoscalar term as well as the original scalar term. Then equation (6) becomes

$$H = \sum_i C_i(\bar\psi_p O_i\psi_N)(\bar\psi_e O_i\psi_\nu) + \sum_i C_i{}'(\bar\psi_p O_i\psi_N)(\bar\psi_e O_i\gamma_5\psi_\nu) + \text{Herm. Conj.}$$
$$\dots(15)$$

C_i is called the parity conserving and $C_i{}'$ the parity non-conserving coupling constant by Lee and Yang.[23] Actually whether C_i or $C_i{}'$ is the parity conserving term depends on the relative parity of the neutrino with respect to the electron. In classical beta decay, it was conventionally assumed that the neutrino and the electron have the same parity; then $C_i \neq 0$ and $C_i{}' \equiv 0$. This is known as 'even' coupling. Otherwise, if the neutrino and e^- are of opposite parity, then the old theory gives $C_i = 0$ and $C_i{}' \neq 0$; which is called 'odd' coupling. There is no way of distinguishing between C_i and $C_i{}'$ without involving the measuring of the spin of the neutrino. Proceeding exactly as before to obtain the energy and angular distribution of the electrons in an allowed transition, one now obtains the expression for the energy and angular distribution of electrons for a parity non-conserving allowed beta transition essentially identical to that derived for a parity conserving beta interaction. In fact, the parity non-conserving expression for any scalar quantities in β decay could be obtained directly from that calculated for the parity conserving beta interaction except for replacing

$$|C_i|^2 \quad \text{by} \quad (|C_i|^2 + |C_i{}'|^2)$$

and

$$C_i C_j{}^\star \quad \text{by} \quad (C_i C_j{}^\star + C_i{}' C_j{}'^\star)$$

No interference terms between C_i and C_i' appear in the above expression, and this is why, with voluminous experimental information on beta decay such as the shape of the beta spectra, the ft-values, the beta–neutrino angular correlations and the β–γ angular correlations, no light was ever shed on the question of conservation of parity in beta decay. This brilliant insight, as concluded from their theoretical analysis, led Lee and Yang to suggest certain crucial experiments in which a pseudoscalar quantity formed out of the experimentally measured quantities should be searched for. For example, a momentum $\mathbf{p}$ (polar vector) and a spin $\boldsymbol{\sigma}$ (axial vector) are measured, the term representing the pseudoscalar CC' $\mathbf{p} \cdot \boldsymbol{\sigma}$ may have a non-zero expectation value. In a beta decay process, if $\boldsymbol{\sigma}$ is the spin of the nucleus and $\mathbf{p}$ the direction of the electron emission, the existence of the pseudoscalar $\langle \mathbf{p} \cdot \boldsymbol{\sigma} \rangle \neq 0$ should show up as the asymmetry* distribution of electrons from polarized nuclei.

6. POLARIZED ^{60}CO EXPERIMENT[24]

The essence of the polarized nuclei experiment is to line up the spins of beta-emitting nuclei along the same axis and then to determine whether the beta particles were emitted preferentially in one direction or the other along the axis. The property by which atomic nuclei can be oriented is the magnetic moment. However, the nuclear magnetic moments ($\mu_n \sim 10^{-3}$ Bohr magneton) are so small that it requires an electromagnet of a strength of the order of magnitude of 10^5 gauss to align these tiny magnets for $T \sim 0 \cdot 01°$ K. Fortunately, strong magnetic fields do, however, exist in the vicinity of the atomic nucleus of a paramagnetic atom. The magnetic moments of such atoms are about a thousand times larger than those of nuclei. Thus paramagnetic atoms can be lined up in a moderately strong magnetic field (hundreds of oersteds) and their tremendous fields in turn orient the nuclear moments. This ingenious method of nuclear orientation was independently proposed by Rose and Gorter in 1948. In order to reduce the thermal agitation which tends to disrupt the orderly orientation, the cerium–magnesium nitrate crystal is cooled down to a temperature of $0 \cdot 01°$ C above absolute zero ($-273 \cdot 17°$ C). The cooling is accomplished by the adiabatic demagnetization method. The paramagnetic radioactive ^{60}Co which decays by pure Gamow–Teller interaction ($\Delta I = 5 - 4 = 1, n_0$) was selected for this test.

---

* Asymmetry is referred to the plane perpendicular to the spin axis.

To study the beta distribution from polarized nuclei in the present problem, two major difficulties had to be overcome. The beta detector should be placed inside the demagnetization cryostat at $\sim 1°$ K, and the radioactive nuclei must be located in a thin surface layer (< 0.1 mm) and polarized. The beta detector was a thin anthracene crystal located inside the vacuum chamber about 2 cm above the ^{60}Co source. The scintillations were transmitted through a glass window and a lucite light pipe 4 ft long to a photomultiplier (6292) which was located at the top of the cryostat. The amount of polarization of ^{60}Co was determined by measuring simultaneously the anisotropy of its gamma radiation.

$$E_\gamma = \frac{I(\pi/2) - I(0)}{I(\pi/2)}$$

A large beta asymmetry was observed. In Fig. 2 the gamma anisotropy and beta asymmetry *versus* time were plotted for polarizing field both up and down. The time for disappearance

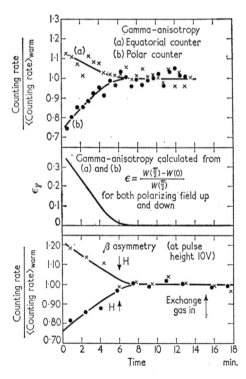

Fig. 2. Asymmetry emission of beta particles from polarized ^{60}CO experiment.

of the beta asymmetry coincides well with that of gamma anisotropy. The sign of the asymmetry coefficient was found to be
negative; that is, the emission of beta particles is more favoured
in the direction opposite to that of nuclear spin. This means that,
viewed from the position of the emitted beta particles, the nuclei
^{60}Co appear to rotate clockwise; left can be distinguished from
right, therefore, parity is *not* always conserved, as shown by this
experiment; moreover, the asymmetry observed is as large as
possible.

In the electron angular distribution

$$I(\theta) = 1 + A \frac{\langle J_z \rangle}{J} \frac{v}{c} \cos \theta \qquad \dots (16)$$

(where θ is the angle between the nuclear spin and electron momentum direction) the measured asymmetry parameter A is nearly
equal to -1. This implies that the parity interference effects are
about as large as they could be. So this first experiment on parity
revealed to us not only that parity and charge conjugation are not
conserved in beta decay but pointed to something even more
drastic and significant. Many important deductions can be
directly derived from the observed asymmetry parameter ($A \simeq -1$)
in the polarized ^{60}Co beta decay experiment. If we write down
the expression A for the beta decay of ^{60}Co, which is a pure G–T
transition:

$$A = \left[\mathrm{Re}(C_T{}^\star C_T{}' - C_A{}^\star C_A{}') - \frac{Ze^2}{\hbar c p} \mathrm{Im}(C_T{}^\star C_A{}' + C_T{}'^\star C_A) \right] \frac{2|M_{GT}|^2}{\xi} \dots (17)$$

where

$$\xi = (|C_T|^2 + |C_T{}'|^2 + |C_A|^2 + |C_A{}'|^2)|M_{GT}|^2$$

The second term with imaginary quantities (we assume the
invariance under time reversal is more or less intact) is in all
probability very small. Furthermore, from the classical theory
of beta decay and the absence of the Fierz term b/E_β, it is concluded that only one of the terms, either A or T, is the dominant
interaction in the G–T transition. (This deduction does not apply
to the two-component neutrinos, see section 11.) So from the
relation

$$A = \mathrm{Re} \frac{(C_T{}^\star C_T{}' - C_A{}^\star C_A{}') \times 2}{|C_T|^2 + |C_T{}'|^2 + |C_A|^2 + |C_A{}'|^2} \simeq -1 \quad \dots (18)$$

it implies either

$$C_A \simeq C_A{}', \quad \text{if } A \text{ is the dominating interaction} \dots (19)$$

or

$$C_T \simeq -C_T{}', \quad \text{if } T \text{ is the responsible interaction} \dots (20)$$

Substituting the above relations into the interaction term, we obtain for the tensor interaction:

$$H_T = C_T(\bar{\psi}_P O_T \psi_N)(\bar{\psi}_e O_T (1 - a\gamma_5)\psi_\nu) \qquad \ldots (21)$$

or axial vector interaction:

$$H_A = C_A(\bar{\psi}_P O_A \psi_N)(\bar{\psi}_e O_A (1 + a\gamma_5)\psi_\nu) \qquad \ldots (22)$$

where a is very close to unity. The total neutrino operator is thus represented by

$$(1 - a\gamma_5)\psi_\nu \quad \text{in tensor interaction} \qquad \ldots (23)$$

and

$$(1 + a\gamma_5)\psi_\nu \quad \text{in axial vector interaction} \qquad \ldots (24)$$

It is well known that the term $(1 \mp \gamma_5)/2$ affects the wave function ψ_ν as a projection operator for the longitudinal polarization, where

$$\{(1 - \gamma_5)/2\}\psi_\nu = \psi_\nu^{R(25)} \quad \text{is for the right polarization}$$
$$\ldots (25)$$

and

$$\{(1 + \gamma_5)/2\}\psi_\nu = \psi_\nu^{L(26)} \quad \text{is for left polarization.} \qquad \ldots (26)$$

Particularly is this the case with mass zero particles, because ψ_ν^R can be uncoupled* from ψ_ν^L, each of which is an eigenstate of the Hamiltonian, and therefore it implies complete polarization of either right-handed or left-handed helicity.

---

* From the Dirac equation, we have

$$\left(\gamma_\mu \frac{\partial}{\partial x_\mu}\right)\psi = -m\psi \quad \text{using} \quad \hbar \equiv c \equiv 1$$

$$\left(\gamma_\mu \frac{\partial}{\partial x_\mu}\right)\gamma_5\psi = +m\gamma_5\psi$$

If we designate

$$\psi^R \equiv \left(\frac{1 - \gamma_5}{2}\right)\psi$$

$$\psi^L = \left(\frac{1 + \gamma_5}{2}\right)\psi$$

Then

$$\left(\gamma_\mu \frac{\partial}{\partial x_\mu}\right)\psi^R + m\psi^L = 0$$

$$\left(\gamma_\mu \frac{\partial}{\partial x_\mu}\right)\psi^L + m\psi^R = 0$$

For $m = 0$, the ψ^R and ψ^L are uncoupled.

From the polarized ^{60}Co experiment, the observed total neutrino operator $(1 \mp a\gamma_5)\psi_\nu$ where a is very close to unity immediately suggests the attractive possibility that the neutrino is longitudinally polarized; that is, it spins about the direction of motion in a definite sense. Moreover, $(1 + \gamma_5)\psi_\nu$ in axial vector tells us that the neutrino possesses a negative helicity (spin and momentum vector aligned in opposite sense) and $(1 - \gamma_5)\psi_\nu$ states a right-handed neutrino in tensor interaction. Furthermore the projection operator $1/2(1 \pm \gamma_5)$ which appears in the total neutrino operator and selects out a given spin state of the neutrino can be written as a projection operator for the electron in the lepton covariant

$$\psi_e{}^\dagger \gamma_4 O_i (1 \pm \gamma_5)\psi_\nu = \psi_e{}^\dagger (1 + \gamma_5)\gamma_4 O_i \psi_\nu$$

(For the details of this derivation, see section 9.) Therefore, the longitudinal polarization of beta particles is theoretically deduced directly from the first polarized ^{60}Co experiment. In conclusion, the observation of the maximum possible violation of parity in polarized ^{60}Co experiment strongly suggested the possibility of a new theory of the neutrino.

7. THE TWO-COMPONENT THEORY OF THE NEUTRINO [25]

This simple and appealing theory of the neutrino was independently proposed by Lee and Yang, and Landau and Salam. In the conventional neutrino theory, there are four components in the neutrino wave function, two for the positive energy state (designated as neutrino ν) with right and left polarization, and two for the negative energy state (designated by anti-neutrino $\bar{\nu}$) also with right and left polarization. The existence of only one completely polarized state each for the neutrino and anti-neutrino reduces Dirac's neutrino wave function from four components to two; therefore the name. From the observed total neutrino wave operator

$$(1 \mp \gamma_5)\psi_\nu \qquad \qquad \ldots\ldots(27)$$

(where '$-$' is for T and '$+$' is for A) by applying the known relations

$$(1 - \gamma_5) = -(1 - \gamma_5)\gamma_5$$

and

$$(1 + \gamma_5) = +(1 + \gamma_5)\gamma_5 \qquad \ldots\ldots(28)$$

the Hamiltonian term is then invariant under the replacements of the neutrino wave function ψ_ν by

$$\psi_\nu \rightarrow \gamma_5 \psi_\nu \quad \text{for } A \text{ interaction} \qquad \dots (29)$$

and

$$\psi_\nu \rightarrow -\gamma_5 \psi_\nu \quad \text{for } T \text{ interaction} \qquad \dots (30)$$

This substitution nevertheless rigorously requires that the mass of the neutrino must be equal to zero for the Dirac equation for a free neutrino

$$\left(\gamma_\mu \frac{\partial}{\partial x_\mu} + m_\nu\right)\psi_\nu = 0 \qquad \dots (31)$$

Substituting

$$\psi_\nu \rightarrow \gamma_5 \psi_\nu ; \qquad \left(\gamma_\mu \frac{\partial}{\partial x_\mu} + m_\nu\right)\gamma_5 \psi_\nu = 0 \qquad \dots (32)$$

Multiplying equation (31) by γ_5

$$\left(\gamma_\mu \frac{\partial}{\partial x_\mu} - m_\nu\right)\gamma_5 \psi_\nu = 0 \qquad \dots (33)$$

The change of the relative sign between the two terms in the above equations (32 and 33) is due to the anti-commuting relation between γ_5 and γ_μ. Therefore, to have both the free neutrino and interaction Hamiltonian invariant under the substitution $\psi_\nu \rightarrow \pm \gamma_5 \psi_\nu$, the mass of neutrino (m_ν) must be equal to zero.

That the masslessness of the neutrino is necessary for the definite intrinsic helicity of the neutrino is physically quite obvious. If there were any mass associated with the particle, the particle would be at rest or with momentum p reversed in a certain frame of reference. It is thus rather meaningless to impose the necessary requirement of alignment of spin σ and momentum p for such a particle. So far, the experimental evidence of the mass of the neutrino indeed indicates its vanishing smallness ($< 1/2,000 \ m_e$) as discussed in section 13.

All through the years, theoretical physicists had entertained the idea of associating certain gauge invariance $(1 \pm \gamma_5)\psi_\nu = 0$ with a massless neutrino. Unfortunately, this leads directly to the two-component theory of the neutrino and therefore violates the law of parity. In 1929 Weyl[2] proposed the mathematical possibilities of such a two-component relativistic particle of spin 1/2. It was rejected by Pauli [2] because it violated the law of parity* and therefore could not be a physical reality! Pauli's reasoning was as follows: one writes down the Dirac equation of a massless neutrino $(m_\nu = 0)$

$$i \frac{\partial}{\partial t} \psi_\nu = \frac{1}{i} \, \alpha \cdot \nabla \psi_\nu \qquad \dots (34)$$

However, α can be expressed by $\alpha = -\gamma_5 \sigma = -\sigma \gamma_5$, where σ_i is the three 2×2 Pauli matrices. Therefore

$$i \frac{\partial}{\partial t} \psi_\nu = \frac{-1}{i} \, \sigma \cdot \nabla \gamma_5 \psi_\nu \qquad \dots (35)$$

For a massless neutrino, one can make the substitution

$$\psi_\nu = \pm \gamma_5 \psi_\nu$$

One obtains

$$i \frac{\partial}{\partial t} \psi_\nu = \mp i \sigma \cdot \nabla \psi_\nu \qquad \dots (36)$$

('$-$' for $\psi_\nu = \gamma_5 \psi_\nu$; '$+$' for $\psi_\nu = -\gamma_5 \psi_\nu$). By Fourier transformation, the above expression becomes

$$H \psi_\nu = \mp (\sigma \cdot p) \psi_\nu \qquad \dots (37)$$

where H is the Hamiltonian operator, or

$$E = \mp (\boldsymbol{\sigma} \cdot \mathbf{p}) = \mp |p| \sigma p \qquad \dots (38)$$

where E is the eigenvalue of the energy state, the positive or negative sign of which is determined by the projection of the spin operator onto the momentum vector. One can also define helicity here as

$$\text{Helicity} = \frac{\boldsymbol{\sigma} \cdot \mathbf{p}}{|p|} \qquad \dots (39)$$

($+1$ for right-handed; -1 for left-handed). The physical

---

* This is true only for unquantized field. Weyl's original version (1929) of the two-component theory was treated before Dirac put forward his theory of holes and therefore as unquantized Dirac fields. Pauli's remarks on the parity violation of Weyl's original version in this *Handbuch* article (1933) were made in that light and are therefore correct. Later on, Majorana (1937) introduced his two-component theory of the neutrino which is a quantized field theory with the identity assumption between the neutrino and the anti-neutrino, $\nu \equiv \bar{\nu}$. In this latter case, the two-component free particle no longer violates the parity law. It is the interaction and the interaction only which violates parity. The relationship between the two versions (Weyl,[2] Landau,[25a] Lee and Yang[25a] and Salam[25a] on the one hand and Majorana[25b] on the other) has been fully discussed by several authors.[25c]

implication of equation (38) means that for a definite momentum p, the particle has two distinct states. These two distinct positive and negative energy states exhibit opposite alignments between the spin direction and momentum vector, and behave like right-handed and left-handed screws. Furthermore, if the axial vector interaction is the correct one, we have $\psi_\nu = \gamma_5 \psi_\nu$ from ^{60}Co experimental results. Then from $E = -(\sigma \cdot p)$, the positive energy state as represented by the neutrino will have the spin σ and momentum vector p aligned anti-parallel (a left-handed screw) and the negative energy state of the particle, known as the anti-neutrino, will be deduced as a right-handed screw. From the 'hole theory' interpretation, the anti-neutrino is considered as a hole in a sea of such right-handed neutrinos in negative energy states. The hole (anti-neutrino) must possess the opposite spin and momentum and therefore the hole in axial vector interaction is right-handed. The helicities of the neutrino and anti-neutrino for the tensor interaction will be just opposite to those in the axial vector interaction as given by the lower relation in equation (38).

Thus a massless neutrino has only two components and the observed experimental results require the helicity of the neutrino to be negative if the G–T interaction is axial vector and positive if it is the tensor interaction.

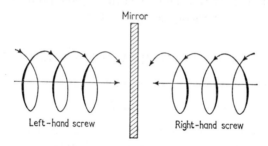

Fig. 3. Mirror reflection of a right-handed and a left-handed screw sense.

The two-component theory of the neutrino violates P and C invariance separately. A left-handed neutrino looks into a mirror and finds a right-handed neutrino, but according to the two-component theory of the neutrino, there is no such possible state (see Fig. 3).

The charge conjugate of a left-handed neutrino is a left-handed anti-neutrino. However, the only allowed anti-neutrino state is right-handed. Thus the charge conjugate of the neutrino state is not an allowed state. This is a clear-cut violation of invariance of charge conjugation. In conclusion, the two-component neutrino violates P and C separately.

All physicists accepted the validity of parity conservation in all interactions until 1956, when the problem of K-meson decay arose to baffle the experts. Earlier, towards the end of 1956, in responding to the parity question raised by Lee and Yang, Landau and Salam independently examined the implications of the possible existence of the two-component neutrino. Landau particularly emphasized in his paper the possible broader symmetry with combined CP operation;* that is, the symmetry is retained under combined charge conjugation and parity operation. Operating with PC changes the particle to anti-particle and reverses helicity. This leads to a possible state under this theory so PC is not violated. In the case of beta decay, then, the invariance of the combined inversion CP implies that the β^+ decay of anti-^{60}Co would then have an angular distribution exactly opposite to that of ^{60}Co.

Until the summer of 1957, Pauli's attitude towards the two-component theory of the neutrino had been very sceptical. As the experimental evidence in favour of this theory mounted and the peculiar two-component formulation became capable of an interesting generalization in all weak interactions, he conceded in the late fall of 1957 that he now entirely gave up his resistance to the two-component theory of the neutrino.

8. LAW OF CONSERVATION OF LEPTONS

The nuclear beta decay can be written as

$$p + e^- \leftrightarrow n + \nu$$

in which one lepton is absorbed and one is created. It suggests that, for proper choice of particle and anti-particle, the total number of leptons in the decay process is always conserved. This prompted Konopinski and Mahmoud[26] to suggest the law of conservation of leptons in order to explain the non-occurrence of certain decay processes. The law states that if a leptonic number is assigned to each particle, then the sum of leptonic numbers

* In an invited paper presented by C. N. Yang at the International Congress on Theoretical Physics, held at the University of Washington (September 17–21, 1956), it was already speculated that by simultaneously going from one coordinate system to the other and switching to the anti-world, i.e. replacing π^+ by π^-, protons by anti-protons, etc., symmetry is regained. (*Rev. mod. Phys.* **29**, 201, 1957.)

must be conserved in all reactions. The assignments generally agreed upon are

lepton l = same (say +1)   for e^-, μ^-, ν (particles)

$\qquad l = -1$ $\qquad\qquad$ for e^+, μ^+, $\bar{\nu}$ (anti-particles)

$\qquad l = 0$ $\qquad\qquad$ for π, γ, K and all heavy particles.

The ν or $\bar{\nu}$ expected in various decays are shown in the following equations:

$$(1)\ n \rightarrow p + e^- + \bar{\nu};\quad p \rightarrow n + e^+ + \nu$$

$$(2)\ \pi^+ \rightarrow \mu^+ + \nu;\quad \pi^- \rightarrow \mu^- + \bar{\nu}$$

$$(3)\ \mu^+ \rightarrow e^+ + \nu + \bar{\nu};\quad \mu^- \rightarrow e^- + \nu + \bar{\nu} \qquad \ldots (40)$$

$$(4)\ \mu^- + p \rightarrow n + \nu;\quad \mu^+ + n \rightarrow p + \bar{\nu}$$

$$(5)\ K^+ \rightarrow \mu^+ + \nu;\quad K^- \rightarrow \mu^- + \bar{\nu}$$

$$(6)\ \pi^+ \rightarrow e^+ + \nu;\quad \pi^- \rightarrow e^- + \bar{\nu}$$

The confirmation of the assignments given by these decays should constitute a strong proof of the law of conservation of leptons; particularly if the helicities of these two neutrinos are opposite, then the predictions of these decay processes become unique. Experimental evidence bears out nearly all of these predictions.

It is true that the most general approach to the theory of beta decay is to assume neither lepton conservation nor the two-component neutrino. This was discussed in great detail by Pauli and others[27] early in 1957. Pauli's attitude towards a law so fundamental as that of lepton conservation was extremely cautious and reserved. However, he expressed his belief in its correctness on many occasions. The general form would be given by

$$H = g \sum_i (\bar{\psi}_P O_i \psi_N)\{\bar{\psi}_e O_i[(C_i + C_i' \gamma_5)\psi_\nu$$
$$+ (D_i + D_i' \gamma_5)\psi_\nu{}^C]\} + \text{Herm. Conj.} \qquad \ldots (41)$$

where $\psi_\nu{}^C$ is the charge conjugate of ψ_ν and D_i and D_i' are the coupling constants for the charge conjugate term. For the single beta decay process, the introduction of non-conservation of leptons results only in replacing the $C_i{}^{\star}C_i'$ term by $(C_i{}^{\star}C_i' + D_i{}^{\star}D_i')$ and therefore no measurements could distinguish between them. Even in neutrinoless double beta decay and Davis's neutrino capture experiment, null results are still anticipated based purely on the requirement of the neutrino helicity in spite of the non-conservation of leptons (see section 15). The relaxation on lepton conservation will have an effect of not more than

18 per cent on the cross-section of neutrino capture by protons
(Cowan and Reines' experiment) but this is beyond the precision
of present techniques. In what follows, lepton conservation will
be assumed to be correct and experimental evidence will bear out
its forcefulness.

9. LONGITUDINAL POLARIZATION OF BETA PARTICLES[28]

Since parity is not conserved, the expectation value of the
pseudoscalar quantity $(\sigma \cdot p_e)$ formed from the measured spin and
momentum vector of the electron may not be zero. In other
words, the decay electrons from unpolarized nuclei can be longitudinally polarized. The results on the longitudinal polarization
of beta particles are startling and simple. The conclusion which
is generally agreed upon is that the β^- particles emitted in radioactive decay exhibit negative helicity (σ and p antiparallel) and
the β^+ particles the positive helicity (σ and p parallel). For
relativistic energies $(v/c \cong 1)$, we have practically completely
polarized electron and positron beams. These results are again in
agreement with the predictions of the two-component neutrino
theory. This is easily understood from the following arguments:
from

$$(\bar{\psi}_p O_i \psi_N)[\bar{\psi}_e O_i (1 \pm \gamma_5)\psi_\nu] + \text{Herm. Conj.} \qquad \ldots . (42)$$

in the lepton covariant term, $\bar{\psi}_e$ can be expressed by $\psi_e^\dagger \lambda_4$, so we
have

$$\psi_e^\dagger \gamma_4 O_i (1 \pm \gamma_5)\psi_\nu \qquad \ldots . (43)$$

('+' for V, A; '−' for S, T, P). The signs for V and S are only
assumed for this derivation because there are no polarized nuclei
experiments to guide us. On the other hand, the measured
helicity of the electrons will yield information on the correlation
of the beta interaction and neutrino helicity. However

$$\gamma_4 \gamma_5 = -\gamma_5 \gamma_4$$

and

$$\gamma_5 O_i = -O_i \gamma_5 \quad \text{where} \quad O_i \text{ is for } V, A$$

$$\gamma_5 O_i = O_i \gamma_5 \quad \text{where} \quad O_i \text{ is for } S, T, P$$

therefore

$$\psi_e^\dagger \gamma_4 O_i (1 \pm \gamma_5)\psi_e = \psi_e^\dagger (1 + \gamma_5)\gamma_4 O_i \psi_\nu \qquad \ldots . (44)$$

Note here that it is $(1 + \gamma_5)$ for all five types of interactions if the choices of equation (43) are made. To write down its Hermitian conjugate, we have

$$\psi_{v'}{}^{\dagger} O_i \gamma_4 (1 + \gamma_5) \psi_e \qquad \dots (45)$$

For relativistic energies, $cp \gg m_0 c^2$, the electron is effectively massless. Since we have shown for the zero mass case that $1/2$ $(1 + \gamma_5)$ is a projection operator to affect complete left longitudinal polarization; thus we have left-handed electrons for all five interactions. If $(v/c)_e < 1$, then the assumption of $m_e = 0$ is not valid. In that case the right and left part of the electron wave function are not uncoupled. In other words, $(1 + \gamma_5)\psi_e$ is no longer the eigenstate of the Hamiltonian. Naturally the above conclusion based on $m_e = 0$ is no longer valid. It is quite obvious physically that the polarization of the electron must vanish at zero electron velocity because there is no momentum direction to which the spin can refer.

However, using the conventional method of projecting the final states of the electron on to eigenstates of $\sigma_e \cdot \mathbf{p}$ and evaluating the various traces, one will get the simple expression of the $\beta^{\mp}$ polarization:

$$\text{(Polarization)} = \langle \sigma_e \cdot \mathbf{p} \rangle = -\frac{v}{c} \frac{E}{|E|}$$

The general expression for a linear combination of beta interactions involving C_i and $C_i'S$ is

(Polarization)$_\beta^{\mp}$

$$= \pm \frac{v}{c} \frac{2 \, \text{Re}[(C_S C_S'{}^{\star} - C_V C_V'{}^{\star}) M_F{}^2 + (C_T C_T'{}^{\star} - C_A C_A'{}^{\star})|M_{GT}|^2]}{(|C_S|^2 + |C_V|^2 + |C_S'|^2 + |C_V'|^2)|M_F|^2 +}$$
$$(|C_T|^2 + |C_A|^2 + |C_A'|^2 + |C_T'|^2)|M_{GT}|^2$$

$$\dots (46)$$

If we assign $C_S = -C_S'$; $C_T = -C_T'$ (for left-handed anti-neutrino) or $C_V = C_V'$; $C_A = C_A'$ (for right-handed anti-neutrino), then

$$\text{(Polarization)}_{\beta^{\mp}} = \mp v/c \qquad \dots (47)$$

The first to observe this longitudinal polarization from beta decay was the Frauenfelder group.[28d] They used a ^{60}Co source and measured $P \simeq -v/c$, which is in good accord with the assigned neutrino helicity from the polarized ^{60}Co experiment. Subsequent polarization measurements on pure Fermi transitions ^{34}Cl and ^{66}Ga [28e] and on mixed transitions ^{13}N and ^{198}Au [28] all confirm the assignments of neutrino helicity as given above (left-handed neutrino in V and A, $\psi_\nu = \gamma_5\psi_\nu$, and right-handed neutrino in S and T, $\psi_\nu = -\gamma_5\psi_\nu$).

At present there are three major methods[28] being used for the determination of electron polarization: (1) Coulomb scattering from heavy nuclei (Mott scattering), (2) circular polarization of forward Bremsstrahlung or annihilation radiation, and (3) free electron–electron scattering (Møller or Bhabha scattering). Working with the polarized beam of beta particles for the last few decades, the firm belief in right–left asymmetry had prevented us from ever discovering it.[29] The polarization experiments are difficult and time consuming. Many systematic uncertainties in the measurements, such as the backscattering effect, depolarization effect, instrumental asymmetry and the screen correction factor, etc., are rather difficult to assess. Probably it is fair to say that in the high energy region of $v/c \geqslant 0\cdot6$, the polarization is nearly v/c with an accuracy of not better than 10 per cent. Below $v/c = 0\cdot6$ very few results have been reported and more work is highly desirable.

10. THE β–γ (CIRCULAR POLARIZATION) CORRELATION[28]

It is quite obvious from the observed beta asymmetry distribution of polarized nuclei that the beta decay should leave the nucleus partly polarized with respect to the direction in which the beta particle is detected. If a gamma-ray follows immediately after the beta decay, it should have circular polarization proportional to the cosine of the angle between the beta particle and gamma-ray. The correlation for the most frequent decay sequence such as

$$J \xrightarrow[\beta]{\text{Allowed}} J' \xrightarrow[\gamma]{2^L \text{ pole } \gamma\text{-radiation}} J''$$

can be expressed by

$$W(\theta) = 1 + \tau A \frac{v}{c} \cos\theta \qquad \dots (48)$$

where $\tau = +$ right circular polarization or

$$P(\theta) = A \frac{v}{c} \cos\theta$$

where $\tau = -$ left circular polarization where

$$
A = \frac{1}{L+1} \left\{ \mu_{JJ'} \left[\pm \operatorname{Re}(C_T{}^\star C_T{}' - C_A{}^\star C_A{}') \right. \right.
$$

$$
\left. - \frac{Ze^2}{\hbar cp} \operatorname{Im}(C_T{}^\star C_A{}' + C_T{}'^\star C_A) \right]
$$

$$
\times |M_{GT}|^2 + \delta_{JJ'} \left(\frac{J+1}{J} \right)^{1/2} \left[\operatorname{Re}(C_T{}^\star C_S{}' + C_T{}'^\star C_S \right.
$$

$$
- C_A{}^\star C_V{}' - C_A{}'^\star C_V)
$$

$$
\pm \frac{Ze^2}{\hbar cp} \operatorname{Im}(C_A{}^\star C_S{}' + C_A{}'^\star C_S - C_T{}^\star C_V{}' - C_T{}'^\star C_V) \right]
$$

$$
\left. \times |M_F| \cdot |M_{GT}| \right\} x \frac{2}{\xi(1 + bmc^2/W)} \qquad \ldots \ldots (49)
$$

$$
\mu_{JJ'} = \begin{cases} 1 & J \to J' = J-1 \\ -\dfrac{1}{J} & J \to J' = J \\ -\dfrac{J+2}{J+1} & J \to J' = J+1 \end{cases}
$$

This method yields the same type of information as that of beta asymmetry from polarized nuclei, but it is easier to carry out although far less sensitive. On the other hand, because the applicability of the present technique of nuclear orientation is very limited, only very few beta emitters can be substantially polarized. Therefore the β–γ (circular polarization) correlation method has been extremely useful. Its greatest contribution is to yield information on the interference term between Fermi and G–T interactions as represented by the term

$$
\operatorname{Re}(C_T{}^\star C_S{}' + C_T{}'^\star C_S - C_A{}^\star C_V{}' - C_A{}'^\star C_V)|M_{GT}| \cdot |M_F| \quad \ldots (50)
$$

This type of interference was indeed observed and attained nearly a maximum. Two important conclusions can be drawn from this: one is that the dominant combination can only be (S, T) or (V, A) and not (V, T) or (S, A); the second is that the invariance of time reversal probably is still intact, or at most its violation is small. The circular polarization of the gamma-ray can be analysed with a cylindrical electromagnet which can be magnetized to saturation either parallel or anti-parallel to the photon direction. The principle of this analysis is based on the existence of a spin dependent part of the Compton cross-section of circularly polarized photons and is treated in detail by Gunst and Page.[30]

Schopper[31] first applied this β–γ (circular) correlation method to ^{60}Co and obtained the parameter $A \cong 1/3$. This is in excellent agreement with the conclusion derived from the polarized ^{60}Co experiment; that is, $C_T = -C_T$ or $C_A = C_A'$. When this method was applied to ^{22}Na, which is a pure G–T positron emitter $(3^+ \rightarrow 2^+)$, the sign of the circular polarization was found to be opposite to that of the electron emitter ^{60}Co as theoretically predicted. Many beautiful β–γ (circularly polarized) correlation studies[32] on the mixed (G–T and Fermi) transitions such as ^{46}Sc, ^{198}Au, etc., by Boehm et al.[32] showed nearly maximum amount of interference between G–T and Fermi interactions. This evidence strongly ruled out a pure VT or SA combination. However, none of these experiments has an accuracy of much better than 20 per cent of the observed effect.

11. CORRELATIONS BETWEEN THE HELICITIES OF LEPTONS AND BETA INTERACTIONS

In the foregoing sections we have deduced theoretically the correlations between the helicities of leptons and beta interactions as summarized in *Table III*. These relations can be easily understood with the aid of Fig. 4.

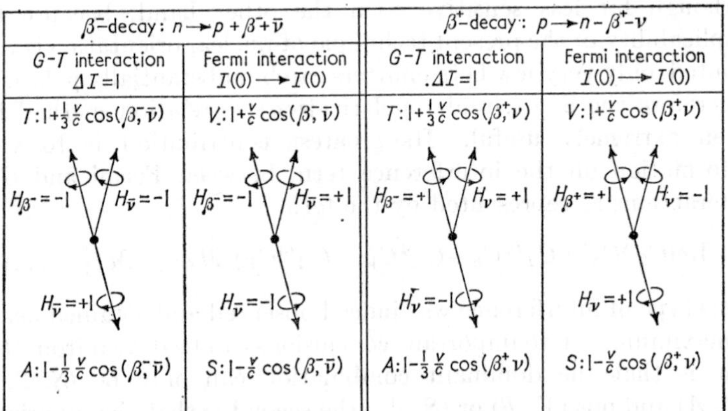

Fig. 4. Correlations of neutrino helicites and β interactions.

In an allowed Gamow–Teller beta interaction, the angular momentum carried away by the leptons is one unit. In the tensor interaction both leptons are emitted preferentially in the same direction. Since the electron is found to possess negative helicity (left-handed screw), the anti-neutrino must have the same helicity. On the other hand, in the axial vector interaction, the electron and the anti-neutrino are emitted preferentially in opposite directions; so positive helicity is predicted for the anti-neutrino and negative helicity for the neutrino. The helicity of the neutrino observed in the electron capture process of ^{152}Eu* (see section 12) is indeed negative and therefore supports the axial vector interaction. In a similar manner, one can figure out the helicity of the anti-neutrino for scalar and vector interactions as shown in *Table III*.

This table also points out two significant conclusions: First, the much used Fierz interference term between S and V expressed as $(C_S C_V^\star + C_S' C_V'^\star)$ and A and T such as $(C_T C_A^\star + C_T' C_A'^\star)$ now automatically vanishes because the neutrino or anti-neutrino associated with S and T or V and A has opposite helicity; therefore no interference occurs. Secondly, and for the same reason, combinations of (V and T) and (S and A) will not result in interference between Fermi and Gamow–Teller terms. The observation of maximum amount of interference between G–T and Fermi interactions in neutron, ^{46}Sc and ^{198}Au, rules out a pure VT or SA combination.

12. DETERMINATION OF BETA INTERACTIONS FROM PARITY EXPERIMENTS

From the original polarized ^{60}Co experiment, which strongly suggested the possibility of two-component neutrinos, the theoretical deduction is that the anti-neutrino has positive helicity for axial vector and negative helicity for tensor interaction. The subsequent results from the investigation of electron polarization from beta decay are completely in agreement with this conclusion. Consequently, the determination of the helicity of a neutrino assumed a crucial role of decision on beta interactions, as can be seen from *Table III*.

A. Electron Capture Process in ^{152}Eu* [33]–Neutrino Helicity

In an electron capture process, a neutrino and the recoil nucleus are emitted in opposite directions.

$$e^- + p \rightarrow n + \nu$$

If the capture process is followed by the emission of a gamma-ray and the spin and parity changes are favourable as shown in the following decay process

$$A(0^-) \xrightarrow{e^- - \text{capture}} B^\star(1^-) \xrightarrow{\gamma\text{-ray}} B(0^+)$$

10+P.M.V.

then by applying the conservation laws of momentum and angular momentum, one can deduce a simple correlation that the helicity of the downward gamma-ray will be the same as that of the upward neutrino as shown in Fig. 5; so the problem of determining the neutrino helicity becomes that of measuring the circular polarization of the gamma-ray. However, to select only those downward gamma-rays following the emission of the upward neutrinos, only the resonantly scattered gamma-ray should be detected. Furthermore, the gamma-ray must have an energy comparable to that of the neutrino and the life-time of the excited level $B^\star$ must be very short ($\sim 10^{-14}$ sec) in order to permit the use of solid material.

The requirements were indeed strict, but the radio-isotope ^{152}Eu* seemed heaven-sent to do this job. Goldhaber, Grodzins and Sunyar [33] knew of this radio-isotope ^{152}Eu* from their previous investigations and realized that it has a rare $E1$ transition and fulfils all the requirements stated above. By measuring the circular polarization of the downward gamma-rays from ^{152}Eu* which are resonantly scattered by Sm, they found that the helicity of the gamma-ray is negative ($H = -0.67 \pm 0.10$)! From this result one concludes that the helicity of the neutrino in electron capture is negative and therefore the Gamow–Teller interaction in electron capture is dominantly axial vector and not tensor.

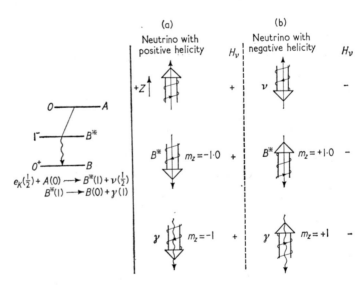

Fig. 5. Helicity of recoil nucleus and gamma-ray following K capture.

B. Beta Decay of Polarized Neutrons [34, 28]

Using a beam of highly polarized (87 per cent) neutrons, Burgy *et al.* determined: (1) the angular distribution of the decay electrons with respect to the neutron spin, and (2) the anti-neutrino distribution with respect to the neutron spin. The detector arrangement for the experiment is shown in Fig. 6. Their results can be represented by

$$W(\theta_{\sigma_n \cdot p_e}) = 1 - (0 \cdot 11 \pm 0 \cdot 02) \cos \theta_{\sigma_n \cdot p_e}$$

where $-(0 \cdot 11 \pm 0 \cdot 02)$ is the value of the asymmetry parameter A and $W(\theta_{\sigma_n \cdot p_\nu}) = 1 + (0 \cdot 88 \pm 0 \cdot 15) \cos \theta_{\sigma_n \cdot p_\nu}$ where $+(0 \cdot 88 \pm 0 \cdot 15)$ is the value of the asymmetry parameter B. These two experiments not only corroborate the existence of a difference in mirror reflection of the neutron decay process, but also their quantitative analysis of the value A and B agrees uniquely with the theoretical prediction of a linear combination of $V-A$.

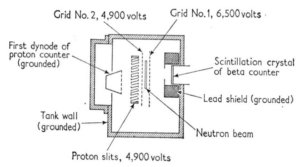

Fig. 6. Detector arrangement for experiment on anti-neutrino distribution with respect to neutron spin.

Look back at the history of the theory of beta decay. It has been filled with surprises and excitement. Now, after a period of nearly 60 years of continuous investigation, finally along comes the non-conservation of parity. These two (classical beta theory and non-conservation of parity) joined forces in reaching the conclusions on the beta interaction. However, we must caution here that whether there is any small mixture of (S, T) in beta interaction is still unknown and its further clarification is highly desired.

13. MASS OF THE NEUTRINO

All experimental evidence indicates that the rest mass of the neutrino must be very small, therefore it is justifiable to assume zero rest mass of the neutrino for simplicity in the Kurie plot.

10*

Actually, the precise shape of the allowed beta spectrum in the vicinity of its upper limit depends on the rest mass of the neutrino. If the rest mass of the neutrino is different from zero and equal to m_ν, the electron distribution then becomes

$$P_0(E)\,dE_\beta \sim \rho(E_\beta)\left[1+\frac{\alpha m_\nu/m_0}{E_\beta(E_{max}-E_\beta+m_\nu/m_0)}\right]dE_\beta \quad \ldots(51)$$

where

$$\rho(E_\beta) = P_\beta E_\beta\left(E_{max}-E_\beta+\frac{m_\nu}{m_0}\right)\left[\left(E_{max}-E_\beta+\frac{m_\nu}{m_0}\right)^2-\frac{m_\nu^2}{m_0^2}\right]^{1/2}$$

($\alpha=-1$ if the electron and neutrino wave functions have the same parity; $+1$ if they have opposite parities).

The relativistic spinor term[35] involving α arises from the summation over spins of the emitted particles. The parameter α may vary between -1 and $+1$ according to: (1) the definite combinations of beta interactions, and (2) the relative parities of neutrino and e^- involved. Because the value of α was not known in the old days, one could only set an upper limit on m_ν for possible values of α varying from -1 to $+1$. For instance, the m_ν estimated from the ^{3}H beta spectrum measured by using a spherical electrostatic integral spectrograph with energy resolution of 0·7 per cent by Hamilton, Alford and Gross[36] gave an upper limit of 500 eV or 150 eV depending on $\alpha=-1$ or $+1$ respectively. In Langer and Moffat's study of the ^{3}H spectrum, the neutrino mass limits are 700 eV or 150 eV depending on $\alpha=-1$ or $\alpha=+1$.

We shall see that this ambiguity is now removed by parity non-conservation in beta decay. The α factor with parity conserving coupling C_i and parity non-conserving coupling C_i' becomes[38]

$$\alpha = \frac{|M_F|^2(-|C_V|^2+|C_V'|^2)+|M_{GT}|^2(-|C_A|^2+|C_A'|^2)}{|M_F|^2(|C_V|^2|C_V'|^2)+|M_{GT}|^2(|C_A|^2|C_A'|^2)} \quad \ldots(52)$$

since parity experiments revealed that $C_A=C_A'$, $C_V=C_V'$, and probably $C_S=C_S'=C_T=C_T'=0$, therefore $\alpha=0$. The upper limit of neutrino mass is now comfortably reduced to 200 eV or 2/5,000 MeV; also, it is not inconsistent with $m_\nu=0$.

14. NEUTRINOS AND ANTI-NEUTRINOS

The classical theory of the neutrino may be formulated in a way similar to that for electrons; that is, by postulating negative energy states which are almost always filled. Holes or vacancies in the negative energy neutrino sea are called anti-neutrinos. However, the difference between the neutrino and the anti-neutrino cannot be detected by electric charge as it can for electrons and positrons. The only possibility of distinguishing them is if they have magnetic moments equal and opposite. Under this circumstance neutrino and anti-neutrino are distinguishable and are called the Dirac neutrinos. The upper limit of the magnetic moment of the neutrino is less than 10^{-7} Bohr magneton from latest experiments.[39] In the classical neutrino theory if a neutral particle possesses no magnetic moment, then there is no place for its anti-particle in the solutions of Dirac equation. There the neutrino and the anti-neutrino are indistinguishable and known as Majorana neutrinos.[40] The formulation of a single beta decay with Dirac or Majorana neutrino leads to the same conclusions as far as the energy and angular distribution are concerned; so all the experimental evidence listed above gives no clue to the question of Dirac or Majorana neutrinos. Fortunately, there are several experiments, and the outcome of their findings will shed some light on this question. This leads us to double beta decay and neutrino-capture reactions.

15. DOUBLE BETA DECAY [41]

Consider an isobaric triplet (N, Z), $(N \pm 1, Z \mp 1)$ $(N \pm 2, Z \mp 2)$ with the intervening isobar of higher mass than either of the pair. This situation only occurs between a pair of stable even Z even N isobars and with an odd Z odd N isobar as the intermediate state. For example, ${}^{48}_{20}\text{Ca}_{28} \rightarrow {}^{48}_{22}\text{Ti}_{26}$, ${}^{150}_{60}\text{Nd}_{90} \rightarrow {}^{150}_{62}\text{Sm}_{88}$ etc. The direct decay of one of these to the other via the intermediate isobar is energetically forbidden. The nucleus (N, Z) can decay to $(N \pm 2, Z \mp 2)$ by double beta decay. The theory of Dirac neutrino requires that four particles must be emitted in the process; that is, two neutrinos (or anti-neutrinos) must accompany the emission of two positrons (or electrons); consequently, the energy distribution of the sum of the two positrons (or electrons) will be continuous. If the neutrinos were of the Majorana type, then a neutrino might be emitted into a virtual state with the emission of the first electron and then re-absorbed in the subsequent emission of the second electron. The energy sum of the two positrons (electrons) will be unique and equal to the energy available in the double beta decay. This feature would improve the sensitivity of its detection greatly. Since energy is only conserved between the initial (N, Z) and the final $(N \pm 2, Z \mp 2)$ states, but not in the intermediate state, the virtual neutrino may assume any energy up to $\cong 35$ MeV, where its de Broglie wavelength becomes short compared to the nuclear radius. The volume of phase space accessible to the intermediate state is therefore very much larger than that for the Dirac neutrinos and hence the greatly increased transition probability for Majorana neutrinos. The theory for double beta decay was investigated in detail by Goeppert–Meyer, Furry, Konopinski and Primakoff.[41]

The exact expression for the life-time in double beta decay is rather involved. The approximate forms as given by Primakoff[41] are

$(T_{1/2})_0$ for neutrinoless double beta decay

$$(T_{1/2})_0 \cong 1 \times 10^{(15\pm2)} \left(\frac{60}{Z}\right)^2 \left(1 - e^{\mp 2\pi Z/137}\right)^2 \left(\frac{A}{150}\right)^{2/3} \left(\frac{8}{W^{(0)}}\right)^6 \text{ years}$$

$$\ldots\text{(53a)}$$

and $(T_{1/2})_{\nu,\nu}$ for two neutrino double beta decay

$$(T_{1/2})_{\nu,\nu}^{\text{Fermi}} \cong 9(T_{1/2})_{\nu,\nu}^{G-T} \cong 6 \times 10^{(19\pm2)} \left(\frac{60}{Z}\right)^2 (1 - e^{\mp 2\pi Z/137})^2$$

$$\times \left(\frac{8}{W^{(0)}}\right)^{10} \text{ years} \quad \ldots\text{(53b)}$$

where $W^{(0)}$ is the kinetic energy release in double beta decay in units of mc^2. The ± 2 in the exponent is an estimate of the overall uncertainty in our calculation of the nuclear matrix elements.

It is interesting to note that for comparable $W^{(0)}$, Z, and nuclear matrix elements, the half-life for the neutrinoless double beta decay is a factor 10^5–10^6 shorter than that for two-neutrino double beta decay. This factor is essentially equal to the fourth power of the energy ratio $\sim [35 \text{ MeV}/1 \text{ MeV}]^4 \cong 1 \cdot 5 \times 10^5$ between that of the virtual neutrinos in the neutrinoless double beta decay to that of the real neutrinos in the two-neutrino double beta decay.

The existence of the conservation law of leptons, together with the two-component neutrino, limits the possible alternatives and demands that the half-life be that of the two-neutrino double beta decay rate. Experimentally no electron line of energy equal to the sum of the two disintegration energies has ever been observed. The observed upper limit of the rate of double beta decay also strongly rejects double beta decay with no neutrinos emitted and favours that with the accompanying two-neutrino emission. *Table III* lists the pertinent data on a few known possible double beta decay transitions.

In the days when the law of parity was believed to be valid for beta decay, the absence of neutrinoless double beta decay was used as a strong argument for both Dirac neutrinos $\nu \neq \bar{\nu}$, and for the validity of conservation of leptons. However, the violation of parity in beta decay revealed 'the two-component neutrino' type coupling which restricts the lepton polarizations and therefore unfortunately introduces a new twist in the meaning of distinguishability between neutrino and anti-neutrino. In one sense, the absence of neutrinoless double beta decay gives good

TABLE III

Double Beta Decay Experiments

Transition	Kinetic energy release (MeV)	$T_{1/2}$ (in years)			Ref.
		Exp.	Theoretical* two-neutrino	neutrino-less	
$^{48}_{20}\text{Ca} \rightarrow {}^{48}_{22}\text{Ti}$	$4 \cdot 3 \pm 0 \cdot 1$	$> 2 \times 10^{18}$ $> 6 \times 10^{18}$	$4 \times 10^{20 \pm 2}$	$3 \times 10^{15 \pm 2}$	†
$^{150}_{60}\text{Nd} \rightarrow {}^{150}_{62}\text{Sm}$	$3 \cdot 7 \pm 0 \cdot 1$	$> 4 \times 10^{18}$	$2 \times 10^{20 \pm 2}$	$2 \times 10^{15 \pm 2}$	‡
$^{96}_{40}\text{Zr} \rightarrow {}^{96}_{42}\text{Mo}$	$3 \cdot 4 \pm 0 \cdot 3$	$> 2 \times 10^{16}$	$1 \times 10^{21 \pm 2}$	$6 \times 10^{15 \pm 2}$	§
$^{130}_{52}\text{Te} \rightarrow {}^{130}_{54}\text{Xe}$	$3 \cdot 2 \pm 0 \cdot 1$	$= 1 \cdot 4 \times 10^{21}$	$2 \times 10^{21 \pm 2}$	$8 \times 10^{15 \pm 2}$	‖
$^{116}_{48}\text{Cs} \rightarrow {}^{116}_{50}\text{Sn}$	$2 \cdot 6 \pm 0 \cdot 1$	$> 10^{17}$	$6 \times 10^{21 \pm 2}$	$2 \times 10^{16 \pm 2}$	¶
$^{100}_{42}\text{Mo} \rightarrow {}^{100}_{44}\text{Ru}$	$2 \cdot 3 \pm 0 \cdot 2$	$> 10^{17}$	$4 \times 10^{22 \pm 2}$	$4 \times 10^{16 \pm 2}$	**
$^{124}_{50}\text{Sn} \rightarrow {}^{124}_{52}\text{Te}$	$2 \cdot 0 \pm 0 \cdot 2$	$> 10^{17}$	$4 \times 10^{22 \pm 2}$	$5 \times 10^{16 \pm 2}$	††
$^{238}_{92}\text{U} \rightarrow {}^{238}_{94}\text{Pu}$	$1 \cdot 1$	$> 6 \times 10^{18}$	$3 \times 10^{25 \pm 2}$	$2 \times 10^{18 \pm 2}$	‡‡

---

* An excellent summary of double beta decay by H. Primakoff and S. P. Rosen (Washington University, 1958), to be published.

† ^{48}Ca: Awschalom, M., *Phys. Rev.* **101**, 1041, 1956: Dobrokhotov, Lazarenko and Luk'yanov, CERN High Energy Physics Conference, 1958

‡ ^{150}Nd: Cowan, Harrison, Langer and Reines, *Nuovo Cim.* **3**, 649, 1956

§ ^{96}Zr: McCarthy, J. A., *Phys. Rev.* **90**, 853, 1953: Awschalom, M., *Phys. Rev.* **101**, 1041, 1956

‖ ^{130}Te: Inghram, M. G. and Reynold, J. H., *Phys. Rev.* **76**, 1265, 1959; **78**, 822, 1950: Hayden, R. J. and Inghram, M. G., *Nat. Bur. Stand. Circ.* **522**, 189, 1953: Kohman, T. P., AEC Report NYO-3626, 1954: Selig, H., *Ph.D. Thesis*, Carnegie Institute of Technology, 1954; *AEC Report NYO-6626*

¶ ^{116}Cd: Winter, R. G., *Phys. Rev.* **99**, 88, 1955: Detoeuf, J. F. and Moch, R., *J. Phys. Radium* **16**, No. 12, 987, 1955: Fremlin, J. H. and Walters, M. C., *Proc. Phys. Soc. Lond.* A **65**, 911, 1952

** ^{100}Mo : See Fremlin and Walters in ¶ and Kohman and Selig in ‖.

†† ^{124}Sn: Kalkstein, M. L. and Libby, W. F., *Phys. Rev.* **85**, 368, 1952: Fireman, E. L. and Schwarzer, D., *Phys. Rev.* **86**, 451, 1952: McCarthy, J. A., *Phys. Rev.* **90**, 853, 1953

‡‡ ^{238}U: Levine, Ghiorso and Seaborg, *Phys. Rev.* **77**, 296, 1950

evidence for the conservation of lepton and Dirac neutrinos $\nu \not\equiv \bar{\nu}$. On the other hand, one could also admit the other extremes that the number of leptons is not conserved and the neutrinos are Majorana type $\nu \equiv \bar{\nu}$; therefore there are two different spin states of a Majorana neutrino. However, the beta interaction is such as to cause the right screw state to appear in negation emission and the left screw state to appear in positron emission. The absence of the neutrinoless double beta decay is consistent with the require-ment of the neutrino polarization and has nothing to do with the neutrino–anti-neutrino distinction. Fortunately, neutrinos are also emitted in π–μ–e decays, in μ-capture and in some decay modes of K-mesons; all the evidence from these various decay modes is in good agreement with the ideas of two-component neutrinos and conservation of leptons. For simplicity we may forsake the second possible alternative and assume Dirac type neutrinos unless later more extensive developments demand otherwise.

16. INVERSE BETA PROCESSES

In the same year, after the publication of the Fermi theory of beta decay, Bethe and Peierls[42] pointed out the possibility of 'inverse beta decay' based on the assumed interaction in Fermi theory. In inverse beta decay a nucleus captures a neutrino or anti-neutrino and simultaneously ejects an electron or positron as

$$(N, Z)^{+\nu}_{+\bar{\nu}} \rightarrow (N \pm 1, Z \mp 1) + e^{\mp}$$

The cross-section for the inverse beta reaction is expected to be extremely small, 10^{-44} cm^2, because of the characteristic slowness of beta interactions. It was only after the intense anti-neutrino flux from nuclear reactors became available that the intense search for so rare occurrences began to be taken up seriously.

A. Anti-neutrino Capture by Protons[43]

The inverse of neutron decay

$$n \rightarrow p + e^- + \bar{\nu} \qquad \qquad \ldots.(54a)$$

can be written as anti-neutrino capture by protons

$$\nu + p \rightarrow n + e^+ \qquad \qquad \ldots.(54b)$$

by merely transposing the e^- to the left side of equation (54a) and then reversing the direction of the reaction. The capture of an anti-neutrino should result in the prompt ejection of a positron and a neutron. The positron should carry all the surplus neutrino energy above threshold but the neutron have a recoil energy only up to a few keV. From the classical theory of beta decay, the cross-section for the inverse reaction can be obtained and expressed in terms of the *ft*-value of neutron decay and the energy of the positron emitted as : [44]

$$\sigma_{\text{inverse } \beta\text{-decay}} = \frac{g^2(|C_V|^2 + 3|C_A|^2)}{2\pi\hbar^4 C^3} p_e W_e \qquad \ldots(55)$$

substituting

$$(ft)_n = \frac{ln2 \cdot 2\pi^3\hbar^7}{g^2(|C_V|^2 + 3|C_A|^2) \cdot m^5 C^4} \qquad \ldots(56)$$

One then obtains

$$(\sigma_{\text{inverse } \beta\text{-decay}})_{\text{classical}} = \frac{\pi^2 \cdot ln2\hbar^3}{(ft)_n \cdot m^5 C^7} p_e W_e \qquad \ldots(57)$$

For two-component neutrinos, and applying the conservation of leptons, the outgoing neutrinos from the reactor have one spin state only instead of the usual two. By a detailed balancing method, the absorption cross-section will be twice [45] as great as the old one:

$$[\sigma_{\text{inverse } \beta\text{-decay}}]_{\text{two comp}} = 2 \times (\sigma_{\text{inverse } \beta\text{-decay}})_{\text{classical}}$$

In Cowan and Reines' experiments, the principle of detection was as follows : the $\bar{\nu}$ entered the cadmium loaded large liquid scintillators which served as proton targets as well as neutron capture material. A prompt pulse due to the annihilation of the positron signalled the absorption of an anti-neutrino. The recoil neutron was slowed down and captured by cadmium in several microseconds. In this radiative neutron capture process, several gamma-rays would be simultaneously emitted and their detection result in a delayed pulse with respect to the annihilation pulse. To identify the observed signals as neutrino-induced, exhaustive supplementary checks were performed to justify the conclusion. Fig. 7 illustrates the essential detection principle. The measured cross-section per fission anti-neutrino for the inverse beta decay of the proton is

$$\sigma_{\text{exp}} = (11 \pm 4) \times 10^{-44} \text{ cm}^2$$

In order to compare with the theoretically expected cross-section, one must know the positron energy or the anti-neutrino spectrum from nuclear reactor very accurately; they are related by $E_{\bar{\nu}} = 3\cdot53 + E_{e+}$ (*mc*² units). To obtain the $E_{\bar{\nu}}$ the beta spectrum from

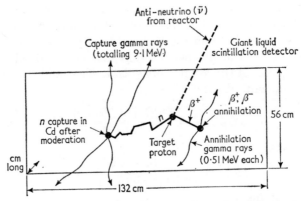

Fig. 7. Schematic of anti-neutrino detector. An anti-neutrino is shown trans-muting a proton to produce a neutron and positron. The positron slows down and annihilates, producing annihilation radiation. The neutron is moderated by the hydrogen of the scintillator and is captured by the cadmium, producing capture gamma-rays.

the fission fragments of ^{238}U was measured from which the anti-neutrino spectrum was thus derived.[46]   The results are:

$\sigma_{theo.} = 9 \cdot 5 \times 10^{-44}$ cm^2 Carter, Reines, Wagner and Wyman [46]
$\phantom{\sigma_{theo.}} = 12 \times 10^{-44}$ cm^2 Muehlhause and Oleksa [46a]
$\phantom{\sigma_{theo.}} = 15 \times 10^{-44}$ cm^2 King and Perkins [46b]

The agreement between σ_{exp} and $\sigma_{theo.}$ is very good.

B. Neutrino Capture [47]

^{37}A decays by an electron capture process as

$$^{37}A + e^- \rightarrow {}^{37}Cl + \nu$$

Its inverse reaction would be

$$^{37}Cl + \nu \rightarrow {}^{37}A + e^-$$

Here a neutrino, not an anti-neutrino, is required for the absorption process according to the lepton conservation.   The intensive flux of anti-neutrinos pouring out of a power nuclear reactor does not provide the correct kind of neutrino for this process, and therefore no ^{37}A activity should be attributed to the reactor neutrino.

Davis' experiment involved irradiating a large volume (1,000 gal) of carbon tetrachloride near a nuclear reactor for a long period of time.   Afterward, ^{37}A was removed and purified by physical methods.   The amount of ^{37}A was measured by counting the X-rays from its electron-capture decays in a low background

Geiger counter. The very small ^{37}A counts $(0\cdot3 \pm 3\cdot4$ counts per day) which Davis observed in his latest improved Geiger counter is equivalent to a cross-section for neutrino capture of $(0\cdot1 \pm 0\cdot6) \times 10^{-45}$ cm^2/atom. This is small in comparison with the theoretically expected inverse cross-section $\sigma \simeq 2 \times 10^{-45}$ cm^2/atom by fission neutrinos if $\nu \equiv \bar{\nu}$. Furthermore, the muon component in the cosmic background under the experimental condition was not known too clearly. The observed residue counts might be accounted for by the muon activation from the cosmic radiation. Therefore no evidence for *a positive effect* from the reactor neutrinos exists at the present time.

17. π–μ–e DECAYS

Pauli's postulation of the existence of a neutrino to save the conservation laws in beta decay found equally important roles in π–μ–e decays, μ-capture and some modes of K-meson decay. Recent experimental evidence from the helicity determination and the asymmetry distribution of the leptons in these various decay modes strongly supports the view that the neutrinos involved in nuclear beta decay are of the same type occurring in other lepton decays.

Here we shall review briefly what types of phenomena in π–μ–e decay are the direct consequences of the two-component neutrino and lepton conservation. In analogy to the beta decay, the interaction term for μ-decay may be represented by

$$f_i(\bar{\psi}_e O_i \psi_\mu)(\bar{\psi}_\nu O_i \psi_\nu) \qquad \dots (58)$$

Let us substitute the two-component neutrino wave functions into the second covariant. We have

$$\tfrac{1}{4} f_i [\bar{\psi}_\nu (1 \mp \gamma_5) O_j (1 \pm \gamma_5) \psi_\nu] \qquad \dots (59)$$

For S, T, P interactions, O_j commutes with γ_5, so the covariant vanishes identically. In the case of V and A, O_j anticommutes with γ_5, we have

$$\tfrac{1}{2} f_i [\bar{\psi}_\nu O_j (1 \pm \gamma_5) \psi_\nu] \qquad \dots (60)$$

Only V and A constitute the μ-decay.

We have grouped the two neutrino wave functions into one covariant for mathematical convenience. It might be argued that since electron and neutrino wave functions are grouped together in one covariant in beta decay, one should probably do the same here for μ-decay. Nevertheless, according to Pauli's rearrangement theorem [5] relating to the permutation of fields, this change of roles will only result in change of the coefficients in the linear combination of the interactions. Particularly, if the linear combination is $V-A$ (Lord is considerate) then it is the same linear combination in both groupings

$$(\bar{\psi}_e\psi_\mu)(\bar{\psi}_\nu\psi_\nu) \quad \text{and} \quad (\bar{\psi}_\nu\psi_\mu)(\bar{\psi}_e\psi_\nu)$$

The three measurements in μ-decay which are of special interest here are: (A) Michel parameter ρ, (B) energy dependence of asymmetry parameter, and (C) polarization of muons and electrons.

A. Michel Parameter ρ [48]

In the μ-decay process, the law of lepton conservation demands that the two neutrinos involved must be a particle and an anti-particle such as

$$\mu^\pm \to e^\pm + \nu + \bar{\nu} \qquad \qquad \ldots (61)$$

If there were no such restriction, the emission of two neutrinos or two anti-neutrinos would also be permissible; that is

$$\mu^\pm \to e^\pm + \nu + \nu \qquad \qquad \ldots (62)$$

or

$$\mu^\pm \to e^\pm + \bar{\nu} + \bar{\nu} \qquad \qquad \ldots (63)$$

From the two-component theory of the neutrino, the shape of the electron energy spectrum depends on whether these two neutrinos involved have the same or different helicities. The electron distribution is [25]

$$N(x)\,\mathrm{d}x = 4x^2[3(1-x) + \tfrac{2}{3}\rho(4x-3)]\,\mathrm{d}x \qquad \ldots (64)$$

where x is the electron energy in units of the maximum energy. The shape of the spectrum depends solely on the single parameter ρ introduced by Michel, a combination of all the coupling constants occurring in the interaction. ρ must equal zero if the electron is accompanied by two neutrinos or two anti-neutrinos and equal 3/4 if one neutrino and one anti-neutrino are emitted. The present experimental values [49] of ρ vary from 0·68 to 0·79, which is certainly close to 0·75, for one neutrino and one anti-neutrino emission and the assumption of two neutrinos or two anti-neutrinos in muon decay can be confidently rejected. This also justifies the assignment of particle and anti-particle roles in section 8. The ultimate accurate evaluation of the value of ρ is highly desirable because of its significant theoretical implications.

B. Energy Dependence of Asymmetry Parameter

The angular distribution [25] of the decay electron from a polarized μ meson at rest is

$$dN = \tfrac{1}{2}\pi x^2[(3-2x) \mp \xi(1-2x)\cos\theta]\, dx\, d\Omega \quad \ldots (65)$$

('$-$' μ^- decay; '$+$' μ^+ decay) where $p =$ electron momentum, $x = p/p_{max}$, $\theta =$ angle between the electron momentum and the spin direction of the decaying muon. For the two component neutrino

$$\xi = \frac{[f_V f_A{}^\star + f_A f_V{}^\star]}{[f_V{}^2 + f_A{}^2]} \quad \ldots (66)$$

The angular asymmetry

$$I(\theta)\, d\theta \propto (1 + A\cos\theta)\sin\theta\, d\theta \approx \left[1 \mp \xi\frac{(1-2x)}{(3-2x)}\cos\theta\right]\sin\theta\, d\theta$$
$$\ldots (67)$$

where A is the asymmetry parameter and is equal to

$$\xi\{(1-2x)/(3-2x)\}$$

which depends on the energy of the electron (x) and is prominent for large values of $|\xi| \approx 1$. The variation of the asymmetry parameter A for μ^- decay is $A = +\xi$ for $x = 1$ (maximum energy), $A = 0$ for $x = 1/2$ (sign reversed at this point) and $A = -1/3\xi$ for $x = 0$ (zero energy). For the integrated spectrum $A = +1/3\xi$.

However, it is not known whether the sign of $\cos\theta$ is positive or negative because we have no direct method to determine the average polarization ($\langle\vec{\sigma}\rangle$) of the muons except that it is parallel to the direction of its motion. From Garwin, Lederman and Weinrich's [50] first experiment on parity non-conservation in muon decay, and also from Friedman and Telegdi's [51] independent results, the large electron asymmetry shows a preponderant fraction of electrons coming out in the backward direction with respect to the muon flight direction. The latest absolute value [52] of $|\xi|$ is equal to 0.97 ± 0.05. In the high energy end of the spectrum, the data on asymmetry are in good agreement with the theory. In the low energy region, measurements are difficult and the statistical accuracy still poor. However, as a whole, the energy dependence of the asymmetry distribution in μ-decay agrees with the prediction of the two-component theory.[52, 53]

C. Polarization of Muons and Electrons

Although the sign of the $\cos \theta$ in the asymmetry distribution is not known because of the lack of knowledge of the muon spin direction, the helicity of the decay electrons can be deduced by the same argument used in the deduction of the longitudinal polarization of beta particles in nuclear decays; that is

$$H_e = \pm \xi v/c \simeq \pm \xi \qquad \qquad \ldots.(68)$$

('+' negative μ-decay; '−' positive μ-decay).

If the negative electron is left-hand polarized and the positron right-hand polarized, then $\xi = -1$. The backward asymmetry observed implies that the negative muon has positive helicity and the positive muon has negative helicity. This can be visualized by considering an extreme case as shown in Fig. 8a. When the

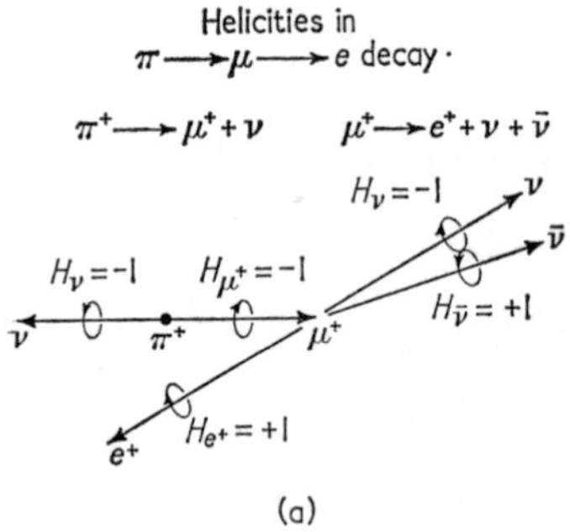

(a)

Fig. 8a.

(b)

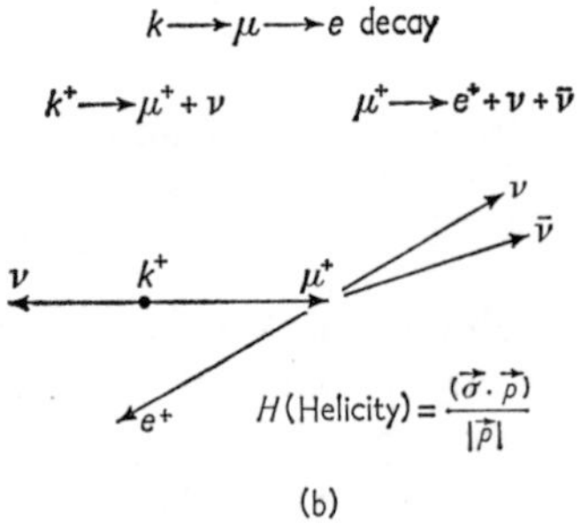

Fig. 8b.

neutrino and the anti-neutrino go in the same direction, the electron which goes in the opposite direction has to carry away the angular momentum of the muon. If μ^+ has a negative helicity, the decay e^+ must possess positive helicity. The experimental results on the polarization of the negative and positive electrons from muon decays observed by measuring the circular polarization of the Bremsstrahlung and annihilation radiation [54] or by the Møller scattering method [55] conclusively show positive helicity for e^+ and negative helicity for e^-. Therefore, the helicity of μ^+ is negative. In $\pi^+ \to \mu^+ + \nu$ decay, the two particles μ^+ and ν must come out in opposite directions and carry no total angular momentum. It predicts negative helicity for the neutrino. Here the results on the helicities of the neutrinos in nuclear beta decays and from π–μ–e decays are in excellent accord.

18. π–e DECAYS

The existence of the pion was originally proposed by Yukawa to account for the strong and short range forces between nucleons. Therefore it is reasonable to expect that a positive pion may virtually transform into a proton–anti-neutron pair

$$\pi^+ \to p + \bar{n}$$

and then be followed by another process of either

$$p + \bar{n} \to e^+ + \nu$$

or

$$p + \bar{n} \to \mu^+ + \nu$$

as shown in Fig. 9. So π^+ should be able to decay by either

$$\pi^+ \to e^+ + \nu$$

or

$$\pi^+ \to \mu^+ + \nu$$

To calculate the π–μ or π–e absolute decay rates one treats the decay as a two-step process, the Yukawa process and the lepton

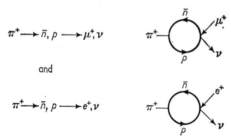

Fig. 9. Feynman diagram of $\pi^+ \to e^+$ and $\pi^+ \to \mu^+$ decays.

capture process. However, the summation over the intermediate state introduces divergence which has to be circumvented by the usual cut-off technique. Therefore, the estimation of its decay rate is only a very approximate one. This uncertainty, however, disappears when evaluating the ratio of these two decay rates, as the troublesome divergence terms due to the intermediate states are exactly the same in the two decay cases and thereby cancel out. The ratio calculated for axial vector interaction is given by [56]

$$R_A = \frac{(\pi^+ \to e^+ + \nu)}{(\pi \to \mu^+ + \nu)} = \frac{m_e^2 (1 - m_e^2/m_\pi^2)^2}{m_\mu^2 (1 - m_\mu^2/m_\pi^2)^2} \approx 1 \cdot 3 \times 10^{-4} \quad \ldots . (69)$$

and shown to be exact to all orders in the strong pion–nucleon couplings.[56]

π–e decay is indeed a very rare event in comparison with π–μ decay. For a long time the π–e decay was extensively searched for but none was observed. The experimental ratio of $\pi^+ \rightarrow e^+ + \nu$ to $\pi^+ \rightarrow \mu^+ + \nu$ seemed to be much less than 10^{-5}. In the days when S and T were favoured in nuclear beta interaction, the absence of π–e decay did not concern physicists too much. The reason is that only two of the five beta interactions, namely the A and P, can be formed out of the pseudoscalar pion field and one four-vector representing the non-local nature of the intermediate state. Therefore they are the only ones which can induce the decay of the pseudoscalar pion; the other three (S, V, T) are forbidden. If A and P are both lacking in beta decay, then $\pi^+ \rightarrow e^+ + \nu$ is naturally forbidden.

However this inability to observe the π–e decay demands serious attention as soon as the experimental evidence strongly supports a universal V–A Fermi interaction in all beta decays. The conclusive findings[57] of the π–e events were reported soon afterwards and were a great triumph for the universal V–A interactions. Since then the ratio of π–e to π–μ has been determined with moderate precision in several laboratories. Results vary from 1.3 to 1.4×10^{-4} and are in good agreement with the theoretical value of 1.34×10^{-4}. Had the π–e decay been successfully observed in early attempts and with correct proportion to π–μ decay, one probably would have pondered on the correctness of the (S, T) interactions in nuclear beta decay.

The ratio for these two decay modes calculated for pseudoscalar interaction is

$$R_P = \frac{\tau(\pi^+ \rightarrow e^+ + \nu)}{\tau(\pi^+ \rightarrow \mu^+ + \nu)} = \left(\frac{m_\pi^2 - m_e^2}{m_\pi^2 - m_\mu^2}\right)^2 \simeq 5.4 \quad \ldots (70)$$

which is just the ratio of the energy densities in phase space. From the present observed ratio (R) of the two modes of pion decay, Treiman and Wyld[58] estimated that

$$|C_P| \leqslant \left(\frac{m_e}{M}\right)|C_A| \approx 5 \times 10^{-4}|C_A| \qquad \ldots (71)$$

The pseudoscalar coupling is indeed negligible.

19. K–μ–e DECAYS

The K–μ–e decay is analogous to π–μ–e decay (Fig. 8b). If the conservation law of leptons holds, the same kind of neutrinos are expected in these two parallel cases. This should, therefore, result in the same asymmetry distribution of electrons with respect to the direction of μ-motion. This predicted asymmetry in K–μ–e decay has been confirmed[59] and therefore further strengthens the validity of lepton conservation.

20. NON-CONSERVATION OF PARITY IN STRANGE PARTICLE DECAYS

It is important and interesting to know whether the non-conservation of parity in weak interactions is limited only to those decay processes involving the neutrino, particularly as it is known that it was the K-meson decay whose apparent violation of parity conservation started the whole investigation.

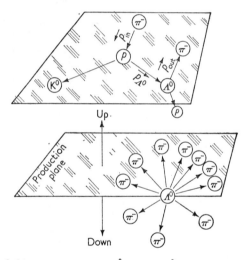

Fig. 10. Up and down asymmetry in $\mathring{\Lambda}$ decay. $\mathring{\Lambda}$ is produced by the reaction $\pi^- + p \rightarrow \mathring{\Lambda} + K^\circ$ and in turn decays by $\mathring{\Lambda} \rightarrow \pi^- + p$. The observation of the up-down asymmetry distribution of the decay pion $\mathbf{p}_{out}$ with respect to the production plane containing the two momentum vectors $\mathbf{p}_{in}$ and $\mathbf{p}_\Lambda$ demonstrates non-vanishing of the expectation value of the pseudoscalar $(\mathbf{p}_{out} \cdot \mathbf{p}_{in} \times \mathbf{p}_\Lambda)$ and therefore the non-conservation of parity in $\mathring{\Lambda}$ decay.

The decay process which has been studied is $\mathring{\Lambda} \rightarrow \pi^- + p$, where the $\mathring{\Lambda}$ particles were produced in the reaction $\pi^- + p \rightarrow \mathring{\Lambda} + K$. The lack of parity conservation was observed[60] in the non-vanishing of the expectation value of the pseudoscalar $\mathbf{p}_{out} \cdot \mathbf{p}_{in} \times \mathbf{p}_\Lambda$ as up-down asymmetry (Fig. 10). The violation of parity was again a maximum. In this case, the neutrino can hardly be blamed for the observed parity violation, because the neutrino is

not involved in the process. All the weak interactions, leptonic
and non-leptonic, are about equally weak. They all violate the
law of parity and charge conjugation. Could it be that they are
all contained in some sort of universal Fermi interaction? Although the rough comparisons of the experimental results with
the universal $V-A$ theory give qualitative confirmation, the
absence of reliable solutions for processes involving the strongly
interacting particles makes the comparison only very tentative.

21. THE UNIVERSAL $V-A$ FERMI INTERACTION

The great similarity in the strength of the coupling constants in
beta decay, μ-decay and μ-capture suggests that the interaction
forms of the three decay processes may also be the same. When
beta decay coupling was concluded to be (S, T) and μ-decay
coupling was deduced to be dominantly V and A from the negative
sign of the asymmetry coefficient, this possibility of a universal
Fermi interaction was naturally ruled out. Now that the
interaction (V, A) has replaced (S, T) in beta decay, the situation
is quite altered.

It is interesting to recall that in 1955, long before the validity
of the parity law in beta decay was questioned, Stech and Jensen[61]
made a strange and heuristic proposal. In order to account for
the lack of the Fierz interference term in beta decay, they proposed the transformations

$$\psi_e' = \gamma_5\psi_e; \quad \text{and} \quad \psi_\nu' = \gamma_5\psi_\nu$$

and introduced the principle that $H_{\text{int.}}$ should be invariant.[72]
Since an overall sign change on transformation is irrelevant, the
new introduction can then have either $[S, T(p)]$ or (V, A) in $H_{\text{int.}}$
but not both. This automatically guarantees the vanishing of
the Fierz term. Although this principle worked, it was not
understood. These principles were considered further by Marshak
and Sudarshan,[62] Feynman and Gell-Mann,[63] and Sakurai[64]
when the new evidence from parity experiments began to make
sense. As we have seen in the two-component theory of the
neutrino, the transformation is applied to the neutrino alone.
The transformation of a pair of the particles simultaneously is a
natural generalization of the former. By using the argument of
chirality invariance,[62] two-component spinor theory,[63] or invariance under mass reversal,[64] the unique expression arrived at is

$$G\{[\bar{A}\gamma_\mu(1+\gamma_5)B][\bar{C}\gamma_\mu(1+\gamma_5)D]+H.C.\} \qquad \ldots\ldots(73)$$

where G is the coupling constant and A, B, C, D are four Dirac particle fields.

Since $\gamma_5(1+\gamma_5)=(1+\gamma_5)\gamma_5=(1+\gamma_5)$ the above expression can be written in terms of

$$G\{(\bar{A}\gamma_\mu B)(\bar{C}\gamma_\mu(1+\gamma_5)D)+(-1)(\bar{A}(-i\gamma_\mu\gamma_5)B)(\bar{C}(-i\gamma_\mu\gamma_5)(1+\gamma_5)D)\}$$
$$\dots(74)$$

This represents the linear combination $V-A$. This universal $V-A$ four fermion interaction, besides giving the unique combination $V-A$, yields a two-component neutrino of negative helicity, leads to conservation of leptons, and is invariant under 'combined inversion of CP.' The discrepancies which stood in the way of its acceptance at the very beginning of its proposal were soon cleared away one after another. At the present moment the experimental results are all in good harmony with the predictions.

The universal $V-A$ expression also demands equal strength of the two types of interactions V and A. However, this has been shown to be not fulfilled in nuclear beta decay. $|C_A|^2$ is estimated to be nearly $1\cdot42|C_V|^2$ from neutron and ^{14}O ft-values. On the other hand, the V and A interactions can be assumed to be equal in muon decay because they are mathematically identical* and there is therefore no need for its distinction. The coupling constant in muon decay turns out in excellent agreement with that of the vector part of the nuclear beta decay. If one applies the constant of the V interaction in nuclear beta decay $g_V=1\cdot41\times10^{-49}$ erg-cm³ the calculated muon life-time

$$\tau_\mu = 192g_v{}^{-2}\pi^3\hbar^7C^{-4}\mu^{-5} = (2\cdot26\pm0\cdot04)\times10^{-6}\text{ sec}\quad\dots(75)$$

which is to be compared with the measured value of $(2\cdot22\pm0\cdot02)\times10^{-6}$ sec. This excellent agreement is by no means a blessing, but rather a puzzle! As it is understood, nucleons can emit and absorb virtual pions. A neutron exists for a substantial fraction of its life as a proton surrounded by the negatively charged pion cloud. It can be presumed that the beta interaction strength of a bare nucleon is considerably different from that of a physical nucleon (a mixture of pion and nucleon). To take into account such a pionic effect, the coupling strength in nuclear beta decay has to be renormalized. On the other hand, the renormalization effect does not occur in muon decay because no pionic effect exists there. Then, why should this agreement be so good? In

---

*   Vector Current   Axial Vector

$$\bar{\psi}_\mu\gamma_\mu\psi_\nu \equiv \bar{\psi}_\mu\gamma_\mu\gamma_5\psi_\nu \quad\text{if}\quad \psi_\nu = \gamma_5\psi_\nu$$

order to explain this unexpected good agreement, Feynman and
Gell-Mann proposed an interesting hypothesis [63] based on the
analogy in electrodynamics that the observed coupling strength e
with electromagnetic field is the same for all particles coupled.
This is possible in the low energy region because, although the distribution of charge is altered with the emission of a virtual meson,
the total charge is not changed. Is it possible that the pions
carry with them the beta interaction strength when they are
virtually emitted from the nucleons, and that the Fermi part of the
nuclear beta-interaction is so arranged as to have no renormalization effects? They suggested that the vector part of the nucleon
transformation current term should be supplemented by a pion
transformation current term. In isotopic spin notation, the sum
of the vector transformation current is

$$J_\mu{}^V = \bar{\psi}_p\gamma_\mu\tau + \psi_n + i[\phi_\pi{}^\star T_+ \nabla_\mu\phi_\pi - (\nabla_\mu\phi_\pi)^\star T_+\phi_n] \quad \ldots\ldots(76)$$

where $\tau = \frac{1}{2}$ for the nucleon and $T = 1$ for the pion. This conserved current leads to a quantity which is unchanged by the
pionic effects.

The observed difference between C_A and C_V as mentioned above
has been tentatively attributed to the renormalization effect on
the axial vector part. Nevertheless, our knowledge of the pion–
nucleon interaction is so meagre and our treatment of the strong
interaction is so inadequate that we may have to wait a long time
before we can solve the renormalization properly.

The proposed direct interaction of pions with the electron and
neutrino gives rise to possibilities of experimental tests of
$\pi^- \to \pi^0 + e^- + \bar{\nu}$ or $\pi^+ \to \pi^0 + e^+ + \nu$. We must still wait for these
results.

22. THE 'CPT' THEOREM: CP AND T INVARIANCE

Pauli's extended discussion on the CTP theorem [3] in 1955 was
most timely in preparing for the later activities concerning the
three operators C, P, T in weak interactions. The CPT theorem is
a general theorem stating the inter-relationship between the
operators C (charge conjugation), P (parity) and T (time reversal)
and proper Lorentz invariance. If a local Lagrangian theory is
invariant under the proper Lorentz transformations, it is invariant
under the product of CPT (and its permutation) although the
theory may not be separately invariant under each one of these
three operators C, P, T.

From this theorem, if P is not conserved in the weak inter-actions, then at least one of the other invariances C or T should not be conserved. From the polarized ^{60}Co experiment and the π–μ–e decays, we learned that charge conjugation as well as parity is not conserved in these weak interactions. Then of particular interest is whether the invariance of time reversal is still intact. If the operation of time reversal (T) is invariant, then from the CPT theorem the combined operation CP is invariant. The invariance of this combined operation CP was predicted by Lan-dau [25] along with his proposal of the two-component theory of the neutrino and also by Wigner [65] in his address to the American Physical Society meeting, January, 1957. In that case, one replaces all particles by their anti-particles in taking a mirror image, and the right–left asymmetry in space is retained. This is indeed a very comforting thought.

At present, there are several experiments in progress to decide the question of the invariance of time reversal. No definite violations of the invariance of T have been detected so far. The underlying principle of proof of T invariance is to measure the relative phases between the coupling constants C_i. If T is in-variant, then C_i are all real, and *vice-versa*. This can be shown by the following arguments:

The time reversal operator T cannot be represented by a unitary operator U_T as in operation C or P, but rather by

$$T = U_T X \text{ complex conjugation} \qquad \ldots(77)$$

Now, the most general beta Hamiltonian is a linear combination of various interactions such as

$$H_\beta = \sum_i C_i H_i$$

Under time reversal, each individual interaction Hamiltonian H_i undergoes

$$TH_iT^{-1} = U_T H_i{}^\star U_T{}^{-1} = H_i \qquad \ldots(77a)$$

which is multiplied by a phase factor. If we allow all such phase factors to be included in $C_i{}^\star$, then the total Hamiltonian under time reversal can be written as

$$TH_\beta T^{-1} = \sum_i C_i{}^\star H_i \qquad \ldots(77b)$$

For $TH_\beta T^{-1} = H_\beta$ (invariance under time reversal), $C_i = C_i{}^\star$. That implies that the coupling constants must be real. From

11 + P.M.V.

the polarized neutron experiment, by measuring $\beta - \nu$ correlation, the existence of a term $\sigma_n \cdot p_e \times p_{\nu-}$ can be detected. This term depends on the imaginary part of the coupling constants. It yields the relative phase angle between C_{GT} and C_F, equals $180° \pm 8°66$ (where $180°$ implies T invariance). The uncertainty is statistical. For the time being, until proven otherwise, we may assume the time reversal invariance still holds and the left–right symmetry is still intact under combined CP invariance.

23. CONCLUSION

It is nearly thirty years since the first idea of the existence of an elusive particle was pronounced by Pauli in an endeavour to save the grave situation in beta decay. Its original idea and concepts have weathered many dramatic developments but still come out intact. The role of the neutrino now has found wide applications in all leptonic decays. Its invariance properties under CP and T operations have suggested the possibility of a deeper symmetry connecting the charge and space. Its peculiar two-component formulation has given us hope that we may generalize all weak interactions into a simple universal $V-A$ Fermi interaction. The class of seemingly diversified weak interactions has therefore emerged into a unique and characteristic group of forces. However, we still do not understand the underlying principle which differentiates the weak interactions from the strong ones. In our ultimate quest for a general theory of elementary particles, the neutrino will undoubtedly play an active role as has been shown brilliantly so far.

REFERENCES

1. Pauli, W. Noyaux Atomiques, *Proc. of Solvay Congress, Brussels, 1933,* p. 324
2. The possibility of a two-component relativistic theory of a spin $1/2$ particle was first discussed by Weyl, H. *Z. Phys.* **56**, 330, 1929. It was rejected on the ground of parity violation. See Pauli, W. *Handbuch der Physik,* Vol. 24, pp. 226–227. 1933. Berlin; Verlag Julius Soringer
3. Pauli, W. *Niels Bohr and the Development of Physics.* 1955. London; Pergamon Press. Schwinger, J. *Phys. Rev.* **91**, 720, 723, 1953; **94**, 1366, 1953. Lüders, G. *Mat.-fys. Medd.* **28**, No. 5, 1954
4. Pauli, W. *Ann. Inst. Poincaré* **6**, 109, 1936
5. Pauli, W. *Z. Phys.* **104**, 553, 1937
6. Ellis, C. D. and Wooster, W. A. *Proc. Roy. Soc. A* **117**, 109, 1927. Meitner, L. and Orthmann, W. *Z. Phys.* **60**, 143, 1930
7. Chadwick, J. *Verh. dtsch. phys. Ges.* **16**, 383, 1914
8. Ehrenfest, P. and Oppenheimer, J. R. *Phys. Rev.* **37**, 333, 1931
9. Heitler, W. and Herzberg, G. *Naturwissenschaften* **17**, 673, 1929. Rasetti, F. *Z. Phys.* **61**, 598, 1930

10. Quoted in a lecture by W. Pauli to the Zürcher Naturforschende Gesellschaft on January 21, 1957 (immediately after the announcement of the first experiments on parity violation), translated by Robert Schlapp. The author is grateful for having received a copy of this translation.

11. Chadwick, J. *Proc. Roy. Soc. A* **136**, 692, 1932

12. Bohr, N. Faraday Lecture: Chemistry and the Quantum Theory of Atomic Constitution. *J. chem. Soc.* pp. 349–384, 1932

13. Fermi, E. *Z. Phys.* **88**, 161, 1934; *Ric. Sci.* **2**, Part 12, 1933

14. Perrin, F. *C.R. Acad. Sci., Paris* 197, 1625, 1933

15. Gamow, G. and Teller, E. *Phys. Rev.* **49**, 895, 1936. Konopinski, E. J. and Uhlenbeck, G. E. *Phys. Rev.* **60**, 308, 1941

16. Wu, C. S. *Beta and Gamma Ray Spectroscopy*, ed. K. Siegbahn. 1955. Amsterdam; North Holland Publishing Company. Wu, C. S. *Rev. mod. Phys.* **22**, 386, 1950. Ridley, B. W. *Progress in Nuclear Physics*, ed. O. R. Frisch, Vol. 5. 1956. London; Pergamon Press. Allen, J. *The Neutrino*. 1957. Princeton University Press

17. $|C_{GT}|^2/|C_F|^2 = 1·16 \pm 0·05$ Kistner, O. and Rustad, B. M. *Phys. Rev.* in press. $(ft)^{14}O$ Gerhart, J. B. *Phys. Rev.* **109**, 897, 1958. $(ft)_n$ Sosnovskii, Spivak, Prokofiev, Kutikov and Dobrinin, *J. exp. theor. phys.* **35**, 1059, 1958

18. Fierz, M. *Z. Phys.* **104**, 553, 1937

19. Wu, C. S. and Schwarzschild, A. *Columbia University Report CU*-173

20. Sherwin, C. W. *Phys. Rev.* **73**, 1219, 1948; **75**, 1799, 1948; **82**, 52, 1951

21. Kofoed-Hansen, O. *Phys. Rev.* **96**, 1045, 1954

22. Snell, A. H. and Pleasonton, F. *Phys. Rev.* **97**, 246, 1955; **100**, 1396, 1955

23. Lee, T. D. and Yang, C. N. *Phys. Rev.* **104**, 254, 1956

24. Wu, Ambler, Hayward, Hoppes and Hudson *Phys. Rev.* **105**, 1413, 1957

25a. Lee, T. D. and Yang, C. N. *Phys. Rev.* **105**, 1671, 1957. Landau, L. *Nuclear Physics* **3**, 127, 1957. Salam, A. *Nuovo Cim.* **5**, 299, 1957

25b. Majorana, E. *Nuovo Cim.* **14**, 171, 1937

25c. Serpe, J. *Physica* **18**, 295, 1952; *Nuclear Physics* **4**, 183, 1957. McLennan, J. A. *Phys. Rev.* **106**, 821, 1957. Radicati, L. A. and Touschek, B. *Nuovo Cim.* **5**, 1693, 1957. Case, K. M. *Phys. Rev.* **107**, 307, 1957. The author is grateful to M. Fierz for enlightening discussions held with him.

25d. Theoretical calculations on various effects due to non-conservation of parity in nuclear beta-decay. Jackson, Treiman and Wyld *Phys. Rev.* **106**, 517, 1957. Morita, M. and Morita, R. S. *Phys. Rev.* **107**, 139, 1316, 1729, 1957; **109**, 2048, 1958; **110**, 461, 1958; **111**, 237, 1130, 1958; **114**, 1080, 1959. Feld, Bernard T. *Phys. Rev.* **107**, 797, 1957. Alder, Stech and Winther *Phys. Rev.* **107**, 728, 1957. Ebel, M. E. and Feldman, G. *Nuclear Physics* **4**, 213, 1957. Curtis, R. B. and Lewis, R. R. *Phys. Rev.* **107**, 1381, 1957

26. Konopinski, E. and Mahmoud, H. M. *Phys. Rev.* **92**, 1045, 1953. Lee, T. D. and Yang, C. N. *Phys. Rev.* **105**, 1671, 1957

27. Pauli, W. *Nuovo Cim.* **6**, 204, 1957. Enz, C. O. *Nuovo Cim.* **6**, 250, 1957. Kahana, S. and Pursey, D. L. *Nuovo Cim.* **6**, 1469, 1957

28. *Proc. Rehovoth Conference on Nuclear Structure*. 1958. Amsterdam; North-Holland Publishing Company. *Bull. Amer. phys. Soc.* Ser. II, **4**, 82, 1959. *Gatlinburg Conference on Weak Interactions* (1958) For electron and gamma-ray polarization in general, please refer to excellent review articles: Page, Lorne A. *Rev. mod. Phys.* **31**, 759, 1959. Fagg, L. W. and Hanna, S. S. *Rev. mod. Phys.* **31**, 711, 1959

28a. *Mott Scattering*
Tolhoek, H. A. *Rev. mod. Phys.* **28**, 177, 1956.   Frauenfelder, H. *et al.* *Phys. Rev.* **106**, 386, 1957.   Alikhanov, Yeliseyev, Linbimov and Ershler.   Cavanagh, Turner, Coleman, Gard and Ridley *Phil. Mag.* **2**, 1105, 1957.   Waard, H. de and Poppema, O. J. *Physica* **23**, 597, 1957. de-Shalit, Kuperman, Lipkin and Rothem *Phys. Rev.* **107**, 1459, 1957. Langevin-Joliot, Marty and Segent *C.R. Acad. Sci.*, *Paris* **244**, 3142, 1957

28b. *Circular polarization of Bremsstrahlung and annihilation radiation*
McVoy, K. M. *Phys. Rev.* **106**, 828, 1957; **110**, 1484, 1958.   Goldhaber, Grodzins and Sunyar *Phys. Rev.* **106**, 826, 1957.   Deutsch, Gittelman, Bauer, Grodzins and Sunyar *Phys. Rev.* **107**, 1733, 1957.   Boehm, Novey, Barnes and Stech *Phys. Rev.* **108**, 1497, 1957

28c. *Moller Scattering*
Møller, C. *Ann. Phys. Lpz.* **14**, 531, 1932.   Page, L. A. *Phys. Rev.* **106**, 394, 1957.   Bincer, A. M. *Phys. Rev.* **107**, 1434, 1469, 1957.   Ford, G. W. and Mullin, C. J. *Phys. Rev.* **108**, 477, 1957.   Frauenfelder, Hanson, Levine, Rossi and De Pasquali *Phys. Rev.* **107**, 643, 909, 910. 1957.   Benczer-Koller, Schwarzschild, Vise and Wu *Phys. Rev.* **109**, 193, 1958

28d. Frauenfelder, H. *et al.* *Phys. Rev.* **106**, 386, 1957

28e. Deutsch, M. *et al.* *Phys. Rev.* **107**, 1733, 1957

29. It is interesting to note the following comments by Mott and Massey on the results of electron polarization in the book *The Theory of Atomic Collisions*, 2nd ed. (Oxford, at the Clarendon Press), p. 83, 'The results of most recent experiments on single scattering of fast electrons from cathode rays are in very good agreement with theoretical prediction', and, p. 84, 'The internal consistency of all the experimental results using beta rays is not good and it is likely that the discrepancies will largely disappear when radioactive sources are replaced by artificial ones of controlled energy.'   Grodzins, L. *Proc. Nat. Acad. Sci. Wash.* **45**, 399, March, 1959; Cox, R. T. *et al.* Apparent Evidence of Polarization in a Beam of Beta Ray.   *Proc. Nat. Acad. Sci. Wash.* **14**, 544, 1928

30. Gunst, S. B. and Page, L. A. *Phys. Rev.* **92**, 970, 1953.   Wheathly, Huiskamp, Diddens, Steenland and Tolhoek *Physica* **2**, 841, 1955. Huiskamp, W. J. *Thesis*, Leiden, 1958.   Schopper, H. *Nuclear Inst.* **3**, 158, 1958

31. Schopper, H. *Phil. Mag.* **2**, 710, 1957

32. Boehm, F. and Wapstra, A. H. *Phys. Rev.* **109**, 456, 1958.   Lundby, Padro and Stroot *Nuovo Cim.* **6**, 745, 1957.   Steffen, R. M. and Alexander, P. *Proc. Rehovoth Conference*, **1957**.   Güngst, W. and Schopper, H. *Z. Naturf.* **139**, 505, 1958

33. Goldhaber, Grodzins and Sunyar *Phys. Rev.* **109**, 1015, 1958

34. Burgy, Krohn, Novey, Ringo and Telegdi *Phys. Rev.* **110**, 1214, 1958

35. Pruett, J. R. *Phys. Rev.* **73**, 219, 1948

36. Hamilton, Alford and Gross *Phys. Rev.* **92**, 1521, 1953

37. Langer, L. M. and Moffat, R. J. D. *Phys. Rev.* **88**, 689, 1952

38. Sakurai, J. J. *Phys. Rev. Letters* **1**, 40, 1958.   Enz, C. P. *Nuovo Cim.* **6**, 250, 1957

39. Cowan, Reines and Harrison *Phys. Rev.* **96**, 1294, 1954

40. Majorana, E. *Nuovo Cim.* **14**, 171, 1937

41. Primakoff, H. and Rosen, S. P. *Double Beta Decay*.   Washington University, 1958 (unpublished).   Goeppert-Mayer, M. *Phys. Rev.* **48**, 512, 1935.   Furry, W. H. *Phys. Rev.* **56**, 1184, 1939.   Konopinski, E. J. *U.S.A.E.C. Report LAMS*-1949.   Primakoff, H. *Phys. Rev.* **85**, 888, 1952

42. Bethe, H. A. and Peierls, R. *Nature, Lond.* **133**, 532, 1934

43. Reines, F. and Cowan, C. L. Jr. *Phys. Rev.* **113**, 273, 1959
44. Quoted from Reference 43
45. Lee, T. D. and Yang, C. N. *Phys. Rev.* **105**, 1671, 1957
46. Carter, Reines, Wagner and Wyman *Phys. Rev.* **113**, 280, 1959
46a. Muehlhause, C. O. and Oleksa, S. *Phys. Rev.* **105**, 1332, 1957
46b. King, R. W. and Perkins, J. F. *Phys. Rev.* **112**, 963, 1958
47. Davis, R. *Phys. Rev.* **97**, 766, 1955. *Bull. Amer. phys. Soc.* Ser. II, **1**, 219, 1956. Private communication, 1958
48. Michel, L. *Nature, Lond.* **163**, 959, 1949; *Proc. phys. Soc. Lond. A* **63**, 514, 1950; *Phys. Rev.* **86**, 814, 1952; *Progress in Cosmic Ray Physics*, ed. Wilson, 1952; *Thesis*, University of Paris, 1953
49. ρ *Value*
    0.68 ± 0.02, Crowe, K.M. *Bull. Amer. phys. Soc.* Ser. II, **2**, 234, 1957. 0.68 ± 0.09, Sargent, C. P. *et al. Phys. Rev.* **99**, 885, 1955. 0.72 ± 0.05, Dudziak, W. and Sagane, R. *Rochester Conference on High Energy Physics*, 1957. 0.67 ± 0.05, Rosenson, L. *Thesis*, University of Chicago, 1957. 0.79 ± 0.03, Plano, R. J. and Courtois, A. Le. *Bull. Amer. Phys. Soc.* Ser. II, **4**, 82, 1959
    Also, Conference on Weak Interactions. *Rev. mod. Phys.* July, 1959
50. Garwin, Lederman and Weinrich *Phys. Rev.* **105**, 1415, 1957
51. Friedman, A. M. and Telegdi, V. L. *Phys. Rev.* **105**, 1681, 1957
52. *Proceedings of CERN Conference on High Energy Physics*, Geneva, July, 1958. Bardon, M., Berley, D. and Lederman, L. M. *Phys. Rev. Letters* **2**, 56, 1959
53. See Conference on Weak Interactions. *Rev. mod. Phys.* July, 1959
54. Culligan, Frank, Holt, Kluyner and Massam *Nature, Lond.* **80**, 751, 1957. Crowe, K. Washington meeting, American Physical Society, 1958
55. Anderson, H. *Proceedings of CERN Conference on High Energy Physics*, Geneva, July, 1958
56. Ruderman, M. and Finkelstein, R. *Phys. Rev.* **76**, 1458, 1949
57. Fazzini, T. *et al. Phys. Rev. Letters* **1**, 247, 1958. Impeduglia, G. *et al. Phys. Rev. Letters* **1**, 249, 1958. Anderson, H. L. *et al. Phys. Rev. Letters* **2**, 53, 1959
58. Treiman, S. B. and Wyld, H. W. *Phys. Rev.* **101**, 1552, 1956
59. Coombes, C. A. *et al. Phys. Rev.* **108**, 1348, 1957
60. Crawford, F. *et al. Phys. Rev.* **108**, 1102, 1957. Eisler, F. R. *et al. Phys. Rev.* **108**, 1353, 1957
61. Stech, B. and Jensen, J. H. D. *Z. Phys.* **141**, 175, 403, 1955
62. Sudarshan, G. and Marshak, R. *Padua-Venice International Conference*, 1957; *Phys. Rev.* **109**, 1860, 1958
63. Feynman, R. and Gell-Mann, M. *Phys. Rev.* **109**, 193, 1958
64. Sakurai, J. J. *Nuovo Cim.* **7**, 649, 1958
65. Wigner, E. P. *Rev. mod. Phys.* **29**, 255, 1957
66. Burgy, Krohn, Novey, Ringo and Telegdi *Proc. Second Internat. Conference on Peaceful Uses of Atomic Energy*, Vol. 30, P/692. Telegdi, V. L. *Rev. mod. Phys.* July, 1959

BIBLIOGRAPHY WOLFGANG PAULI

Prepared by CHARLES ENZ

A. BÜCHER UND BEITRÄGE ZU SAMMELWERKEN

Relativitätstheorie, *Encyklopädie der Math. Wissensch.*, Vol. V, Teil 2, pp. 539–775, 1921 und Separatausgabe, Leipzig, 1921
Neuausgaben mit Vorwort und Zusätzen (W. Pauli, 1956):
Englische Übersetzung *Theory of Relativity*, Pergamon Press, 1958
Italienische Übersetzung *Teoria della Relatività*, Torino, 1958
Stichwort 'Störungstheorie' in *Physikalisches Handwörterbuch*, Berliner und Scheel, pp. 752–756, 1924
Quantentheorie, *Handbuch der Physik*, Geiger und Scheel, Vol. 23, pp. 1–278, 1926
Über das H-Theorem vom Anwachsen der Entropie vom Standpunkt der neuen Quantenmechanik, in *Probleme der modernen Physik, Arnold Sommerfeld zum 60. Geburtstage, gewidmet von seinen Schülern*, pp. 30–45, Leipzig, 1928
Theorie der schwarzen Strahlung, *Müller-Pouillets Lehrbuch*, 11. Auflage, Vol. II, Teil 2, pp. 1483–1553, 1929
Allgemeine Grundlagen der Quantentheorie des Atombaues, *Müller-Pouillets Lehrbuch*, 11. Auflage, Vol. II, Teil 2, pp. 1709–1842, 1929
Die allgemeinen Prinzipien der Wellenmechanik. *Handbuch der Physik*, Geiger und Scheel, 2. Aufl., Vol. 24, Teil 1, pp. 83–272, 1933. Revidierte Neuausgabe in *Handbuch der Physik*, Flügge, Vol. V, Teil 1, pp. 1–168, 1958
Meson Theory of Nuclear Forces, New York, 1946, second edition, 1948
Einstein's contribution to quantum theory, in *Albert Einstein: Philosopher-Scientist*, Vol. VII of the Library of Living Philisophers, pp. 149–160, 1949
Deutsche Übersetzung, Einsteins Beitrag zur Quantentheorie, in *Albert Einstein als Philosoph und Naturforscher*, pp. 74–83, Stuttgart, 1955
Der Einfluss archetypischer Vorstellungen auf die Bildung naturwissenschaftlicher Theorien bei Kepler, in *Naturerklärung und Psyche*, Zürich, 1952
Englische Übersetzung, The influence of archetypal ideas on the scientific theories of Kepler, in *The Interpretation of Nature and the Psyche*, New York and London, 1955

Remarques sur le problème des paramètres cachés dans la mécanique quantique et sur la théorie de l'onde pilote, in *Louis de Broglie, Physicien et Penseur*, pp. 33–42, Paris, 1953

Matter, in *Man's Right to Knowledge*, An International Symposium Presented in Honour of the Two-Hundredth Anniversary of Columbia University, 1754–1954, Second Series: *Present Knowledge and New Directions*, pp. 10–18, New York, 1954

Exclusion principle, Lorentz group and reflection of space-time and charge, in *Niels Bohr and the Development of Physics, Essays dedicated to Niels Bohr on the occasion of his seventieth birthday* (edited by W. Pauli), pp. 30–51, London and New York, 1955

Physik und Erkenntnistheorie. Vorträge und Abhandlungen, Braunschweig, 1960

B. PUBLIKATIONEN UND DISKUSSIONSBEITRÄGE IN ZEITSCHRIFTEN UND KONFERENZBERICHTEN

Mercurperihelbewegung und Strahlenablenkung in Weyls Gravitationstheorie. *Verh. dtsch. phys. Ges.* **21**, 742–750, 1919

Über die Energiekomponenten des Gravitationsfeldes. *Phys. Z.* **20**, 25–27, 1919

Zur Theorie der Gravitation und der Elektrizität von Hermann Weyl. *Phys. Z.* **20**, 457–467, 1919

Theoretische Bemerkungen über den Diamagnetismus einatomiger Gase. *Z. Phys.* **2**, 201–205, 1920

Die Ausbreitung des Lichtes in bewegten Medien. *Math. Ann.* **82**, 113–119, 1920

Quantentheorie und Magneton. *Phys. Z.* **21**, 615–617, 1920

Zur Theorie der Dielektrizitätskonstante zweiatomiger Dipolgase. *Z. Phys.* **6**, 319–327, 1921

(Born, M. und Pauli, W.) Über die Quantelung gestörter mechanischer Systeme. *Z. Phys.* **10**, 137–158, 1922

Über das Modell des Wasserstoffmolekülions. *Ann. Phys. Lpz.* (4) **68**, 177–240, 1922*

Über die Gesetzmässigkeiten des anomalen Zeemaneffektes. *Z. Phys.* **16**, 155–164, 1923

(Kramers, H. A. und Pauli, W.) Zur Theorie der Bandenspektren. *Z. Phys.* **13**, 351–367, 1923

Über das thermische Gleichgewicht zwischen Strahlung und freien Elektronen. *Z. Phys.* **18**, 272–286, 1923

Zur Frage der Zuordnung der Komplexstrukturterme in starken und in schwachen äusseren Feldern. *Z. Phys.* **20**, 371–387, 1924

* Münchener Dissertation.

Bemerkungen zu den Arbeiten 'Dimension der Einsteinschen Lichtquanten' und 'Zur Dynamik des Stosses zwischen einem Lichtquant
und einem Elektron' von L. S. Ornstein und H. C. Burger Z. Phys.
22, 261–265, 1924

Zur Frage der theoretischen Deutung der Satelliten einiger Spektrallinien und ihrer Beeinflussung durch magnetische Felder. *Naturwissenschaften* **12**, 741–743, 1924*

Über den Einfluss der Geschwindigkeitsabhängigkeit der Elektronenmasse auf den Zeemaneffekt. *Z. Phys.* **31**, 373–385, 1925

Über den Zusammenhang des Abschlusses der Elektronengruppen im
Atom mit der Komplexstruktur der Spektren. *Z. Phys.* **31**, 765–783,
1925†

Über die Intensitäten der im elektrischen Felde erscheinenden
Kombinationslinien. *Dan. Vid. Selsk. Math.-fys. Medd.* **7**, No. 3, 1925

Über die Absorption der Reststrahlen in Kristallen. *Verh. dtsch.
phys. Ges.* (3) **6**, 10–11, 1925

Über das Wasserstoffspektrum vom Standpunkt der neuen Quantenmechanik. *Z. Phys.* **36**, 336–363, 1926

(Mensing, L. und Pauli, W.) Über die Dielektrizitätskonstante von
Dipolgasen nach der Quantenmechanik. *Phys. Z.* **27**, 509–512, 1926

Über Gasentartung und Paramagnetismus. *Z. Phys.* **41**, 81–102, 1927

Zur Quantenmechanik des magnetischen Elektrons. *Z. Phys.* **43**,
601–623, 1927

(Baade, W. und Pauli, W.) Über den auf die Teilchen in den Kometen-
schweifen ausgeübten Strahlungsdruck. *Naturwissenschaften* **15**,
49–51, 1927

Cinquième Conseil de Physique Solvay, *Electrons et Photons*, Bruxelles
1927, discussions pp. 46, 95–98, 134–135, 256–258, 276–277, 280–282,
286, Paris, 1928

(Jordan, P. und Pauli, W.) Zur Quantenelektrodynamik ladungsfreier
Felder. *Z. Phys.* **47**, 151–173, 1928

(Heisenberg, W. und Pauli, W.) Zur Quantendynamik der Wellenfelder.
Z. Phys. **56**, 1–61, 1929

(Heisenberg, W. und Pauli, W.) Zur Quantentheorie der Wellenfelder
II. *Z. Phys.* **59**, 168–190, 1930

Les théories quantiques du magnétisme : l'électron magnétique. In:
Sixième Conseil de Physique Solvay, *Le Magnétisme*, Bruxelles 1930,
pp. 175–238, discussions pp. 74, 240–242, 244, 269, 272, 275–276,
Paris, 1932

(Güttinger, P. und Pauli, W.) Zur Hyperfeinstruktur von Li+. *Z.
Phys.* **67**, 743–765, 1931

(Solomon, J. und Pauli, W.) La théorie unitaire d'Einstein et Mayer et
les équations de Dirac. *J. Phys. Radium* (7) **3**, 452–463, 582–589,
1932

---

* Kernspin Hypothese.
† Pauli-Prinzip.

Diracs Wellengleichung des Elektrons und geometrische Optik. *Helv. phys. Acta* **5**, 179–199, 1932

Einige die Quantenmechanik betreffenden Erkundigungsfragen. *Z. Phys.* **80**, 573–586, 1933*

Über die Intensität der Streustrahlung bewegter freier Elektronen. *Helv. phys. Acta* **6**, 279–286, 1933

Über die Formulierung der Naturgesetze mit fünf homogenen Koordinaten. *Ann. Phys. Lpz.* (5) **18**, 305–336; 337–372, 1933

Paul Ehrenfest †, *Naturwissenschaften* **21**, 841–843, 1933

Septième conseil de Physique Solvay, *Noyaux Atomiques*, Bruxelles 1933, discussions pp. 175, 180, 213–214, 215, 324–325†, 330, Paris, 1934

(Pauli, W. und Weisskopf, V.) Über die Quantisierung der skalaren relativistischen Wellengleichung. *Helv. phys. Acta* **7**, 709–731, 1934

Beiträge zur mathematischen Theorie der Dirac'schen Matrizen, in *Zeeman, Verhandelingen 1935*, pp. 31–43, Haag, 1935

Raum, Zeit und Kausalität in der modernen Physik. *Scientia* **59**, 65–76, 1936

(Pauli, W. and Bose, M. E.) Remarks on the polarization effects in the positron theory. *Phys. Rev.* **49**, 462–465, 1936

Contributions mathématiques à la théorie des matrices de Dirac. *Ann. Inst. Poincaré* **6**, 109–136, 1936

Théorie quantique relativiste des particules obéissant à la statistique de Einstein–Bose. *Ann. Inst. Poincaré* **6**, 137–152, 1936

(Pauli, W. und Fierz, M.) Über das H-Theorem in der Quantenmechanik. *Z. Phys.* **106**, 572–587, 1937

(Pauli, W. und Fierz, M.) Zur Theorie der Emission langwelliger Lichtquanten. *Nuovo Cim.* **15**, 167–188, 1938

On asymptotic series for functions in the theory of diffraction of light. *Phys. Rev.* **54**, 924–931, 1938‡

Einige prinzipielle Betrachtungen über die Theorie des β-Zerfalls (russisch). *Bull. Acad. Sci. U.R.S.S., Série phys.*, pp. 149–152, 1938

Über ein Kriterium für Ein- oder Zweiwertigkeit der Eigenfunktionen in der Wellenmechanik. *Helv. phys. Acta* **12**, 147–168, 1939

(Pauli, W. und Fierz, M.) Über relativistische Feldgleichungen von Teilchen mit beliebigem Spin im elektromagnetischen Feld. *Helv. phys. Acta* **12**, 297–300, 1939

(Fierz, M. and Pauli, W.) On relativistic wave equations for particles of arbitrary spin in an electromagnetic field. *Proc. Roy. Soc.* **173**, 211–232, 1939

(Pauli, W. and Belinfante, F. J.) On the statistical behaviour of known and unknown elementary particles. *Physica* **7**, 177–192, 1940

The connection between spin and statistics. *Phys. Rev.* **58**, 716–722, 1940

---

* Antwort auf Fragen von P. Ehrenfest.
† Neutrino Hypothese.
‡ A. Sommerfeld zum. 70, Geburtstag.
11*

Über die Invarianz der Dirac'schen Wellengleichungen gegenüber Ähnlichkeitstransformationen des Linienelementes im Fall verschwindender Ruhmasse. *Helv. phys. Acta* **13**, 204–208, 1940

Relativistic field theories of elementary particles. *Rev. mod. Phys.* **13**, 203–232, 1941

(Pauli, W. and Dancoff, S. M.) The pseudoscalar meson field with strong coupling. *Phys. Rev.* **62**, 85–108, 1942

(Pauli, W. and Kusaka, S.) On the theory of a mixed pseudoscalar and a vector meson field. *Phys. Rev.* **63**, 400–416, 1943

(Einstein, A. and Pauli, W.) On the non-existence of regular stationary solutions of relativistic field equations. *Ann. of Math.* **44**, 131–137, 1943

On Dirac's new method of field quantization. *Rev. mod. Phys.* **15**, 175–207, 1943

On applications of the λ-limiting process to the theory of the meson field. *Phys. Rev.* **64**, 332–344, 1943

(Pauli, W. and Jauch, J. M.) On the application of Dirac's method of field-quantization to the problem of emission of low frequency photons. *Phys. Rev.* **65**, 255–256, 1944

Niels Bohr on his 60th birthday. *Rev. mod. Phys.* **17**, 97–101, 1945

(Pauli, W. and Hu, N.) On the strong coupling case for spin-dependent interactions in scalar- and vector-pair theories. *Rev. mod. Phys.* **17**, 267–286, 1945

Remarks on the history of the exclusion principle. *Science* **103**, 213–215, 1946

Diracs Feldquantisierung und Emission von Photonen kleiner Frequenzen. *Helv. phys. Acta* **19**, 234–237, 1946

Exclusion Principle and Quantum Mechanics. Prix Nobel 1945. Neuchâtel, 1947; Stockholm, 1948.

Difficulties of field theories and of field quantization. *Phys. Soc. Cambridge Conf. Report* pp. 5–10, 1947

Der Einfluss archetypischer Vorstellungen auf die Bildung naturwissenschaftlicher Theorien bei Kepler. Psychologischer Club, Zürich, *Jahresbericht* 1947/48, pp. 37–44

Sommerfelds Beiträge zur Quantentheorie. *Naturwissenschaften* **35**, 129–132, 1948*

Editorial. Die Idee der Komplementarität. *Dialectica* **2**, 307–311, 1948

Communication. In: Huitième Conseil de Physique Solvay, *Les particules élémentaires*, Bruxelles 1948, pp. 287–289, discussions pp. 193, 284. Bruxelles, 1950

Note after the conference of Prof. Born, The foundation of quantum statistics. *Nuovo Cim.* **6**, *Suppl.* pp. 166–169, 1949

(Pauli, W. and Villars, F.) On the invariant regularization in relativistic quantum theory. *Rev. mod. Phys.* **21**, 434–444, 1949

* A. Sommerfeld zum 80. Geburtstag.

On the connection between spin and statistics. *Progr. theor. Phys.* 5, 526–543, 1950

Die philosophische Bedeutung der Idee der Komplementarität. *Experientia* 6, 72–81, 1950

Etat actuel de la théorie quantique des champs. La rénormalisation. In *Particules fondamentals et noyaux*, Paris 1950. *Colloques internat. Centre nat. Recherche Sci.* 38, 67–77, 1953

Arnold Sommerfeld, *Z. angew. Math. Phys.* 2, 301, 1951

Arnold Sommerfeld †, *Z. Naturf.* 6a, 468, 1951

Die Geschichte des periodischen Systems der Elemente (Autoreferat zum Vortrag vom 28. Jan. 1952 in Zürich). *Vierteljahrsschrift naturf. Ges. Zürich* 97, 137–139, 1952

Theorie und Experiment. *Dialectica* 6, 141–142, 1952

On the Hamiltonian structure of non-local field theories. *Nuovo Cim.* 10, 648–667, 1953

Der Begriff der Wahrscheinlichkeit und seine Rolle in den Naturwissenschaften. *Verh. Schweiz. naturf. Ges.*, Bern, 1952, pp. 76–79, 1953

Wahrscheinlichkeit und Physik. *Dialectica* 8, 112–124, 1954

Rydberg and the periodic system of the elements. *Proc. Rydberg Centennial Conference on Atomic Spectroscopy, Lund, 1954*, pp. 22–26, Lund, 1955.

Dixième Conseil de Physique Solvay, *Les électrons dans les métaux*, Bruxelles 1954, discussion p. 282. Bruxelles, 1955

Impressionen über Albert Einstein, *Neue Zürcher Zeitung* Nr. 1055, 22. April, 1955

Naturwissenschaftliche und erkenntnistheoretische Aspekte der Ideen vom Unbewussten. *Dialectica* 8, 283–301, 1954

(Källén, G. and Pauli, W) On the mathematical structure of T. D. Lee's model of a renormalizable field theory. *Dan. Vid. Selsk. Mat.-fys. Medd.* 30, No. 7, 1955

Remarks on problems connected with the renormalization of quantized fields. *Nuovo Cim.* 4, *Suppl.* pp. 703–710, 1956

Die Wissenschaft und das abendländische Denken, in *Europa—Erbe und Aufgabe*, Internationaler Gelehrtenkongress, Mainz, 1955, pp. 71–79, Wiesbaden, 1956

Abgedruckt in *Schweiz. Bauzeitung* 77, Heft 1, pp. 1–4, 1959

Opening Talk; Schlusswort durch den Präsidenten der Konferenz; Relativitätstheorie und Wissenschaft, in *Fünfzig Jahre Relativitätstheorie*, Bern, 1955. *Helv. phys. Acta, Suppl.* IV, pp. 27; 261–267; 282–286, 1956

Announcement, *CERN Symposium 1956*, Vol. 2, p. 258, 1956*

Zur älteren und neueren Geschichte des Neutrinos (Autoreferat zum Vortrag vom 21. Jan. 1957 in Zürich). *Vierteljahrsschrift naturf. Ges. Zürich* 102, 387–388, 1957

* Nachweis des Neutrinos.

On the conservation of the lepton charge. *Nuovo Cim.* **6**, 204–215, 1957
Phänomen und physikalische Realität. *Dialectica* **11**, 36–48, 1957
Albert Einstein in der Entwicklung der Physik, *Neue Zürcher Zeitung*
Nr. 89, 12. Jan. 1958
Abgedruckt in *Universitas* **13**, 593–598, 1958
Die Verletzung von Spiegelungs-Symmetrien in den Gesetzen der
Atomphysik. *Experientia* **14**, 1–5, 1958
Zur Thermodynamik dissoziierter Gleichgewichtsgemische in äussern
Kraftfeldern, in *Festschrift Jakob Ackeret. Z. angew. Math. Phys.*
9b, 490–497, 1958
The indefinite metric with complex roots, *Proc. 1958 Annual International Conference on High Energy Physics at CERN,* pp. 127–128,
discussions pp. 122–126, 130, 133, 140, 1958

C. BUCHBESPRECHUNGEN

E. Buchwald, Das Korrespondenzprinzip. *Naturwissenschaften* **12**,
36–37, 1924
E. P. Adams, The quantum theory. *Naturwissenschaften* **12**, 412–413,
1924
M. Born, Vorlesungen über Atommechanik, 1. Teil. *Naturwissenschaften* **13**, 487–488, 1925
A. S. Eddington, Relativitätstheorie in mathematischer Behandlung.
Naturwissenschaften **14**, 273–274, 1926
Ergebnisse der exakten Naturwissenschaften, Band 7. *Naturwissenschaften* **17**, 257–259, 1929
H. A. Lorentz, Vorlesungen über theoretische Physik. *Naturwissenschaften* **17**, 279, 1929
Ergebnisse der exakten Naturwissenschaften, Band 8. *Naturwissenschaften* **18**, 568–570, 1930
M. Born und P. Jordan, Elementare Quantenmechanik. *Naturwissenschaften* **18**, 602, 1930
P. A. M. Dirac, The principles of quantum mechanics. *Naturwissenschaften* **19**, 188, 1931
W. Heisenberg, Die physikalischen Prinzipien der Quantentheorie.
Naturwissenschaften **19**, 188–189, 1931
A. March, Die Grundlagen der Quantenmechanik. *Naturwissenschaften*
19, 867, 1931
Ergebnisse der exakten Naturwissenschaften, Band 10. *Naturwissenschaften* **20**, 186–187, 1932
G. Gamow, Der Bau des Atomkernes und die Radioaktivität. *Naturwissenschaften* **20**, 582, 1932
J. H. Van Vleck, The theory of electric and magnetic susceptibilities.
Naturwissenschaften **21**, 239, 1933
Ergebnisse der exakten Naturwissenschaften, Band 11. *Naturwissenschaften* **21**, 301–302, 1933

P. Debye, Kernphysik. *Naturwissenschaften* **23**, 772–773, 1935

H. Reichenbach, Philosophic foundations of quantum mechanics. *Dialectica* **1**, 176–178, 1947

A. Sommerfeld, Vorlesungen über theoretische Physik, Band IV: Optik. *Z. angew. Math. Phys.* **2**, 215, 1951

D. ter Haar, Elements of statistical mechanics. *Z. angew. Math. Phys.* **7**, 467, 1956

D. VORLESUNGEN

The theory of the positron and related topics. Notes by B. Hoffmann. IAS, Princeton, 1936

Statistische Mechanik, ausgearbeitet von M. R. Schafroth. ETH, Zürich, 1947

Optik und Elektronentheorie, ausgearbeitet von A. Scheidegger, zweite Auflage von P. Erdös. ETH, Zürich, 1948, 1957

Elektrodynamik, ausgearbeitet von A. Thellung. ETH, Zürich, 1949

Ausgewählte Kapitel aus der Feldquantisierung, ausgearbeitet von U. Hochstrasser und M. R. Schafroth. ETH, Zürich, 1951

Thermodynamik und kinetische Gastheorie, ausgearbeitet von E. Jucker. ETH, Zürich, 1952

Continuous groups in quantum mechanics. Notes by A. R. Edmonds. CERN-Report No. 31, Genève, 1956

Continuous groups and reflections in quantum mechanics. Notes by R. J. Ridell, jr. UCRL-Report No. 8213, Berkeley, 1958

Wellenmechanik, ausgearbeitet von F. Herlach und H. E. Knoepfel. ETH, Zürich, 1959

AUTHOR INDEX

(R) is used for references

SUBJECT INDEX